PERSONAL COMPUTERS IN THE HAM SHACK

PAUL DANZER, N1II · RICHARD ROZNOY, K1OF

Published by:
The American Radio Relay League
225 Main Street
Newington, CT 06111-1494

Contents

Foreword

If you have been a ham for a while, you have your own list of major advances that have changed the way you "do" ham radio. Although I've been a ham for several decades, mine is short: SSB, transistors, FM repeaters and now personal computers. PCs have changed the modes we transmit and receive, the design and construction of our equipment, the control of our stations—and even the size and quality of our club newsletters.

The League did a survey recently to see what hams were doing with PCs and what type of PCs hams use. We were not surprised to find that the majority of hams had, and use, PCs in their shacks. Some were using older machines they had picked up at flea markets or had purchased a few years before. But we were surprised to find that the greatest number of hams had up-to-date systems with large hard disks, CD-ROM drives and fast processors. Hams are clearly determined to exploit the power and versatility of computer technology.

When SSB first became popular, it was clear to many that it would soon become the dominant mode of HF voice communication. Many of us could foresee the impact when transistors and FM repeaters arrived on the ham scene.

Personal computers are a little different. Things change so fast in the hardware and software realms that predictions can become outdated before they get to appear in print! For this reason, you may find that names, addresses and prices have changed since this book was published. You'll find up-to-date information on the ARRL Web site (**http://www.arrl.org**) and in *QST*. Not yet online? Call or write the ARRL Technical Information Service at ARRL Headquarters in Newington, Connecticut.

What's in store for the next edition of this book? That depends on what you, and I, do with computers in our ham shacks.

Despite the distance PC technology has come, it's safe to say that the best is yet to come.

David Sumner, K1ZZ
Executive Vice President

Newington, Connecticut
January 1997

vi

Preface

The first ham radio use of personal computers was as calculators—designing circuits, antennas and filters. It was not long before enterprising hams ran a few wires directly from a PC to the ham rig. Suddenly, hams had discovered that PCs can also be used to communicate and control.

This book was written to help hams get the most from their PCs. The authors are ARRL headquarters staff members and avid users of PCs in their ham activities. If you find a problem or have a good idea, use the feedback form at the back to let us know about it. Your idea could be featured in the next edition.

This book is organized to cover the most common uses of PCs in a ham shack. Chapter 1 contains a few basic definitions, followed by a discussion of PC hardware, operating systems and software. Chapter 2 looks at the PC as a communications terminal. Connected to your rig, it can get you on packet, RTTY, AMTOR, SSTV and many other modes—most often with a direct connection through a simple op-amp or transistor switch, instead of an expensive software-laden terminal unit. Chapters 3 and 4 examine the PC (strangely enough) as a computer—as a record-keeper (station logs and similar database managers) in Chapter 3 and as a design tool in Chapter 4. After reading Chapter 4, you can play *what-if* with antenna and hardware designs without ever heating up your soldering iron.

Want to roll your own? Want to connect your PC to some part of your ham station through one of the PC ports? Chapter 5 describes how to do it, and suggests some software approaches.

Imagine worldwide propagation without interference, sunspot effects or fading. Want some new software? Want to track down a problem you have been having with a piece of gear? You guessed it—the Internet will have the answers. Chapter 6 discusses Internet techniques and tricks, and the authors' favorite sites.

No one book can contain everything. Often there are additional places to look, comments to make and data you might need. Rather than try to fit this information into the fine print as footnotes, we've compiled it into one place—Chapter 7, the Resources Guide.

Enjoy—and don't forget to share your expertise with us!

Acknowledgments

The following individuals made valuable contributions to this book:

James Craswell, WBØVNE
The Fairfield County Users Group (FCUG), Charles Bryk, President
John Langner, WB2OSZ
Craig Lee, AA3HM
Cop MacDonald, VY2CM
David Newkirk, W9VES
Lauren Rudd, KD8PZ
William Sabin, WØIYH
Robert Schetgen, KU7G
Warren Toomey, VK1XWT

Particular thanks are due to R. Dean Straw, N6BV, for his guidance to the antenna-related software—much of which he wrote, and Joel Kleinman, N1BKE for his editorial contributions and guidance.

Software Available

Files related to this book are available for downloading from the ARRL ftp site (**oak.oakland.edu**) or the ARRL Hiram Bulletin Board (telephone 860-594-0306). Also check the ARRL Web site (**http:www.arrl.org**) for any updates. If you would prefer to receive the files on a 3^1/$_2$-inch IBM-format disk, send a check for $5, payable to ARRL, to the ARRL Technical Secretary, 225 Main St, Newington, CT 06111-1494. Request the **PCHS disk**.

A WORD ABOUT STYLE USED IN THIS BOOK

The authors have used *italics* for the names of programs mentioned in this book, while **boldface type** is used for Web addresses. In addition, Web addresses that have punctuation after them have been enclosed in parentheses, as in (**http://www.arrl.org**). Please note that the parentheses *are not part of the address*—they merely set off the actual address from the rest of the sentence.

What Every Ham Should Know About The PC

Hams have been involved with personal computers since the first one was advertised, for a few hundred dollars, in an electronics magazine. The concept of *hacking*—doing-it-yourself, often by trial and error—is basically what hams have been doing from the outset.

This book discusses the things you should know to get the most enjoyment from the computer in your shack. If you are going to run a database program to keep track of your QSLs, and put the computer to no other ham use, that's one thing. But if you want to use it to communicate through your ham gear, that brings forward all kinds of challenges—those we'll be exploring in this book.

Personal computers, or more accurately the machines described by the letters *PC*, refer to the IBM PC design and its many descendants. Apple IIs, Macs, Ataris and others all have their advocates. Hams use them all, but not to the same extent as PCs. Much of what will be discussed in this book applies to all personal computers, independent of platform, but the emphasis will be on the IBM PC family.

Some degree of computer literacy is assumed—or at least the desire to look up any unfamiliar terms in a reference book. This chapter contains a discussion of PC hardware, operating systems and software as they relate to ham use of computers. The Resources Chapter lists some suggested books for further study.

Every profession has its language; every technology its jargon. Terms you will see often in this book are defined in Appendix B.

OLD COMPUTER OR NEW?

If we were to define an "older computer"—the clock speed, the processor, the hard disk size (if any!), the RAM and the video bus—we would probably insult more than a few reading this book. That little beauty you looked at, drooled over and finally stretched your pocketbook to buy just a few short years ago is likely today considered an "older computer."

When we use that term, we are referring to a computer you might get either free or for $25 at a flea market. It works, and works well, but it won't achieve any speed records. It may have a hard disk, but is probably too small to run *Windows*. If you are lucky, you may have gotten several dozen low density disks with it, containing copied versions of obsolete software.

Is this baby useless? Not necessarily. It will still do light word processing, database management and—here is the nice part—it will probably do very well as a devoted terminal and testbed in your shack. Older computers can work fine, as long as you understand their limits.

Processing speed is not critical, assuming you are not going into any of the new high speed data modes or FAX/TV/graphics modes. If you buy an operating 4.7-MHz PC for $10 or $20, and then try it for the things you want, your risk is small.

The presence (or absence) and size of the hard disk is one consideration. There is a good reason hard disks are so popular: Without one, and a large enough one at that, you will find yourself constantly searching for and switching floppies. The floppy type also is important, as few modern programs can fit on a low-density (360K) disk.

If you are planning to limit the use of your computer to text modes only—no SSTV or FAX—the video type is less critical. Otherwise, stick to machines having VGA or better video cards and monitors.

Each of these limitations can be fixed by installing other cards, assuming the BIOS (see Appendix B) in the computer is compatible with these newer cards. *This is a very big assumption!* Many times, if you walk the aisles with a sharp eye, cards with more capability can be found at flea markets, but it is a matter of luck if you and the card will make contact.

Generally speaking, it would be wisest not to upgrade that little flea market beauty. Even if you can find the needed parts and cards, they may cost as much as the entire computer did when it was new! More often, however, the available cards will not come with books or instructions for setting DIP switches and jumpers, and you are on your own! Upgraded BIOS chips for your particular machine may have been readily available 5 years ago, but it could be another story today.

INTERFACING—CAN YOU BLOW IT UP?

Well, yes and no. It is usually very difficult to damage a PC. Some monitors will accept video scan rates (from video cards) higher than their design capability, and the resulting duty cycle may be higher than you should use for that monitor. You could say they never should have been designed to work at those rates, and you would be correct. But there have been several on the market that could be damaged at high video rates. For the most part, using the video modes common in ham software, this is not a problem.

If you want to electrically connect to your computer—interface with it—you could cause some problems. Chapter 5 contains descriptions of direct interfacing methods—hardware and software. Common choices for interfacing are the parallel port (Centronics compatible printer port), serial port (RS-232) and the joystick port. Less common, but useful, are the internal bus (just like bus mice) and sound cards. See Figure 1.1.

The most common choices are the RS-232 serial and parallel (Centronics compatible) ports. If you stick to building devices that comply with RS-232 standards for the serial port, and the Centronics interface for the parallel port, you will be safe. But being a ham, you might be inclined to cheat a little, and perhaps not run the same tests on your design that a major, multimillion dollar corporation might run for their design. What then?

Go ahead and build it. You only risk the I/O board, not the whole computer. And the I/O board is generally replaceable. One caution, however—some computers were built with oddball combination multipurpose boards. Your I/O board may be combined with a floppy disk controller. If you blow the I/O board, you may have to replace it with two boards, one for I/O and one to control the floppies. Some portables were built with I/O on the mother board; if you blow a port you probably lost the computer.

Exercise a bit more caution, if you chose to interface with the internal computer bus or the sound card. An electrical problem here can result in damage to the motherboard or sound card.

Experienced hams (and computer repair people) will tell you never to connect or disconnect anything when the computer is turned on. This is a good rule, and one that is often violated—at least when it comes to the external ports. Many people consider it an acceptable risk—after the seventh time they have shut power off, made a change in an external circuit, turned power back on to the computer, rebooted the software, and tested the external circuit—they give up and just plug and unplug the external circuit to the computer port, while the computer is live. Can you get away with it? Yes, most of the time. But remember, there is a risk, and the inoperative external circuit may be due to a blown computer port, rather than a malfunction in the circuit you are testing.

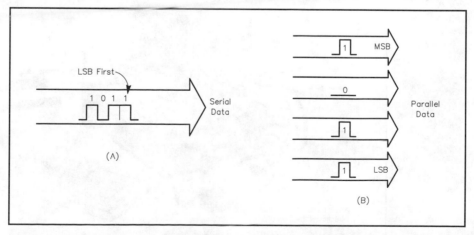

Figure 1.1—The same four digital bits can be transmitted either serially or in parallel. If the width of one bit remains the same, it will take 4 times as long to transmit the full serial word. *LSB* is the least significant bit, and *MSB* is the most significant bit.

SAFETY

If you are used to working on solid-state circuits, a PC offers no new safety challenges. Generally, the line voltage is contained within the power supply module. The power supply is a three-wire grounded supply, and as long as no one has modified it and you use a three-wire ac socket, there is little risk to you. Remember, you are working with a system that may have been modified, or the (usually unknown overseas) manufacturer may have cheated a bit. There is no guarantee that the system is safe for you to handle with power on—especially from the point of view of ac line safety.

Monitors do present a challenge. The CRT anode voltage is usually generated in a feedback high voltage power supply. This section is the most likely to fail. You will probably be trying to fix a monitor that becomes an immediate danger—if you succeed. The best bet is to treat the monitor as though the high voltage will go back on any second, as well it might. See the Resources Chapter for additional safety references.

RFI

We are all used to the idea of TVI—when you use a ham transmitter, you can interfere with a TV either through *fundamental overload* or *harmonics*. Fundamental overload is simply putting too much energy, on the transmitter's output frequency, into the TV circuit at one point or another. This energy interferes with the normal functioning of the TV set and the result is interference, either in the video or audio portion of the program.

Harmonic energy is the other common source of TVI. Although the transmitter has been set to transmit on one frequency, some power is generated at multiples of that

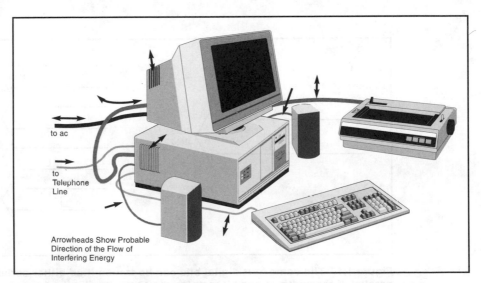

to ac

to
Telephone
Line

Arrowheads Show Probable
Direction of the Flow of
Interfering Energy

Figure 1.2—Cables and line cords may have to be shielded and filtered to remove the effects of RFI.

frequency. If this multiple occurs on a TV channel, and is not suppressed before it leaves the transmitter, the result is TVI.

Less well known, ITV means *Interference* from a *TV*. The usual cause is the 15,750-Hz horizontal oscillator. This oscillator produces a triangular waveform, rich in harmonics. The power output from this oscillator can be considerable, since it is used both to synchronize the horizontal deflection of the CRT scan and to drive the *flyback* system that generates the CRT high voltage. The output of this oscillator is often heard as annoying buzzes every 15 kHz on 80 meters, and occasionally on higher bands.

Many hams have found this source of interference a surprise, when they tried to use a Commodore or VIC-20, which required a black and white TV as the output monitor. Coupled to an inexpensive ac/dc TV set, this (fortunately now obsolete) collection of equipment could completely blank the lower HF bands.

PCs can be even worse than these TV sets. What we know about radiation *from* computers dates back to some of the original computers at the Moore School of Engineering (University of Pennsylvania). This school is recognized as the home of the UNIVAC series of computers, and therefore the source of the first commercial computers. Very early on, one enterprising engineer found that the computer generated RF interference, and proceeded to program it to play a crude variety of music. Another engineer, monitoring the computer performance overnight, used a broadcast-band radio to monitor the interference. If the sound of the interference changed, he knew the computer was in trouble. (See the Resources Chapter.)

Unfortunately, the ability of computers to make RF noise has continued to this day. The only difference is we now speak of RFI, *radio frequency interference*, and EMI, *electromagnetic interference*. Generally EMI includes RFI as well as magnetic field and other field energy sources. However, only the RFI portion is relevant here. See Figure 1.2.

RFI consists of two parts, corresponding to TVI and ITV. The radiation part is predictable, since each computer has at least one *clock*—and the clock oscillator produces a digital waveform. The oldest PC used a 4.77 MHz clock, counted down from a 14.31818-MHz oscillator. As the development of computers progressed, clock speeds went to 8, 16, 33, 66, 75, 100, 120, 133, 150 and then 200+ MHz. Each clock pulse is rectangular—to call them square waves is not totally correct. The up and down portions of the waveform are not identical—they often have less than a 50% *duty cycle*.

Since they are rectangular, they are very rich in harmonics. Thus a 16-MHz computer clock system will have harmonics related not only to multiples of 16 MHz, but also related to the reciprocal of the time interval of the up and down portions of the waveform. For a complete analysis, see the Resources Chapter.

You might say: "I will buy a computer with a 75-MHz clock, and all the problems will be at 75 MHz or higher. No problem on HF, right?" Wrong! The clock is *divided* down to subharmonics for various purposes, and when data is transmitted, the sequence of 1's and 0's produce energy at all sorts of oddball frequencies related to the data waveform. This is particularly true for serial data, such as might be found on a cable from the computer to an external modem or serial port printer.

So What Are You Going to Do?

What would you do with any transmitter that is radiating all over the spectrum?

The first step, perhaps, is not to buy the particular transmitter, or in this case that computer. The FCC requires computers and accessories to be certified (see the Resources Chapter) to a standard defined in Part 15B of the FCC Rules. Do all computers used in the home have to be tested and certified to this standard? Yes! Are they all? Well, sort of.

Often a prototype will be tested and certified. If certain changes are made, recertification is required. Often, however, substantial changes are made and somehow a new unit is not sent for testing. Occasionally, relatively minor changes can be made, such as using a better (faster) chip. The newer chip has faster rise times on waveforms, and then, although the clock frequency and all other waveforms remain the same, the faster rise times can result in increased radiation on additional frequencies.

Your best bet, if you are buying a new computer, is to buy it with an agreement that lets you return it. Then you can test the new unit, and see if the noise level exceeds your needs. You may have perfectly good, working computer, and it will be difficult to explain the problem to the sales people, so make sure the return policy is unconditional.

If you are trying to use an old computer, the story is much different. Here shielding and filtering are the only solutions. Some of the old tricks to TVI-proof a transmitter will have to be tried. This includes grounding everything in sight, filters on all external cables (especially the power cord) and a host of other fixes. Two good starting points are *Radio Frequency Interference: How to Find It and Fix It*, published by the ARRL and the RFI Chapter of *The ARRL Handbook for Radio Amateurs*. See the Resources Chapter.

Cables are a real source of noise, even on a "clean" computer. Shielded cables are available, or you might consider making your own. Often, all you have to do is remove one end of the commercial cable, cover the cable with shielding braid removed from a length of coax cable, and reconnect a new connector in place of the one you removed (you did note the colors of the wires and connecting pins, didn't you?). Then

Part 15B—Thou Shalt Not Interfere

Part 15 of the FCC Rules covers things that radiate, but are not transmitters. Transmitters and other purposeful generators of RF fall under other parts of the rules and are usually licensed. Thus, any radiator not covered elsewhere ends up under the control of Part 15.

Subpart B applies to noncommercial equipment, and very specifically personal computers for use in a home. Personal computers must be certified and a formal application for certification filed with the FCC. Subpart A applies to commercial equipment. Don't let the *A* fool you: Subpart B is stricter than Subpart A.

Unfortunately, even a Subpart B-approved computer is no guarantee of compatibility with your ham equipment. The current rules look for conducted emissions, such as you might find on a power cord or printer cable, from 450 kHz to 30 MHz. The allowable signal levels still could interfere with your receiver. Radiated emissions, such as those that could come from openings in the computer case, are examined only above 30 MHz. There are no requirements below this frequency!

Susceptibility—how well the computer will operate in the presence of RF from your transmitter—is not tested at all.

provide a good ground at one or both ends of the cable, starting with the end at the computer. Another good approach is the addition of ferrite beads to each lead. See the books referenced above for more information.

It Works Two Ways

Now for the second half of the story. In an ideal world, every computer would be well shielded, and every digital signal would have to go to a positive level of 100 volts to be a digital one, and minus 100 volts to be a digital zero. The signal swing would be a total of 200 volts, and *noise immunity* would be a good part of this 200 volts—say 180 volts. Your transmitter would have to put a 180-volt pulse into some part of the computer circuitry to make the computer malfunction.

So much for the ideal world. Noise immunities of 3.5 volts are very common with power supplies of 5 volts. Newer computers, to reduce the power consumed, are going to supplies of 3.5 volts and soon—to be very common—to power supplies of slightly over 1 volt!

Guestimating a noise immunity of about 80% of the power supply voltage, you can see the computer can be very vulnerable to transmitters. So what do you do?

First, make sure your transmitter and *antenna system* (antenna, feed line, and tuner or matchbox) are putting RF into the antenna, not into the shack. Coax feed lines, with SWRs of 3:1 or less, are a starting point. That random length wire antenna, with 10 feet of radiating wire in the shack, is not the way to go. If you are experiencing RF on your microphone, you can bet you will have a problem with RF entering your PC. Unlike the preceding section, to expect the computer manufacturer to protect the computer from your transmitter is unreasonable.

After making sure the RF is going out of the shack, the next step is similar to that in the preceding section. RF seals may be added to openings and cables replaced by shielded cables. It also may be necessary to disconnect certain external accessories, such as the printer or an external modem, when you are transmitting.

Don't overlook the "little things." A telephone wire, connected to your modem, may be conducting RF into the computer, as might speaker leads for your sound card. Again, if you follow the procedures associated with reducing TVI, you can get to a workable situation.

See the Resources Chapter for additional places to look for help.

PICKING A TOTAL COMPUTER PACKAGE

Probably, the most common question is "What do I need in computer hardware and software in my shack?" To paraphrase the title of this section, a computer consists of several connected parts. The hardware is connected to the BIOS, the BIOS is connected to the operating system and finally the operating system is connected to the software. An oversimplification? Probably, but there are some unique things relating the hardware, BIOS and software in PCs to ham radio requirements.

Again, let's start with a few definitions. The *hardware* is the metal, plastic, silicon—the things you can touch and hopefully fix when they are broken. Shipped with each computer, usually *burnt in* or stored in a read-only-memory (*ROM*) memory chip, is the *BIOS* (Basic Input Output System). This software, often called *firmware,* contains the code to start the computer and the code to control the hardware, especially

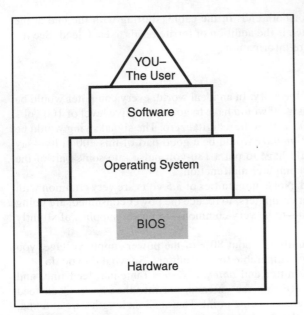

Figure 1.3—The hardware is the base of the system. Each building block must be matched to the other, adjacent blocks. This matching often takes the form of an *INSTALLATION* program.

the input and output functions. It is called firmware since it *usually* cannot be changed, except by replacing the memory chip holding the code. See Figure 1.3.

Generally, the BIOS is whatever it is— it comes with the computer and we have very little choice. The only unique "ham" consideration of BIOS was discussed earlier in this chapter: A BIOS in an older computer may not be compatible with the expansion boards you want to add to your "flea market special," and you may not be able to add that alternative floppy drive or larger hard disk.

The *operating system* is the next level. Here we usually have a choice, but as we will see later some are so slow they will not let you run communications software—at least any that requires real-time signals going into and out of a port in the computer.

Finally, our *software*. Sometimes you get what you pay for and sometimes you don't. Sometimes excellent software is available as either free as *freeware* or at a modest cost as *shareware*. See the sidebar on shareware. The software you select also determines the operating system and hardware you need. In other words, if you want to run a particular software package, you must be running an operating system compatible with that software package. In addition, you must have hardware compatible with both the operating system and the software. An example of this is in Figure 1.4.

Again, in our ideal world, you would pick the one and only perfect software package, select a compatible operating system, and then buy a computer that can use the operating system and software to advantage. In this non-ideal world, often the process works backwards. You buy the "best" computer you can afford, pick an operating system that the computer can handle and then select software that will run under the hardware and operating system you now own. To live in this nonperfect world, let's look at some of the limits and considerations you should be aware of.

NO SOFTWARE, NO WORK!

Most people worry about their computer speed, and how fast it operates the software, because they just don't want to wait. If you have a computer (and program) that takes 15 seconds to search for a file, and then change to another computer that takes only 1 second, you will find going back to the first computer almost intolerable. The hardware and software operate *non-real time*—except for your impatience, there is no reason even to measure the time it takes. Word processors, database managers, file managers and spreadsheets are all examples of this type of operation. For more infor-

Now for the Commercial on Shareware

At one point I was looking for a certain type of program to use at League Headquarters. I downloaded almost 15 programs from various libraries on CompuServe and the internet. Each was installed, tested and evaluated. When I was finished, I selected the one I liked the best, filled out the payment form included in the .ZIP file, and sent a check (less than $35) to the author of the program.

This is *shareware*. It is not free—nor is it always perfect. But it allows you to take a copy of the program, test it, see if it is what you want, and if it is, pay the author or company for its time and effort. Some very good software is available as shareware, and some very poor software is available as shareware. But then again there is very good and very poor software at my local computer store. With shareware, there is no need to return software if it is not to your liking. Just erase the disk! There is a great deal of competition, so the asking prices are usually reasonable—reasonable enough that you should pay for it if you plan to use it for more than the usual 30-day evaluation period.—*N1I*

mation on loading and installing software, see the Resources Chapter.

Hams use software just like anyone else, but they also use another class of software—software with a *real-time* interface. Communications programs, packet, RTTY and SSTV all send signals through a computer port, and the computer must be ready to accept or transmit this signal when it appears. If the computer is not ready—if it is occupied with something else—the signal will just disappear, and an interrupted RTTY message or noisy (partly missing) SSTV picture will result.

A computer in your ham shack is just like any other computer when it comes to running the first class of software. But when it comes to real-time operations, some precautions are necessary.

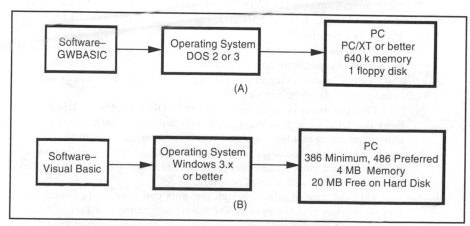

Figure 1.4—*GWBASIC* is an older software program that can run on early versions of DOS—2.x or 3.x. *Windows* or *OS/2* is not needed. The PC requirements are very few, and a floppy disk drive or two can handle the whole problem. If you go to more demanding *Windows*-based software, you'll need more machine capability.

Which Operating System?

In the last 10 years, millions of words have been written (and millions of dollars spent) in a battle to persuade you to buy one operating system or another. But as a ham, you may not have much choice. Software—the non real-time variety—is written to run under one or more operating systems. It may be written for DOS, in which case you can usually also run it under *Windows* or *OS/2*. If it is written for *Windows*, you cannot run it under DOS, but you may be able to run it under *OS/2*. Simply put, if you have a software package you want to use, your operating system must be compatible—and vice versa.

There is some overlap. For example, you can usually install DOS programs under *Windows*, but not all DOS programs will run under *Windows*. Some of the older DOS programs, still perfectly usable and very good for their intended purpose, take direct control of the computer assets—something that newer operating systems such as all versions of *Windows* and *OS/2* frown upon. And when an operating system frowns upon a program's action, it usually means the computer will just stop, requiring you to reboot.

Most hams use DOS and a version of *Windows*. You can define the date for "right now," because if anything changes very quickly, it is computer standards. In a year, or perhaps in 5 years, the words *DOS* and *Windows* may not even exist, except in a historical context.

Real Time Software

It is time to speak the truth! Operating systems are generally very slow, and the more complicated (and capable) the operating system, the slower it is! Even without memory size considerations, the increased size and complexity and the need to perform more operations with newer operating systems are the main reasons you see so many advertisements for 150+ MHz Pentium-based PCs. You can send a single character to your monitor—the letter **E** for example—just as well from a 286 as from a 166-MHz Pentium.

Often, operating systems just get in the way. Software designers, therefore, trying for the best performance, "will write to the metal," bypassing the operating system and addressing computer internal registers directly. And just as often, this software cannot run under *Windows* or *OS/2*.

This statement is especially true for "a DOS window in *Windows*." Just because there is a DOS prompt on the screen does not mean you are really in DOS. Unfortunately, operating in a DOS window means you can incur all the disadvantages of operating in DOS plus the disadvantages of operating under *Windows* or *OS/2*. *Windows 95*, being more complicated and more capable than *Windows 3.X*, often will be even slower to operate with a DOS program.

This sad state of affairs, which prevents you from using a modern operating system with many real-time communications programs, is a fact of life right now. But this does not mean it will continue that way forever—or even after next year! In the meantime, what should you do? The answer may lie in how you start your computer, and how you organize your start-up files.

Booting for Ham Radio

Few of us can afford to have two "good" computers. The same machine we use to write letters, track household finance and maintain our files most often doubles as our ham shack computer. *Windows*, TSRs and similar items are needed for non-ham use, while the same computer, used as a ham radio terminal, cannot afford to have this "junk" taking up room in memory.

The start-up routine determines what gets loaded into your computer's memory. When you turn your computer on (or press **RESET**) the start cycle is a system-wide reset pulse followed by the "boot routine." This boot, or bootstrap routine, starts the software control. It is resident in ROM. Part of this routine is a set of commands to look for the rest of the start-up cycle on disk.

Unless modified, the standard is for the computer to look first at drive A. If there is no disk in drive A, the computer next looks in drive C.

Using DOS as an example, the first files found are the operating systems files—*COMMAND.COM* and one or two hidden systems files. You have very little choice up to this point—the computer requires this information to operate. Next, the computer looks for *CONFIG.SYS*, which contains your setup commands, such as the drivers to use and number of files and buffers. None of the commands in *CONFIG.SYS* can be entered from the keyboard. These commands must be listed in the *CONFIG.SYS* file to work. Some also may be available as executable *.COM* or *.EXE* files, producing the same results.

Finally the computer looks for the *AUTOEXEC.BAT* file, which does consist of commands that could be executed from the keyboard. Since you use the same sequence every time you boot, however, this batch file executes and saves you the trouble of typing the same commands over and over. Both the *AUTOEXEC.BAT* and *CONFIG.SYS* files must be in the root directory.

How Do We Take Advantage of It?

Clues to the answer to that question lie in the preceding paragraph. But before we look at the answer, let's describe what we want to do.

⌨ Sometimes we want to boot with *Windows*, and run *Windows*-hosted software.

⌨ Other times we want to boot only DOS, and not boot any TSRs. We also want a very minimal configuration, with perhaps simple (or fewer) drivers. This configuration makes the most machine available to communications programs.

⌨ We may want to run in a full-up DOS mode, with TSRs and a complex configuration (large number of files and buffers, many drivers, large environment space). This is for those who run only DOS, and are proud of it!

The answer to the question is *dual boot*—the use of two or more autoexec and config files, plus a way to select or control the selected boot configuration. There are several ways to accomplish dual boot.

For Windows 3.1X and DOS Users

First let's talk about the minimalist approach. You really don't want to have two computer configurations—all you want to do is decide, each time you turn on the computer, whether or not to run *Windows*. The command **WIN** is probably the last command in your *AUTOEXEC.BAT* file, so one approach is to add a few statements to your *AUTOEXEC.BAT* file. Make the end of the file look like:

@ECHO To run DOS, press CTRL +C
To load Windows, PAUSE
WIN

CTRL+C (control C) interrupts any batch file, and your *AUTOEXEC.BAT* is a batch file, so pressing CTRL+C interrupts the execution of the file before the last statement — **WIN**—is executed. Therefore, your computer will remain in the DOS mode. Pressing any other key, which is prompted by the **PAUSE** command, makes the batch file continue execution, and therefore the next command, to run *Windows*, is executed.

The second approach, if you do want to modify your *AUTOEXEC.BAT* and *CONFIG.SYS* files, is to have two sets of these files, and select one set each time you boot. In the simplest approach you might boot from a floppy disk, and each time you boot, choose the disk to place in drive A. Alternatively, you could have one configuration on a floppy for drive A, and a second configuration on drive C. Normally, you would boot with the drive C configuration, by not placing a disk in drive A. Want the other configuration? Just boot with the floppy in drive A.

A third, and perhaps "slicker" approach, uses two sets of autoexec and config files on drive C. Let's call one set of files *AUTOEXEC.BAT* and *CONFIG.SYS*, and the other *AUTOEXEC.ALT* and *CONFIG.ALT*. You boot with the current set of autoexec and config files, and then decide if this is the way you want to operate or not. If not,

The MODE Command

Microsoft, in their *User's Guide* for Microsoft DOS 6, says the **MODE** command "Configures a printer, serial port, or display adapter,. . . redirects printer output,. . . displays the numbers of character sets (code pages),. . . displays the status of all the devices installed on your computer." These are important words, since some software packages expect you to have a computer set to their requirements. This is especially true of older DOS programs. For DOS 5 and later the on-line help file contains all you need to know about using this command. For earlier versions of DOS, you might consider buying a user's manual. Many books cover the DOS commands in an appendix.

Some older programs require an 40 column black and white display. **MODE BW40** will set this mode of operation, and **MODE CO80** will bring the display back to an 80 column color mode. Your COM port also may have to be set. **MODE COM1:9600,E,8,1** will set the COM1 port to 9600 baud, even parity, 8 data bits and 1 stop bit.

The mode command syntax you actually are able to use depends on the version of DOS loaded on your computer. There is not total backwards compatibility, and a mode command that might work on a version of DOS 2.1 may not work with DOS 5, or at least in the same way—in fact, it may result in the all-too-common SYNTAX ERROR message on the screen. Occasionally, the command will work, but the hardware is not capable of responding. Your computer may hang up, requiring a reboot.

If the software does not ask you to set the mode, don't worry about it. But if it does, the MODE command is probably your answer. Remember, the computer accepts what you give it. If the command requires two commas, with no space, type just that, or the command will not be accepted or interpreted correctly.

exchange names between pairs of files. *AUTOEXEC.BAT* becomes *AUTOEXEC.ALT*, and *AUTOEXEC.ALT* becomes *AUTOEXEC.BAT*. Then just reboot with the new pair of files.

Sound clumsy? Not really, if you use a utility program to do the work for you. Surprised such a program exists? Well, you are not the first to face this problem. See Figure 1.5 for one method, or look for REBOOT.COM or RECONFIG.COM on many on-line services on the Internet.

If you use any version of DOS 6, you can include multiple configurations in one file. See the sidebar on DOS 6.

What about Windows 95, OS/2 and NT?

The information in the last section described operation under DOS and *Windows 3.1x*. If you use a later (newer) operating system, such as OS/2 or WIN 95, you may be more fortunate. Their setup programs offer dual-boot capabilities. Linux, popular in some ham circles, uses a program called *LILO* (Linux Loader) as the boot routine; it contains provisions to allow you to make a choice of Linux or another operating system (such as plain DOS) at start-up time. Users of UNIX (and varieties of UNIX) usually do their own setup. Little information is available about the operation of most ham software packages under UNIX and NT. See the Resources Chapter for more information on Linux.

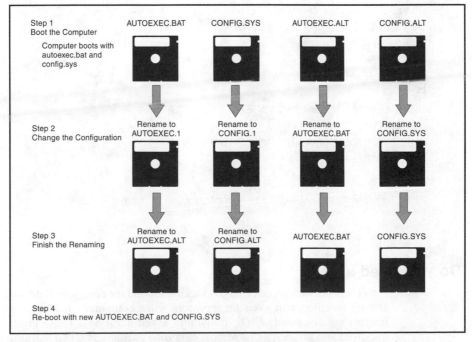

Figure 1.5—Boot with one configuration, and if you want to change, just reboot after renaming the controlling files. The "new" AUTOEXEC.BAT and CONFIG.SYS now give you the new configuration.

Do It With DOS

If you are using DOS 6 ...

And not an earlier version, you can have multiple boot configurations by using the **[MENU]** command. It allows you to write *CONFIG.SYS* and *AUTOEXEC.BAT* files that contain two or more boot configurations. The example *CONFIG.SYS* file below gives you two configurations: one to run *WINDOWS 3.11* and one to run a very striped-down configuration for a ham communications program. The object of the stripped-down configuration is to have as much memory space free (in the lower 640 kb) as possible.

```
rem:CONFIG.SYS

[MENU]
REM: Defines a menu with two items, WINDOWS and HAMRADIO
MENUITEM=WINDOWS
MENUITEM=HAMRADIO

[COMMON]
REM: Items common to both configurations go here
BUFFERS=10,0

[WINDOWS]
REM: Items for the WINDOWS only configuration go here
DEVICE=C:\windows\HIMEM.SYS
DEVICE=C:\DOS\EMM386.EXE NOEMS
FILES=30
DOS=UMB
LASTDRIVE=H
FCBS=4,0
DEVICEHIGH /L:1,12048 =C:\DOS\SETVER.EXE
DOS=HIGH
SHELL=C:\DOS\COMMAND.COM C:\DOS\ /p
STACKS=9,256

[HAMRADIO]
REM: Items for the HAMRADIO only configuration go here
```

Do you Need a . . .?

There is a new piece of jargon kicking around the computer field—on the internet, at club meetings and even on repeaters when computers and other topics of wide interest are discussed: *FAQ*—frequently asked questions. These are the nitty-gritty questions and problems that almost everyone encounters when learning to use a new piece of technology, new software or even a new ham rig. They range from the "Where is the ON/OFF switch?" variety to the highly complex questions. Here are a few that

```
FILES=10

[COMMON]
REM:End of the CONFIG.SYS file
```

There is a matching *AUTOEXEC.BAT* file:

```
rem:AUTOEXEC.BAT

GOTO %CONFIG%
REM: Defines multiple configurations

:WINDOWS
REM: AUTOEXEC commands for the WINDOWS only configuration
@LOADHIGH C:\DOS\SHARE.EXE /l:500 /f:5100
LH /L:0;1,45456 /S C:\DOS\SMARTDRV.EXE
PATH C:\;C:\WINDOWS;C:\DOS;C:\MOUSE
SET TEMP=C:\WINDOWS\TEMP
LH /L:1,35472 C:\MOUSE\MOUSE/C1
WIN
GOTO END

:HAMRADIO
REM: AUTOEXEC commands for the HAMRADIO only configuration
PROMPT Current Directory is $P$G
PATH C:\;C:\DOS;C:\MOUSE
GOTO END

:END
REM:End of the AUTOEXEC.BAT file
```

The *Users Guide for MS-DOS 6* and the on-line help have descriptions of this approach to multiple boot files. The individual entries in the files above will probably have to be modified to work on your computer. Thanks to Bob Schetgen, KU7G, for pointing out this approach for DOS 6.

apply to ham software and computers:

⊟ *Do I need a memory manager?* For ham radio software, probably not. If fact, you might be better off disabling the memory manager, if you usually use one, when you run ham communications software.

⊟ *What languages should I have on the machine? Do I have to know how to use Visual Basic?* Unless you intend to write your own ham software, no languages are needed. If you have never programmed and want to try it, or want to use some of the computer control and interface circuits described in Chapter 5, you'll need a variety of *BASIC*. *QBASIC* comes with later versions of DOS; *GWBASIC*, although not freeware, is readily available. Most people who are testing the programming waters for the first time start with a variety of *BASIC*.

🖫 *What is a language, an interpreted language and a compiled language?* A language is simply a way to talk to the computer. It consists of words the computer (or computer software) can understand, and like the language you speak, it has words with meaning and grammatical rules. An interpreted language is accepted by the computer, each statement in the program read and each statement understood and executed— one by one, one after another. To use a *compiled language,* you have to write the program and process it with a piece of software called, not too surprisingly, a *compiler*. The output of the compiler (for a PC) is either a .COM or .EXE file. See the sidebar on executable files for more information.

🖫 *I have a small hard disk. Can I continue to use disk compression? How about cache programs?* For most ham software, the answer is sure! Disk compression is a problem only if it slows down file access, which is usually not a problem with ham software. But just as with any software, make sure you do an orderly shutdown— don't just dump the power if you are using a cache program.

🖫 *Where should I put my ham software?* For non-*Windows* software, put each program with associated files into a separate directory. The first time you find a new piece of software whose *READ.ME* or *README.1ST* file has overwritten the *READ.ME* file of an older piece of software—you too will start to use separate directories. *Windows*-based software, with a good installation program, usually suggests a directory name. Unless you are using that directory name for another purpose, go along with this default. It is the safest way.

🖫 *I know what will happen: I will probably have a dozen or so ham software packages. Should I use a menu program?* In DOS, I certainly would. There are some excellent menu programs that take up very little computer room and work well. Hunt around on BBSs or the internet. Often, an older version of a commercial menu program is declared "freeware" by the manufacturer in the hope you will try it and like it—and then go to the store to buy the latest version.

🖫 *Viruses—what to do?* Hams are people, and they are as careful and sloppy as other people. You can run a virus checker each time you boot your computer, or you can just virus check each time you get a new floppy disk.

Executable Files

Executable files on a PC are those files that are programs that run when you type the first part of their filename. Generally there are three common types, which can be run from the keyboard. Their filenames end in *.BAT, .COM* and *.EXE.* Thus, if you have a program named *QSL.EXE*, typing *QSL* followed by pressing the ENTER or RETURN key will make the program execute or run (assuming you are logged onto the directory holding *QSL.EXE* or have a *PATH* statement pointing to that directory). Programs ending in *.BAT* have the same property, but they are usually shorter, simpler programs you write yourself in an English-like language. The computer will run *.BAT* programs when you type in the first part of the filename.

HARDWARE PIECES

We would all like to own a dream machine; one that has every feature you can think of. We would all like to read the weekend computer store advertisement, go over each offering, and be able to say, "I already have that." That is why it is called a dream machine. But let's face it—some of us are running Pentium Pros, and some 8086s. Some of us can brag about a 200-MHz clock speed, and others walk along at 4.7 MHz. The trick, for ham radio purposes, is to know what you can do with the machine you have or are considering buying.

The basic elements of a computer are shown in Figure 1.6 (you really didn't think we could get away without including at least one picture of a computer, did you?)

The elements, no matter what you have, are the same—a system unit including processor and memory, disk drives, a keyboard, mouse and perhaps some peripherals and accessories such as a modem, CD-ROM drive and printer.

Processors and Other Chips—What Do the Numbers Mean to Hams?

The processor and its speed directly affect the software you can run. An older PC, PC/XT or similar era clone can do very well with some older and current computing software, such as the freeware written and distributed by VE3ERP (see the Resources Chapter), but stumble and often fail with most newer communications packages. They generally will not support any software that includes high-resolution graphics, and the use of *Windows* is out of the question.

To work properly, many communications programs look for signals on the computer ports (I/O) by directly examining the contents of and writing to various regis-

Figure 1.6—Desktop or tower case, old or new, the PC adds a new, powerful capability to your shack. The minimum configuration consists of the main unit, keyboard, monitor and (usually) a printer. (Photo courtesy of MICRON ELECTRONICS, INC.)

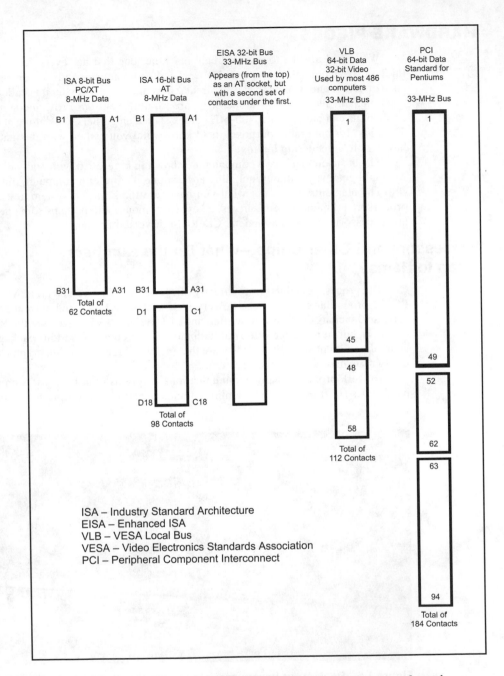

ISA 8-bit Bus
PC/XT
8-MHz Data

ISA 16-bit Bus
AT
8-MHz Data

EISA 32-bit Bus
33-MHz Bus
Appears (from the top)
as an AT socket, but
with a second set of
contacts under the first.

VLB
64-bit Data
32-bit Video
Used by most 486
computers
33-MHz Bus

PCI
64-bit Data
Standard for
Pentiums

33-MHz Bus

B1   A1   B1   A1

B31   A31   B31   A31

Total of
62 Contacts

D1   C1

D18   C18

Total of
98 Contacts

1

45

48

58

Total of
112 Contacts

1

49

52

62

63

94

Total of
184 Contacts

ISA – Industry Standard Architecture
EISA – Enhanced ISA
VLB – VESA Local Bus
VESA – Video Electronics Standards Association
PCI – Peripheral Component Interconnect

Figure 1.7—Plug-in cards are built to match the type of computer. A card designed for an XT or AT will plug into, and probably work with a newer system, such as one with an AT bus. A card built to work with a newer bus will not work with an older bus system, however, even if you can plug in the card.

ters. Chapter 5 describes some of these I/O functions, and how to use them for your own programs.

As an example, the 8250 UART (universal asynchronous receiver and transmitter) chip was used in most early PCs. If the communications software you want to use was written to connect through the serial port, and does not require a speed higher than 9600 baud, you can probably use this hardware/software combination—assuming the PC bus speed is high enough. If the software requires a higher speed, a 16450 or 16550 chip interface will be required.

No problem, you might say. Just change the I/O card to a newer one, and presto—you are using a 16550. Not quite! If your PC clock and bus speed are the limit, you are still in trouble. In addition, the computer BIOS probably does not support the newer I/O card requirements.

That's the bad side. Now, what is the good side? For most common communications programs and non-*Windows* computational programs, a 16-MHz 386-based computer is usually all that is needed. Sure there are exceptions, but if this is what you have, you just have to select software capable of running on it.

A Word About Upgrades

You are a ham. Your buddy tells you all the connectors on a PC motherboard are standard, so disconnecting your current motherboard and reconnecting a new one should be easy. Go for it! See Figure 1.7.

Well, that is only part of the story. It is very tempting to buy a new motherboard for $100, plug your existing power supply into the new board, and upgrade. Unfortunately, there are a few cautions. Yes, the connectors are generally standard. Some clones used a telephone type connector for the keyboard plug, and this is not compatible with new boards. But for the most part, these are simple problems that can usually be solved with a converting cable or plug combination.

One real problem revolves around memory. First find out if your existing memory chips can be used—or if you want to use them—on a newer motherboard. You may find you will have to buy new memory, which will change the economic picture considerably. In addition, some of your existing plug-in cards either may not be compatible with the BIOS on the new motherboard, or may not use the new motherboard to good advantage. Before you choose this road, get a good book on upgrading. See the Resources Chapter for some recommendations.

Add Capability by Plugging in Cards

Today's PCs are based on an *open architecture*—the details are publicly documented. If you want to manufacture and sell a card that thousands of people can plug into their computer, you can safely base your design on this public documentation. Once again, you have to exercise caution when adding capability to an old computer. For example, some PCs have disk controllers and I/O interfaces built onto the motherboard. Others have multipurpose boards—a video board that also includes both a printer port and a game port is a common configuration. If you wish to plug in a hard disk controller so you can add a hard disk you may have to disable the current floppy controller. Without documentation, this can be difficult. It may prove next to impossible if the computer BIOS does not support various hard disk sizes, and no software patch is available.

The same problem arises if you want to add an I/O card to give you a second serial port and a second printer port. You may have to disable ports currently active, or remove current multi-purpose boards and replace them with non-overlapping boards. You could wind up paying more for these new boards than you did for the entire flea-market computer!

More Memory—It's Alphabet Soup Time!

One easy way to upgrade computer performance—for an older machine or a brand new one—is to add memory. The good news is memory is getting cheaper. The bad news is that memory types evolve, so the hardware needed for last year's computer will not be suitable for this year's, and sometimes even last month's will not be the best for this month's!

There are three basic questions to be answered before buying more memory:

- The electrical size and arrangement, such as 1 meg by 9 bits
- The physical form, such as DIP, SIPP or SIMM
- The speed rating—60, 70, 80 or 90 ns

The earliest PCs (and their predecessors, such as the Apple IIs), used *DIPs*—dual in-line packages—for memory. These were simply individual microcircuits, very similar to the 14 and 16-pin chips commonly used for logic circuits today. They mounted either on the motherboard or, if there was not enough space on the motherboard, on a plug-in card.

If you are considering adding memory to an older computer, the telltale sign of the presence of DIP memory is the absence of the other types of memory described in this section, since the memory chips look just like all the other chips in the computer. You will probably want to increase the memory size to 640 kbytes. Other arrangements—with expanded memory and memory managers, allowing 1 meg of RAM—are possible. To go this route, see the Resources Chapter for recommended references on memory expansion.

Single in-line pin packages, or *SIPPs*, are a pre-assembled memory module designed to plug directly into a motherboard. At first glance, they appear to be a circuit board, about one inch high and several inches long, with a row of 30 pins sticking out from one long side. Although several configurations were made, they generally contain 9 memory chips. Some replacements for the 9-chip *SIPPs* contain only 3 chips, but are functionally equivalent.

Your computer may use a later evolution of the SIPP, called a *SIMM*—single in-line memory module. The first SIMMs were a 16-bit wide memory module with 30 contacts along one edge. Newer versions have 72 contacts, and contain either 32 or 36-bit wide memory organization. Small converting sockets make it possible to use older 30-contact SIMMs in a computer requiring 72-pin units.

As you can see, there is a wide variety of memory available and needed for today's (and yesterday's) computers. Without an instruction manual (and details on the motherboard), memory expansion can be a nightmare. Mail order and flea market vendors sell a wide variety of new and used products. One tip—try the Internet. If you can describe the motherboard, a search for the manufacturer on both web sites and newsgroups can turn up a surprising amount of information. Perhaps someone else has tried to add memory to the same computer you now own. See Chapter 6 for more information.

Hard Disks, Floppy Disks and No Disks

In the beginning there were cassette recorders. This may be no surprise if you saw an original Radio Shack TRS-1. The agony of loading software and reading software from a cassette recorder is akin to a visit to the dentist in the early 1800s. It was usually effective, but once was enough. The advent of floppy disks, even those that held less than 200 kbytes, were nothing short of a miracle. Of the various sizes and capacities used, only the 1.2-Mbyte 5 1/4-inch and the 1.44-Mbyte 3 1/2-inch floppies are current, with older 5 1/4-inch drives capable of only 360 kbytes found primarily in used PCs. Often, software found at flea markets and bought from mail-order shareware suppliers use the obsolete 360-kbyte format.

Adding another disk drive, or changing a drive from an older, low-capacity drive to a higher capacity is relatively simple—at least mechanically. Cables from the disk drive controller usually allow connections of any of the three floppy types. Even if the existing cable does not, a new cable is inexpensive. The real problem is the BIOS. Earlier computers, built before there were any alternatives to the 5 1/4-inch 360-kbyte drives, may not recognize the new drives. Changing the BIOS is possible, but will cost you both time and effort—if anyone still stocks one for the machine you are working with.

A similar problem exists for hard disks. Early PCs did not come with hard disks, and some had hard disks added as a plug-in card. One popular trade name was *Hard-Card*. A software patch installed the *Hard-Card*, and bypassed BIOS problems. Other early computers had hard disks, but their capacity was limited to 10, 20 or perhaps 40 Mbytes. Often, these computers can be upgraded to larger hard disk capacity than their BIOS can recognize by using special software packaged with the new hard disk. A typical large replacement drive and upgrade software is described in the Resources Chapter.

Getting Information In and Out—Those Connectors in the Back

Suppose you bought a new rig. You took it out of the box, unpacked it and turned it around to connect it to the rest of your equipment. On the back were a set of connectors, but no labels or tags to identify them. You look in the instruction manual, and there you find a cryptic statement that all the connectors are "standard." Sound bizarre? Well, that is exactly what many of us face with our computers—except often, with used machines, there is no instruction book.

Fortunately, there is a degree of standardization, but you have to have a key or magic decoder to identify them. The sidebar on connectors will provide a starting point.

Variations and nonstandard models are in wide use. Instead of a 5-pin DIN male connector for the keyboard, some units use a modular telephone-like RJ plug. Others have a right-angle 5-pin DIN connector, which will not fit into certain computers, where a slightly recessed 5-pin socket is mounted directly on the motherboard. They were designed for a straight-in DIN connector.

The designation male or female always refers to the pins. Depending on the type of connector, there may be a male or female skirt, shield or insulating structure around the pins or the entire connector.

Mice usually come with a standard serial port mating connector. Some also come with a miniature female 6-pin DIN-like connector, as well as a converting cable to a serial port jack.

What Connects Where?

There are standards (sort of) so when you look at the rear of your PC, you can tell what an unlabeled jack is supposed to do. There is no guarantee, but if the connector fits, try it. Supposedly you will not be able to damage anything. The most common connectors you will run into are:

- *50-pin female connector, for a 50 wire flat cable*—This is the interface connector for SCSI-1 and SCSI-2 (small computer systems interface) bus. A similar 68-pin connector is used for the Fast-Wide SCSI. Don't expect to see these at flea markets in the near future!

- *36-pin female*—occasionally found on the rear of certain IBM models. It was used to connect external storage devices to the internal bus. Some early computers used this connector for a printer connector.

- *25-pin female*—parallel printer port. Note the mating cable is usually terminated at the far end in a 36 male parallel contact (not pin) connector with wire clips. This is the standard Centronics printer connector. Most often, only one such connector is supplied, but occasionally 2 (LPT1 and LPT2) are present. New machines have an *EPP*, enhanced parallel port, which is bidirectional.

- *25-pin male*— Serial or RS-232 port, primarily on older PCs. Newer PCs more often use a 9-pin male.

- *15-pin female in 3 rows*—VGA and higher resolution monitor connector. Notice, this means you cannot plug a CGA monitor into a VGA video card.

- *15-pin female in two rows*—game port

- *9-pin male*—Serial or RS-232 port. Early computers were able to have only two serial ports, and often only one was used for external devices. The other remained internal, and was used for a modem. New computers usually have up to four serial ports, with two external 9-pin connectors.

- *9-pin female*—CGA and EGA video connector. The mating cable goes to the monitor.

- *6-pin mini-DIN female*—mouse connector. The male connector has a small protruding rectangular pin in its center. Some newer keyboards also use this mini-connector.

- *5-pin DIN female*—keyboard connector. If there is a second 5-pin DIN connector (most likely only on a very old IBM PC), this second connector is for the cassette recorder.

- *Three RCA jacks from a single plug-in card plus another connector*—nonstandard video card. The three RCA jacks are the three color signals, and the extra connector carries the amplitude and sync signals on separate wires. While not a real PC standard, this arrangement was used in a number of industrial monitors, and these monitors often show up at flea markets.

- *Two RJ-11 4-wire modular telephone plug sockets*—connections to the rear panel of a modem card.

- *3-pin ac male connector*—On many PCs, the male 3-pin connector is used with a line cord to supply primary ac power. Some monitors have a power cord terminated in a 3-pin male, which plugs through a line cord into a mating female connector on the rear of the computer, to supply prime power to the monitor.

- *Single RJ-45 8-wire modular telephone plug socket*—network or LAN connection. Some older keyboards also used this connector.

- *Single RCA phono jack*—composite video to a TV type monitor.

- *Single BNC connector*—network or LAN connection.

- *Several (2 or 3) $1/8$-inch audio jacks*—mounted on the rear of one plug-in card, this is usually the inputs and outputs of a sound card. Occasionally, RCA phono jacks are used on the same card for speaker connections.

Printers

To print out log sheets, contest totals and even interesting text you have captured on packet, you'll need a printer. Fortunately, prices of new printers have come down. High-quality laser printers sell for prices unimagined several years ago. Near-laser-quality inkjet printers are now very reasonable. If you're in the market for a bargain or a second printer, there is nothing wrong with a $150 dot-matrix printer; even better is the $25 flea-market special.

Occasionally, the program you are using will do strange things with a noncompatible printer. This may result in control signals doing such things as ejecting paper or advancing continuous-feed paper one sheet. The software will usually permit you to select a "vanilla" setting, however, such as "TTY," "serial TTY" or "standard printer." These will produce very usable text.

The most common printer standards (called emulations) are IBM, Epson and Hewlett-Packard. Most software will allow you to choose one of these as your printer, in addition to other brands of printers. Many printers allow selection, either through software or by setting a switch, of one of these printer emulations.

CD-ROMs, IRQs and Shovelware

A few years ago a CD-ROM drive was an unusual accessory—found only where the PC user felt it was the way to access a great deal of data available quickly. As cost went down, CD-ROMs became more and more common.

Installation of a CD-ROM drive can be a real problem, especially if your computer is loaded with accessories and multiple ports. Interrupt conflicts—the infamous IRQ problem (see Appendix B)—can result in a crippled or completely hung-up machine.

One of the easiest ways to add CD-ROM capability is by adding it as part of a sound card and CD-ROM package. The CD-ROM drive electrically interfaces with the plug-in sound card, and the accompanying installation software usually sorts out the interrupt questions. It is not foolproof—but can be much better than trying to find out why your computer hangs up for "no apparent reason."

Utility programs, including one usually supplied as part of a *Windows* package, allow you to examine the IRQs in use on your PC. Run this software before you install the CD-ROM so you will know what answers to give the installation software.

Initially, CD-ROMs for the ham community were simply collections of existing freeware and shareware, shoveled onto a CD-ROM to fill the disk to capacity. Thus the name *shovelware*. This material has its own value—a number of handy utilities, logging programs and other gems can be found buried on these disks. This is especially true if you are running an older machine. Much of this software was written for a PC, XT or AT (and similar clones) and do not require much machine capability.

The second generation of ham CD-ROMs are ham databases, such as call-sign directories. The newer generation of CD-ROMs contain magazine back issues. You no longer have to store the last few years of *QST* in your shack, or keep years of back issues in moldy boxes in the garage. Plop in a CD—and scan back to the material you want! See Chapter 3 for more information on these items.

It's Your Eyeballs

As a ham, you won't just sit down and write a letter or two on your computer.

More likely, you will spend an evening operating or a weekend staring at the computer monitor during a contest. Eyes become tired, and the better display you can use, the better it is for your eyes.

Low resolution *CGA* (color graphics adapter), the first color standard for PCs, is probably the worst choice you can make, unless you use it in a single color mode. Commercial computer users discovered this fact very quickly, and many users replaced CGA with *EGA* (extended graphics adapter). But even this was not good enough, and EGA was quickly replaced with *VGA* (video graphics adapter). Unfortunately, many old computers can support only CGA, or perhaps EGA at best.

VGA is the real standard for many applications. Although you'll often see *SVGA* (super VGA) on the label, its features are rarely used. Other standards are around, and occasionally referenced, but the three primary (CGA, VGA and SVGA) types are now the most common.

Monitor size also is important. For straight text, a 14-inch monitor may be acceptable, but for modern *Windows* applications 15-inch, 17-inch or larger units are desirable. Dot pitches of 0.25 to 0.29 mm are standard and provide good resolution.

If you are considering buying a new monitor, read the spec sheet carefully. While dot pitches of less than 0.30 mm are readily available, so are low-cost monitors with a dot pitch of .48 or larger. The display size refers to the diagonal screen measurement. Many "17-inch" displays have a diagonal of only 16 or 15.8 inches; others are even smaller.

Examine the monitor with live video. Some are not usable within $^1/_2$-inch (or more) of the edge of the screen. Thus, you may be better off buying a better quality, smaller monitor for the same usable area.

A good monitor, meeting all your requirements, could cost over $1000—which may well not be feasible. So what do you do?

⌨ Consider mono applications. If you are not using SSTV or color fax, a monochromatic display—either green on black or some variation of black and white—may be your choice. Many CGA displays have a mono switch on the back, which lets you operate in a green and black mode. You also can combine the three color signals in an adapter, and run them to just one grid in the monitor. If you select the green video input, all video will show as green. Figure 1.8 contains the wiring of the CGA connecting plug, if you wish to try this approach. The Resources Chapter contains additional information on this wiring.

⌨ If you use glasses to read, talk to a qualified eyeglass provider about a pair for the computer. He or she will discuss your monitor size and the distance you sit from the monitor, and then you can order reading glasses matched to the distance. Bifocals can be a problem, since you may have to keep your head tilted back to see the screen through the reading portion of the lenses.

⌨ Timeshare your monitor. If you have a computer with a good monitor outside your shack, consider moving it into the shack temporarily—at least until the contest is over.

Where Do We Go From Here?

We've discussed the most common hardware and software questions: Choosing hardware, new or used, and upgrading used hardware. Most importantly, you should know what you want to do with the computer before you buy anything. The software

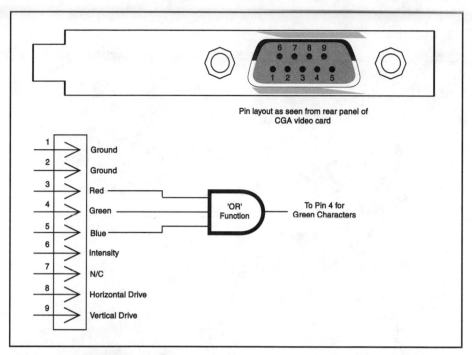

Pin layout as seen from rear panel of
CGA video card

Figure 1.8—CGA wiring is easy to modify. You can select all-green text (the usual choice) or all-blue or all-red.

has to work under your operating system, and both must be within the capabilities of the hardware.

The chapters that follow have examples of the many things you can do with your personal computer. The Glossary in Appendix B has definitions of many common computer terms.

Your PC as a Communications Terminal

Presumably you already own a computer. But if you don't, read this chapter and you will likely want to run out and get one. We will show how your computer can be used at little or no additional cost to receive and send SSTV (Slow Scan Television); become a packet TNC; send and receive CW, RTTY and AMTOR; decode WEFAX (Weather Fax) transmissions and even act as an "Automatic Packet Reporting System" (APRS). A few years back you would have to buy separate units to be able to use these modes. The hardware in a modern 386/486 or Pentium is so powerful it performs these tasks easily. Software engineers realized that they could exploit this hardware power by creating applications that completely replace existing standalone hardware. Imagine—a whole slow-scan TV system on a floppy downloaded from a BBS.

What makes all this possible is the ability of a digital device—the computer—to process analog information. If all we need to determine is the frequency of an analog signal, rather than its amplitude, this is an easy task for a computer. Fortunately, all the above-mentioned applications convey their information in the frequency domain—they are frequency encoded.

Figure 2.1 shows how the frequency of a sine wave can be converted into a string of numbers that a computer can "understand." In this example, the increasing frequency of a sine wave is converted into a string of numbers that change in proportion to frequency. The signal at A is the speaker output of a receiver, and is squared up by the limiting action of a simple op-amp, producing the waveform at B. This signal is fed directly into the computer serial port, and the time between the rising and falling edges is calculated by the computer. When the frequency increases, the period between zero crossings (rising and falling edges) decreases.

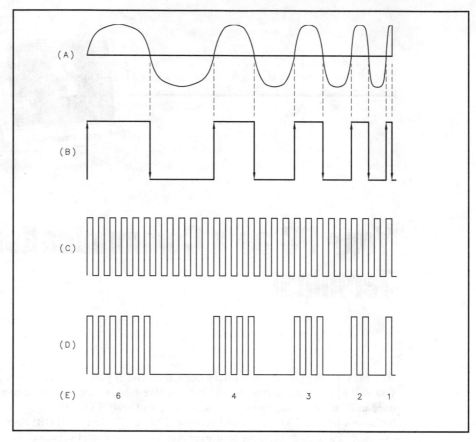

Figure 2.1— The process used to convert an audio tone into computer video. At A, an audio tone increasing in frequency represents a video change from black to white. The signal at B has been limited by overdriving an op-amp. It produces a level that is sufficient to drive the serial port. The waveform at C graphically represents a clock that is generated by the application software. The signal at D illustrates how the software determines the period of B. Clock pulses are only counted between the rising and falling edges of waveform B. At E the varying number of pulses have been converted into numbers that the computer program uses to set the video level. In this example a video level of 6 represents black and a value of 1 represents white.

If the computer's internal clock (C) is much higher than that of the incoming signal, the computer can count how many clock pulses occur between zero crossings with a high degree of resolution. The process is not exact, but the higher the internal clock speed of the computer, the more finely the changes in frequency can be measured. Figure 2.1E shows that the incoming period was decreasing (increasing frequency) from 6 to 4 to 3, etc. to 1. For clarity, the internal clock is shown as a much lower frequency than that actually used by the computer. In reality, thousands of internal clock pulses will occur during a single period of the incoming signal.

If this were an SSTV signal, the information being sent might represent the brightness at a given time. In our simple example, a count of six pulses might represent a dark portion of the picture, and a count of one or two might represent a brighter portion. For an RTTY or packet signal, a count greater than four might represent a mark tone and anything less than four counts as a space tone. Once the incoming waveform has been converted to numbers inside the computer, there are thousands of ways software can display the information. For SSTV it might be the brightness of a color; for packet, RTTY and CW it may be alphanumeric characters on the screen.

The process is completely reversible and the computer can transmit these specialized signals. The serial port can be programmed to output a waveform similar to Figure 2.1B. A simple RC low-pass filter is often used between the computer and the mike input to remove most high-frequency components by rounding the leading and trailing edges of the square waves.

COMMON DENOMINATORS

It is important to realize that these modes have something in common, which makes it possible for them to run on a PC: They all convey their information as a varying audio tone. This audio tone may be transmitted, like your voice, using either SSB, AM, FM or any other modulation technique, as long as the demodulated signal returns a replica of the original. A simple circuit gets the low-level analog signal from the speaker into the computer. Because the computer uses a digital logic level (see Chapter 5) at the serial port, the speaker output (500 mV typical) must be amplified. A

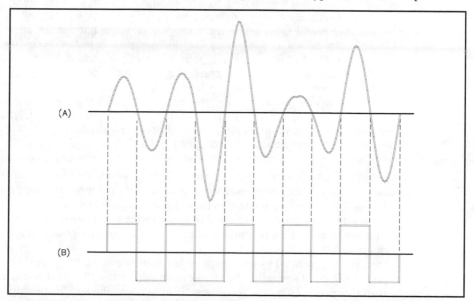

Figure 2.2—The waveform at A is an audio signal with amplitude variations caused by QSB. The signal at B has the variations removed by the limiting action of an op-amp. The amplitude information has been lost—the only information left is due to frequency changes.

Serial Port Plays A Dual Role

The role that the serial (com) port plays can be confusing and easily misunderstood. This port is the main avenue for getting external signals (data) in and out of your computer. Confusion often results because the serial port may also be referred to as the RS-232 port. RS-232 defines a specific way the serial port works. The voltage levels and functionality of each pin have been pre-defined by the Electronic Industries Association (EIA). Their definition was based on the supposition that the serial port would be connected to a modem-compatible device and used for data communication. Because RS-232 usage is so popular, a dedicated piece of hardware was developed to convert the CPU's data into RS-232-compatible data. This device, called a UART (Universal Asynchronous Receiver Transmitter), is found in every PC with a serial port. The UART is largely a self-contained system providing its own clock and data buffering. As a result, external data cannot be directly read though the RS-232-defined TX and RX data pins on a real-time basis. This creates a bottleneck for applications that need to access the CPU in the fastest possible time.

Clever programmers soon figured out a way to get data into the CPU by utilizing the serial port in a nonconventional fashion. They realized the RX and TX pins were always buffered by the UART. The handshaking lines were not buffered, however, and could signal the CPU through an interrupt request. In a 386/486 machine, the interrupt cycle is fast enough for the data to be processed in near real-time.

CPU speeds increased to a point where analog signals, such as audio, could be sampled with a simple limiter similar to the HamComm interface. Input to the CPU would be fed through one of the handshake lines. The PC now had the ability to process any audio signal up to 3000 Hz. This is nothing short of revolutionary! Your PC can now perform both analog-to-digital and digital-to-analog conversions. Any analog signal that comes out the speaker of your rig can be processed by the computer. Think of all the hardware devices using the speakers' audio that can now be replaced by software—TNCs, SSTV systems, modems, audio spectrum analyzers and data analyzers to name just a few. For more information on electrically interfacing with your computer, see Chapter 5.

simple op-amp does the trick, acting as both an amplifier and limiter. All the amplitude variations are removed, leaving only the FM components (zero crossings). See Figure 2.2. If the op-amp derives its power directly from the serial port, its output will be in saturation, producing a bipolar output swing that is suitable for driving the input of a serial port. This is a nice feature, because external power supplies are not required.

Tones generated by the computer are available at the PC's speaker or at the serial port TXD pin. Generally, the signal generated at the PC speaker has better fidelity than that produced by the serial port. In either case the level is too high and contains harmonics that should be filtered before they are put into the microphone connector. A simple RC low-pass filter, as shown in Figure 2.3B, will filter and attenuate the signal. R3 is used to set the signal level. Although transformer T1 is optional, it is highly recommended since it eliminates ground loops that often cause feedback.

Although the serial port is commonly called the RS-232 port, all control is assumed by the application program and none of the standard RS-232 conventions are used. For example, RX data is never used as data input for these programs because the computer has no direct way to sense the level of this pin. The UART gets in the way by buffering the data, thus precluding real-time processing. The application program has to bypass the use of the UART by sensing the level on one of the other control pins such as DSR. A de facto standard has developed, known as the *HamComm interface,* which assigns specific pins for data in/out, power supply and PTT control. Figure 2.3 is a schematic diagram of the HamComm interface. The op-amp used in the receive circuit (Figure 2.3A) brings the audio signal from the receiver up to the RS-232 level. The supply current is drawn from DTR and RTS. Diodes D1-D4 act as steering diodes to ensure that the op-amp sees the correct polarity supply voltage regardless of the states of DTR and RTS. The input signal level should be at least 100 mV (peak-to-peak). C1 is a dc blocking cap. The op-amp runs with maximum gain (open loop) and produces a more or less rectangular waveform. Most op-amps will work, but the 741 is often used because it is inexpensive, is widely available and can run on the few mA that the DTR and RTS pins supply.

HAMCOMM

W. F. Schroeder, DL5YEC, has created a sophisticated shareware program, *HamComm*, which supports reception and transmission of CW, RTTY in Baudot or ASCII, AMTOR, ARQ/FEC, Sitor A/B and even Navtex modes. SSTV software developers have followed his standard using his pin-outs. Thus, a single op-amp interface can be used for a whole range of software programs. The circuit shown in Figure 2.3 will fit inside a 25-pin connector case on a small piece of perf-board or can be wired "rats nest" style using point-to point connections. A sidebar at the end of this chapter discusses feedback problems you could find when transmitting. We will use *HamComm* in this chapter as representative of a popular, multipurpose communication program.

HamComm version 3.0 is shareware, and may be freely copied and distributed. It is granted on a limited basis on a 30-day trial basis; after that, a $30 registration fee is expected by the author. It is DOS-based and will run under DOS 3.0 or higher on most PCs with at least 370 kB of free memory. Some functions may not work as expected on older 8088 machines. It cannot run under any kind of multitasking environment like Windows or OS/2, since it needs direct control of the interrupt controller, timer chip and serial I/O hardware. Periodic updates are issued.

On start-up the program tries to identify the video card and automatically selects a graphics mode for highest resolution. If this fails, a command-line option can be used to force the desired video display mode. One nice feature of this program is its ability to utilize any port address and IRQ number. Many programs of this class let you use only the common defaults or a narrow range of choices. If you have many external devices attached, it is desirable to be able to select independent IRQs.

The program is easy to run, with many built-in features that can outperform dedicated hardware systems. The built-in tuning screens are superb. An audio spectrum analyzer shows the actual received mark and space frequencies relative to the decoder's passband. You can glance at the screen and determine the shift of the received signal

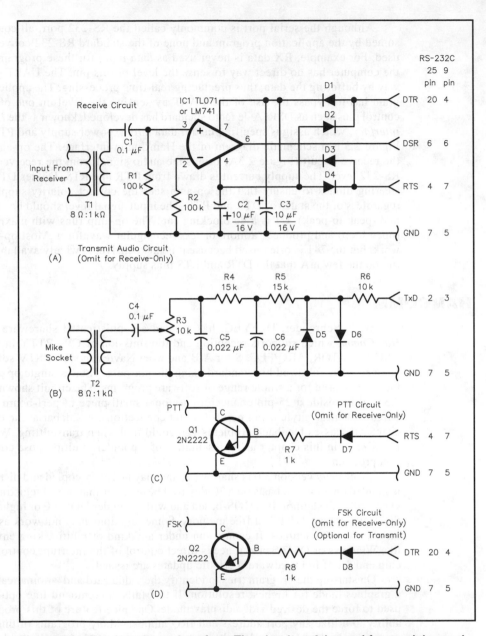

Figure 2.3—*The HamComm* Interface. The circuit at A is used for receiving and the circuit at B for transmitting. The circuit at C keys the transmitter's PTT. If you manually switch from transmit to receive, it is not necessary for receive and may be omitted for transmitting. All resistors are ¹/₄ W. The transformers are Radio Shack no. 273-1380. All diodes are 1N914, 1N4148 or similar. Any small-signal NPN transistor (such as a 2N222 or 2N3904) will work for Q1 and Q2.

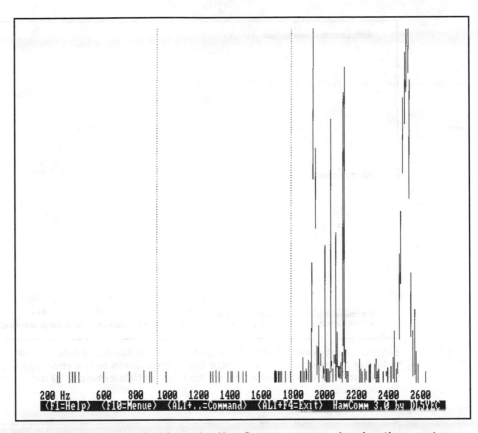

Figure 2.4—A screen shot from the *HamComm* program showing the spectrum analyzer function. The F7 function key activates this feature. A 600-Hz shift RTTY signal is shown tuned too high in frequency on the receiver. Dotted vertical lines represent the currently selected mark and space filter frequencies. Mark is 1800 Hz and is space is 950 Hz, indicating a shift of 850 Hz (1800–950=850). The received signal is shown as the broken lines centered around 2000 and 2600 Hz. The receiver should be tuned to shift the signal lower in frequency (to the left) so that it falls in between the dotted lines.

to see how far off frequency you are tuned. Figure 2.4 shows the spectrum analyzer screen. The display is so sensitive to frequency shifts that fine-tuning adjustments not perceivable by ear are seen clearly on the screen. Another handy tuning feature is the statistical baud rate indicator as shown in Figure 2.5. It indicates the receive baud rate and is an indispensable feature. Figure 2.6 shows the signal frequency versus the center frequency of the modem. In the past even the best hardware decoders left you in the dark regarding the correct tuning and speed settings. See the sidebar at the end of this chapter for tips on tuning digital modes.

AMTOR

Derived from the maritime SITOR system, AMTOR (Amateur Teleprinting Over

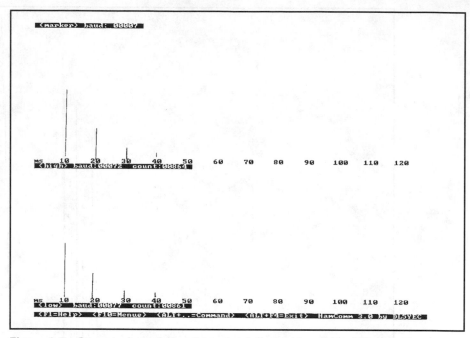

Figure 2.5—Screen shot of *HamComm*'s statistical baud rate display. The time with the highest vertical indicator bar corresponds to the received baud rate. The baud rate is the reciprocal of the time. In this example 10 ms corresponds to 100 baud.

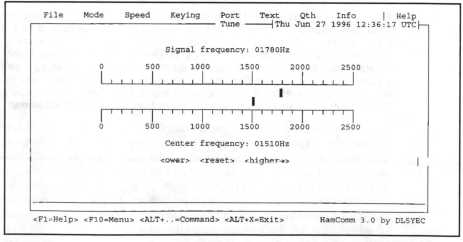

Figure 2.6—Screen shot of *HamComm*'s Center Frequency tuning display. In this example CW is being received, producing a 1780-Hz tone. The receiver should be tuned to lower the pitch of the CW signal to fall on top of the 1510-Hz center frequency.

Radio) is an effective method of sending digital information on HF. Unlike RTTY, AMTOR uses error detection and correction and is a popular mode on the amateur bands. As a side benefit, if you tune outside the amateur bands, you will be able to monitor ship-to-shore Telex messages and maritime weather broadcasts as well. All AMTOR and SITOR transmissions are 100 baud with a 170-Hz shift. AMTOR provides two modes of communication, *ARQ* and *FEC*. In the ARQ (Automatic ReQuest) mode, data is sent in blocks of three characters and the receiving station replies with one character (ACK) for acknowledgment if received correctly.

If an error was detected, a Negative Acknowledge (NAK) is returned to the transmitting station so the data can be sent again. ARQ is the mode used on the amateur bands. Stations listening in can monitor the QSO but will not see the benefit of error correction. The two connected stations will enjoy error-free QSOs, however. When a one-way broadcast is desired, all the listening stations can enjoy the benefits of Forward Error Correction (FEC). Each character is sent twice, but not in succession. This greatly reduces the chances that interference or noise will obliterate both characters. When a missed character is sensed, the program will wait until that character is sent again and then print the correct character. HamComm prints the corrected character in red. This is a neat feature, allowing you to actually see the corrected data; the power of error correction is clearly visible.

W1AW regularly sends bulletins in the FEC mode. The schedule appears in the rear of this book. Maritime coastal stations are another good source for AMTOR reception. See the Resources Chapter. Schedules do change every so often, and updates are usually available on the internet.

Transmitting AMTOR requires fast T/R switching. Most modern transceivers can switch fast enough, but if you plan to use a power amplifier with a "slow" T/R relay, precautions must be taken. If you are not already familiar with the timing restrictions of this mode, further information may be found in the Modulation Sources Chapter of recent editions of *The ARRL Handbook for Radio Amateurs*.

RTTY

The earliest RTTY systems have their roots more in the Industrial Revolution than in the Computer Age. The first RTTY machines were made of gears, cams and motors and could spew out enough oil to ruin your shirt if you were anywhere near them with the cover open. Spouses and families complained about the continual clattering and smell of hot oil. No wonder RTTY fell off in popularity.

Any device using mechanical means to decode data is very slow by today's standards. Despite this, many amateurs still use RTTY because it easily interfaces to your rig. There are no T/R timing restrictions. Transmitting RTTY requires a continuous duty cycle, so care must be taken not to overheat your transmitter. A 170-Hz shift at 45 baud is the amateur standard. To decode an RTTY signal the decoder's center frequency has to be midway between the received mark and space tones. Activating the **F9** function key (under *HamComm*) pops up a tuning bar. All you have to do is tune your receiver so the tuning bar is between the mark and space indicators. RTTY transmissions are often found at the upper end of the CW band segment.

CW

CW is unique because it is the only digital mode that can be decoded in your head. Computers can't compete with the brain when it comes to decoding CW. *HamComm* does a good job when compared to other hardware or computer techniques, but it cannot copy as well as a human. The program has two difficult tasks to perform: first, to figure out when a tone is present and second, to calculate the spacing between tones and determine which character was sent. The second task is particularly difficult and is why a human can outperform a computer.

The first problem is tough because CW has only one tone to decode. (AMTOR and RTTY have two states—frequencies which are constantly being switched back and forth.) All data transmissions require a minimum of two states. For CW these states are the tone and the background noise. It maybe surprising to hear that a certain amount of noise is required by HamComm to be able to tell when the tone is on or off. The best way to tune for CW reception is to use the center frequency marker (F9 function key) and tune the radio so that when the CW tone is heard, it falls on top of the center frequency tuning bar.

Weather Decoding

Although weather decoding is not useful in the ham bands, it is fun to experiment with. Weather reports are transmitted by many stations throughout the world 24 hours a day. In North America try CFH (Halifax, Nova Scotia) on 4271, 6496.5 and 10536 kHz. There are many others between 4000 and 5000 kHz. Transmissions are normally in Baudot, 425-Hz shift, 50 or 75 Baud. The SYNOP format is used for reports from land stations and the SHIP format is used for reports from ships.

The messages include data about temperature, wind speed/direction, cloud cover, precipitation, dewpoint, pressure and other meteorological information. SHIP reports also include the current position of the vessel. Land stations are identified by a five-digit station number. These are fixed stations, so their geographical position is not transmitted with a SYNOP report. To give you a better idea where the reporting station is located, *HamComm* comes with a list of about 10,000 station numbers, their names and geographical position. The program will automatically pick the correct entry from this list while decoding a SYNOP report. A typical message is shown in Figure 2.7

This is the screen you will see if the SHIP/SYNOP decoder function of HamComm is switched off. The first line of a message starts with *zczc* and a three-digit transmission sequence number. The second line is a header describing the following information. Here *sien42* indicates a "synoptic report at intermediate hours" for northern Europe, *edzw* is the international four-letter location indicator of the station originating or compiling the bulletin and *141500* means 1500 UTC on day 14 of the current month. The indicator for SYNOP reports is *aaxx*, and *nnnn* marks the end of a message. Other formats are used for different kinds of information.

When the WX decoder is switched on from the TEXT menu, the screen appears as shown in Figure 2.8. *HamComm* displays the incoming text just as before. The WX decoder watches the characters go by, waiting for certain keywords like *zczc* (start of message), *aaxx* (SYNOP report), *bbxx* (SHIP report) and *nnnn* (end of message) to synchronize with an incoming message. If it thinks it knows what the text is about, it starts to insert comments. The comments are surrounded by square brackets and therefore easily distinguished from the normal text (there are no square brackets in the Baudot character set).

```
zczc 548
sien42 edzw 141500
aaxx 14154
01465 42889 42715 10084 20022 40159 52033 81048=
02060 41480 40000 11088 21113 40060 52035 72272
83530 333 83694=
nnnn
```

Figure 2.7—*HamComm* screen shot showing a typical RTTY weather report. These reports are sent from both land and ships at sea. This screen contains the raw data before decoding. It is sent in this form for brevity. All reports start with the letters *zczc* and end with *nnnn*.

```
zczc [start] 548 [message 548]
sien42 [Synoptic reports at intermediate hours (SYNOP, SHIP)]
[Northern Europe]
edzw [Offenbach (MET/COM Centre)]
141500 [day:14 UTC:1500]
aaxx [SYNOP]
14154 [day:14 UTC:1500] [Wind speed obtained from anemometer (knots)]
01465 [Norway, 58ø24'N 008ø48'E TORUNGEN (LGT-H)]
42889 [manned] [cloud height:2000-2500m] [visibility:75km]
42715 [cloud cover:4/8] [wind dir:270 deg, speed:15]
10084 [air temp:+8.4]20022 [dew-point temp:+2.2]
40159 [pressure at sea level:1015.9hPa]
52033 [pressure:increasing] [change in 3h:3.3hPa]
81048 [cloud info]
02060 [Sweden, 68ø41'N 021ø32'E NAIMAKKA]
41480 [manned] [cloud height:300-600m] [visibility:30km]
40000 [cloud cover:4/8] [wind dir:calm, speed:0]
11088 [air temp:-8.8]
21113 [dew-point temp:-11.3]
40060 [pressure at sea level:1006.0hPa]
52035 [pressure:increasing] [change in 3h:3.5hPa]
72272 [past wx: snow, or rain & snow mixed,cloud cover > 1/2 of sky]
[wx now: Snow]
83530 [cloud info]
333 [section 3]
83694 [clouds:3/8, stratocumulus, 1000-1500m]
nnnn [End of Message]
```

Figure 2.8—*HamComm* screen shot showing a decoded weather report. The program watches for certain keywords and inserts English text in brackets to explain the codes.

SLOW-SCAN TELEVISION

SSTV has probably evolved more than any other facet of Amateur Radio due to advances in PC technology. We can even credit a ham with its invention—Copthorne (Cop) Macdonald, VY2CM, started it all back in 1958. The first commercial hardware was made by Robot and cost over a thousand dollars. For many years there was no alternative until systems using the Amiga and Atari ST computer became available. The first SSTV pictures were sent as 120 lines in eight seconds. Video was sent as a varying audio tone between 1500 Hz for black to 2300 Hz for white. A 1200-Hz tone was sent as the horizontal sync pulse. Today there are a number of different modes being sent, with new ones developing as computer technology continues to evolve. Interestingly, video information is still essentially conveyed as an audio tone varying from 1500-2300 Hz. Actually, those frequencies even predate Macdonald's work, and were used to send commercial facsimile over telephone lines in the '30s and '40s.

All the new systems use a PC as the hardware and many will work with the simple op-amp *HamComm* interface. Some may require a different pin-out for the power and signal input and output. Only these computer-based systems, using a simple op-amp interface, will be covered in this chapter. The older hardware-oriented systems offer no more performance than that provided by the low-cost op-amp interface.

SSTV is not as standardized as AMTOR or packet because the hams who are developing it like to "push the envelope" and take advantage of the very latest computer advances. As PC video graduated from black and white to CGA to VGA and now SVGA, slow-scan video kept pace. Luckily, the differences are all in the software and no additional hardware is required to view these newer modes. Continuing with this trend, the PC's sound card may now be used in place of the simple op-amp for some programs. You can't get much simpler that that. If you have a PC with a Sound Blaster or compatible sound card, you can get on SSTV just by plugging in a cable from your rig to the computer and running SSTV software.

Modes

Figure 2.9 shows how the early black and white systems used a tone varying from 1500 Hz to 2300 Hz to convey video information. Sync was sent at 1200 Hz. The first attempt at sending color pictures required that each picture be sent three times, once in red then blue and then green. This frame-sequential system was particularly susceptible to interference. A better approach was to send each line in sequential fashion. The three primary colors were sent as shown in Figure 2.10.

Most SSTV modes are named after the programmers who developed them. The Martin, Scottie and Wraase modes all use the line-sequential method. The Wraase SC-1 mode is an example of an early color line-sequential system that used a sync pulse for every line. The problem with this approach was that the receiving station would lose track of which line was which with the slightest bit of interference. The resulting picture would have mixed-up colors. The Martin and Scottie modes got around this problem by sending a single horizontal sync pulse for each set of red, blue and green lines. If synchronization was lost, it would be corrected in only one line and the overall picture quality was much better under noisy conditions.

The Scottie S1 mode is the most widely used in the United States; in Europe, Martin M1 is more popular. Other modes, such as Robot 36 and 72, and ATV 90 and 94, are used but are not as popular. The techniques used to encode the video differ for each mode. Modes that take longer to transmit produce a clearer picture because they have more scan lines. Transmission characteristics are summarized in Table 2.1 (thanks John Langner, WB2OSZ).

The JV-Color mode combines properties of both FAX and SSTV transmission. This is a good mode for use on a noise-free channel where maximum resolution is desired. Unlike the other SSTV modes, the actual number of lines per minute is user selectable. This requires both the transmitting and receiving stations run JV-Fax software.

As more modes developed, it became apparent that a means of identifying them was required. VIS, Vertical Interval Signaling, codes were adopted to determine, automatically, which mode was being sent. The Robot 1200C was the first system to employ VIS codes. The vertical sync pulse was lengthened from the original 30 ms pulse to 300 ms to accommodate 7 data bits plus a start, stop and parity bit. The 1100, 1200 and 1300-Hz tones are used as shown in Figure 2.11. All current SSTV systems use the VIS code.

Most SSTV modes send 16 lines of gray-scale information at the top of the picture. Generally they will not be saved when the image is saved to a file. Figure 2.12 is a sample of actual off-the-air SSTV pictures received by DL8EBM. They are even more striking when viewed in color on a monitor.

Operating SSTV

The majority of SSTV takes place on 80 and 20 meters. Some

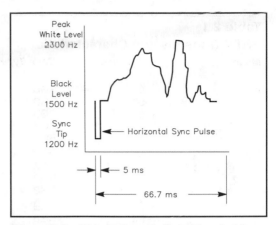

Figure 2.9—This is the relationship of video level to frequency for most early SSTV systems. Peak white was sent as 2300 Hz and black at 1500 Hz. Sync pulses were a 5 ms burst of 1200 Hz. A complete frame was sent as 120 lines in 8 seconds. Each line was 66.6 ms long.

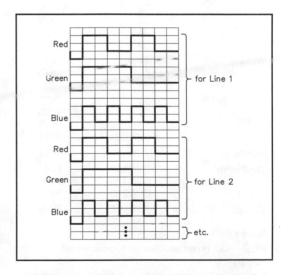

Figure 2.10—This is a typical line-sequential color SSTV transmission. Each line is sent three times: once in each of the primary colors, red, blue and green. After they have been received, the computer combines them into a single full color line.

Table 2.1
SSTV Transmission Characteristics

Mode	Designator	Color Type	Scan Time (sec)	Scan Lines	Notes
ATV	24	RGB	24	120	D
	90	RGB	90	240	D
	94	RGB	94	200	D
	188	RGB	188	400	D
	125	BW	125	400	D
Martin	M1	RGB	114	240	B
	M2	RGB	58	240	B
	M3	RGB	57	120	C
	M4	RGB	29	120	C
Pasokon TV	P3	RGB	203	16+480	
	P5	RGB	305	16+480	
	P7	RGB	406	16+480	
Robot	8	BW	8	120	A,E
	12	BW	12	120	E
	24	BW	24	240	E
	36	BW	36	240	E
	12	YC	12	120	
	24	YC	24	120	
	36	YC	36	240	
	72	YC	72	240	
Scottie	S1	RGB	110	240	B
	S2	RGB	71	240	B
	S3	RGB	55	120	C
	S4	RGB	36	120	C
	DX	RGB	269	240	B
Wraase SC-1	24	RGB	24	120	C
	48	RGB	48	240	B
	96	RGB	96	240	B
Wraase SC-2	30	RGB	30	128	
	60	RGB	60	256	
	120	RGB	120	256	
	180	RGB	180	256	
Pro-Skan	J120	RGB	120	240	
WinPixPro	GVA 125	BW	125	480	
	GVA 125	RGB	125	240	
	GVA 250	RGB	250	480	
JV Fax	JV Fax Color	RGB	variable	variable	F

Notes

RGB—Red, green and blue components sent separately.

YC—Sent as Luminance (Y) and Chrominance (R-Y and B-Y).

BW—Black and white.

A—Similar to original 8-second black & white standard.

B—Top 16 lines are gray scale. 240 usable lines.

C—Top 8 lines are gray scale. 120 usable lines.

D—AVT modes have a 5-second digital header and no horizontal sync.

E—Robot 1200C doesn't really have B&W mode but it can send red, green or blue memory separately. Traditionally, just the green component is sent for a rough approximation of a b&w image.

F—JV Fax Color mode allows the user to set the number of lines sent, the maximum horizontal resolution is slightly less than 640 pixels. This produces a slow but very high resolution picture. SVGA graphics are required.

Figure 2.11—The composition of the Vertical Interval Signal (VIS), used to select the correct SSTV mode automatically. The signal is tri-polar—it has three states. Data is sent as a 1100, 1200 or 1300-Hz tone lasting 30 ms. There are 7 data bits plus a start, stop and parity bit. In this example, the code for Robot 36 Color is shown as binary 00010001.

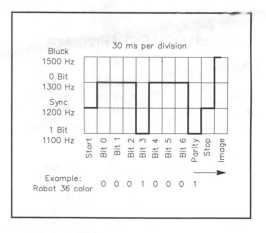

Figure 2.12—Joerg Bauerfeld, DL8EBM, captured these off-air SSTV pictures. When viewed on a monitor, they appear in full color and are quite striking. As you can see, there is a wide variety of subjects being sent. This makes SSTV exciting—you never know what you will be seeing next.

Table 2.2
Comparison of SSTV Programs

	Modes	CPU Requirement	Video Requirements
JVFAX 7.1	B&W 8, 16, 32 M1, M2, S1, S2 SC-DX, WEFAX, MSAT, HamColor, NOAA	386 with 640 kB RAM, runs under DOS	256 color SVGA or hi-color card
PC SSTV 5.0 Color SSTV (Blaster)	BW 8,12,24,36 sec S1, S2 M1, M2 Robot 36 & 72	min 286 386/486 preferred, 640 kB RAM, 5 MB HD space	VGA (640x480), 256-color with 512 K memory`
SSTV Explorer	Robot Color 12, 24, 36, 72 Robot B&W 8, 12, 24, 36 M1, M2, M3, M4 S1, S2, S3, S4 Wrasse SC-1, 24, 48, 96	min 286 640K RAM	VGA
WinPix Pro	AVT 24, 90, 94, 188 AVT BW 125 GVA 125,250 GVA BW 125 M1, M2, M3, M4 Pasokon 3, 5, 7 PD 65, 180, 240 Robot 12, 24, 36, 72 Robot BW 8, 12, 24, 36 S1, S2, S3, S4, DX Wraase SC1, 24, 48, 96 Wraase BW SCI, 8, 16, 24, 32 Wraase SC2, 30, 60, 120, 180	486/33DX 8 MB RAM Windows 3.1 or Win95	
GHS-PC	M1, M2, M3, M4 S1, S2, S3, S4, DX Wraase SC-2 30, 60, 120, 180 Robot Color 12, 24, 36, 72 Robot BW 8, 12, 24, 36	386/DX 640K RAM	VGA, 1 MB VESA mode
Proskan ver 2.07	S1, S2, DX, DX2 M1, M2 Robot BW 24, 36 Robot Color 72 AVT 24,90,94 J-120 wefax	386/33DX 600K conventional memory	SVGA 640×480, 256
EZSTV	S1 Robot 36 color	386 or better 640 K RAM	Color VGA Use of VESA driver will result in best resolution
Vester	ATV 90, 94 Wraase 96 FAX 480 wefax S1, S2 M1,M2	286 386/16 or 33 better	SVGA color 640×480, 256

Cost	Tuning Indicator	Type of Interface
Shareware, voluntary contribution	Yes	HamComm others
$30 shareware S1 mode only $80 all modes RX only $100 full working version		Sound Blaster
$50 includes software and hardware adapter		HamComm
30 day free demo $149 to purchase		Sound Blaster 16 bit Windows Compatible
Shareware $35 registered	Spectrum analyzer or Oscilloscope	HamComm
Shareware $40	graphic display showing sync	HamComm
Free demo version	Tuning bar	HamComm
Free	None	simple op amp type, however the pin outs are different from the HamComm standard

2-meter repeaters even allow SSTV under prearranged circumstances. Figure 2.13 lists the most common SSTV frequencies. See the Resources Chapter for more information on frequency updates. You don't have to be set up for HF to enjoy SSTV, nor do you necessarily have to transmit SSTV to enjoy this specialized mode. Most of the SSTV programs are DOS based because they need to run uninterrupted. They cannot operate under Windows, OS2 or any environment where TSRs are used.

You might ask, what extra equipment (other than a *HamComm* type interface) will I need to get started? The answer is none. Most SSTV operation does not involve live picture transmission so images taken from your computer are fine. Broadly speaking, there are three common image sources: pictures generated with a camera, images generated with a graphics program and images altered by a graphics program. If you have Internet access, many images can be downloaded for SSTV transmission. Most people do not send pictures directly from a camera because of the high cost of a camera.

If you own a camcorder you are in luck, since these images may be "captured" with a frame grabber or image capture card. Recently a better solution has been provided by Connectix Corporation. They have developed inexpensive CCD cameras that are perfect for SSTV because they are low cost and do not require an extra grabber/capture card. Their golf ball size camera plugs directly into the parallel port (serial port if used on a Mac) of the computer. A black-and-white model goes for less than $99 and the color model for around $200. These cameras are becoming popular for SSTV, and it is likely you will be seeing more live video as a result. The most memorable pictures are those of operators in their shacks.

You don't even need the simple *HamComm* interface if you have a Sound Blaster compatible audio card. Programs that use a sound card can work under the *Windows* environment, since the critical timing issues are taken care of by the sound card. If you don't have a modern *Windows* machine, an old 286 can run the Vester system. Table 2.2 summarizes the most popular SSTV programs. As you can see, there are programs for many different platforms, so you should be able to choose one that is just right for you.

List of popular SSTV frequencies:
3.845
3.857
7.171
14.230
14.233
21.340
28.680

Figure 2.13—Listen on these popular SSTV frequencies. 14.230 MHz is the most popular with activity heard anytime the 20-meter band is open. Although 14.233 and 3.857 are not part of generally agreed-to band plans (see the Resources Chapter), SSTV is often heard on these frequencies when 14.230 and 3.845 are busy.

Interfacing the Rig and Computer

The *HamComm* interface is very simple to build and gives excellent results; however, there are some possible problem areas. For example, programs such as JVFAX require an IRQ to be configured in the program to match the IRQ of the selected computer port. Another area of concern is the transmit audio source. The transmit audio is available from either the serial port or from the PC's built-in speaker. This choice is made during the initial installation of the program. Some programs claim better transmitted picture resolution is possible by using the audio from the PC's speaker. The actual difference is very slight, and may not outweigh the complications of getting inside your PC and modifying the speaker circuitry.

One common problem is "RF feedback" when transmitting SSTV. In many instances this problem is not really RF feedback. In reality it is caused by a dc ground loop between the chassis of the computer and the rig; therefore, the common cures for RF feedback, RF chokes and bypass capacitors will not work. The use of an audio coupling transformer between the mike input and the computer is the solution and is *definitely* recommended. (See Figure 2.3B earlier in this chapter.)

When first running an SSTV program, you may notice that the picture slants to the left or right. This is a common problem because the program has no way of knowing in advance your CPU's speed. Upon installation, a simple software calibration routine corrects the program timing to match your specific computer. This Slant Correction procedure is usually performed once, since the program remembers the correction factor for future use.

PACKET RADIO

Packet radio is a popular way of connecting two computers over Amateur Radio. Digital data is processed by the computer; the actual transmission over radio is accomplished by modems in analog fashion, however. Almost anything sent in or out of the RS-232 port may be conveyed on packet radio. There are some practical limitations, since packet speed is slow compared to computer transfer rates. Packet users run 1200 baud on VHF (and 10 meters) and 300 baud on HF. Backbone linking systems found on UHF run 9600 or higher baud rates. Common uses of packet radio

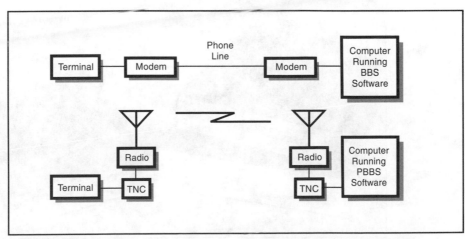

Figure 2.14—A landline modem-to-modem connection and a packet radio connection are similar. In each case the terminal station is able to access a BBS system.

include keyboard-to-keyboard QSOs, logging on BBS systems, checking into a DX Cluster to find out what and where the DX is, sending a file to a friend and even sending messages via packet satellites. Figure 2.14 shows a simple comparison of a landline BBS and a packet station.

The advantage packet has over simpler modes such as RTTY is its ability to correct transmission errors. As the name implies, information is sent in *packets,* with each packet containing the desired data information and additional bits that are used for error correction. A packet or frame consists of *flag* bits, *address* bits, *control* bits, *pid* or protocol identifier bits, *information* bits (the actual data you are sending) and *fcs* or frame check sequence bits. As you can see, there is a lot of "extra" information being sent along with the *information* bits.

Further information on packet formats appears in the Resources Chapter. Fortunately, most operators never have to bother with the individual bits because a TNC (Terminal Node Controller) processes them. The TNC divides the message into separate packets, keys the transmitter and sends the message. Upon receiving a message, the TNC decodes it, checks for errors and displays it if it is error free. If it is not error free, it requests the incorrect packets be sent again, and sometimes again and again until it is received correctly. Time is saved by resending only the incorrect portion of the message. The best part for us is the satisfaction of knowing that the TNC does all of this without our knowledge. What we receive as the final message is an exact copy of what was sent; the system is said to be *transparent.*

The TNC is usually a piece of hardware costing around $200; however, software is available that can emulate the TNC for a lot less money. Hardware TNCs were developed when computers did not have enough speed to perform both the display (terminal) function and process raw packet information. Hardware TNCs contain a modem and a microprocessor and are connected to the computer through the RS-232 port. Four popular TNCs are shown in Figure 2.15. The TNC sends ASCII information to the computer, and the computer assumes the role of a somewhat "dumb"

Figure 2.15—Four popular 1200 bit/s packet TNCs: On the left—the AEA PK-88 and MFJ-1207C. On the right—the DRSI DPK-2 and the Kantronics KPC-3.

display terminal. The computer allows information to be saved to disk, something a true "dumb" terminal can't do.

If a computer has enough speed to process both raw packet information and display the data, then only the modem section of the TNC is required. BayCom is one popular TNC emulation program developed in Germany. It is shareware and may be found on many amateur BBS's and on the Internet. It may be downloaded from the ARRL HIRAM BBS as *baycom.zip* from the the *tcpip* directory. The only hardware required—other than the radio and computer—is a modem. Tigertronics sells a compact modem including a copy of the BayCom software for $49. (See the Resources Chapter.) This is, no doubt, one of the least expensive ways to get started on packet radio. There is even a program that is powerful enough to perform both as a TNC-emulator and modem for receive-only applications. Look for *pktmon12.lzh*. This program is not intended to be a full function packet radio program, since it is receive only. However, it does demonstrate the trend toward software solutions solving hardware problems. *Software-only* packet radio appears to be just around the corner.

Radio Requirements

Figure 2.16 shows how the radio is connected to the computer. Transmit au-

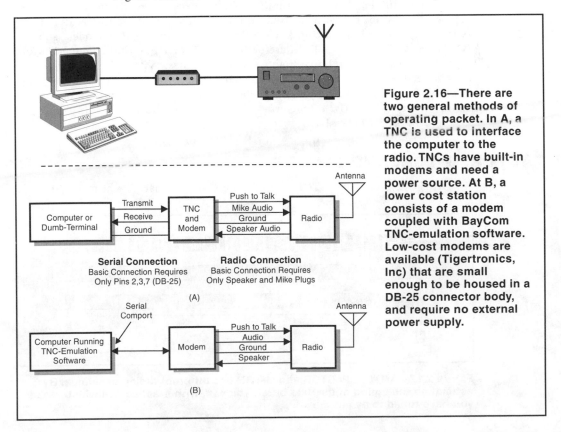

Figure 2.16—There are two general methods of operating packet. In A, a TNC is used to interface the computer to the radio. TNCs have built-in modems and need a power source. At B, a lower cost station consists of a modem coupled with BayCom TNC-emulation software. Low-cost modems are available (Tigertronics, Inc) that are small enough to be housed in a DB-25 connector body, and require no external power supply.

dio is fed from the TNC or modem into the microphone jack or auxiliary audio input. Receive audio is taken from the radio's external speaker jack. These simple connections work for 1200-baud VHF packet and 300-baud HF. For 9600 baud and higher, connections must be made directly to the circuitry inside the radio or the radio must be specifically designed for 9600 baud. In the mid 1990's some amateur transceivers were manufactured as "data ready"; many didn't perform as well as expected for data transmissions, however. Later, data-dedicated radios were introduced with improved performance. Excellent results may also be obtained by modifying a commercial radio such as the Motorola *Mitrek*.

For most of us, a regular 2-meter rig will work without modification for 1200-baud packet. There are, however, some precautions you should be aware of. When an external power amplifier is used, care must be taken to ensure that data is not sent before the antenna relay contacts have a chance to close. This is easily accomplished by adding a small delay between the time the PTT control line signals the relay to close and the start of data. This is called *TX Delay*, and is one of the parameters that may be changed through software. If you use an HT, the battery saver feature must be turned off because it causes a dead period when the receiver is muted, and packets may be lost. For the most part these are minor problems, and a typical 2-meter HT or base rig will work without complications.

On HF, 300 baud is used with the TNC connected directly to an SSB transceiver. Most of this operation is used for long-distance message forwarding; there is relatively little keyboard-to-keyboard communication. Other modes, such as AMTOR, PACTOR and G-TOR, are better suited for HF digital communication. Figure 2.17 shows the relative timing for these modes. With a bit of practice you should be able to identify which mode is being sent by the lengths of the data and acknowledge bursts. Activity can be found in the following frequency ranges: 80 meters—3580-3635 kHz; 40 meters—7080-7105 kHz; 20 meters—14070-14095 kHz and 141005-14112 kHz.

PACTOR, G-TOR, AND CLOVER

AMTOR, PACTOR, G-TOR and CLOVER are four HF digital modes that are

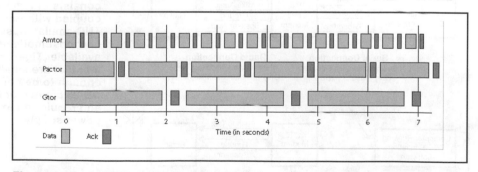

Figure 2.17—AMTOR, PACTOR and G-TOR use different timing baselines. By estimating the timing of the data burst, you can, with practice, tell which mode you have tuned to by ear.

more efficient than packet. Designed to overcome the shortcomings of RTTY, AMTOR is the oldest of the "TOR" (teleprinting over radio) modes. Similarly, PACTOR and CLOVER were designed to overcome problems associated with packet and AMTOR. G-TOR (Golay-Teleprinting Over Radio) is advertised as an improvement over PACTOR, and there is little doubt that before too long a still-better mode will replace G-TOR. Conventional packet was never intended to be used on interference-filled channels because it was originally designed to be used over relatively quiet telephone circuits. As a result, newer modes were developed to offer maximum performance on circuits with multipath interference and QRM.

CLOVER is designed to overcome multipath fading. By using multilevel tone, phase and amplitude modulation, this mode adapts to changing conditions to produce the maximum throughput. A Reed-Solomon algorithm is used to provide error correction by selecting one of six possible modulation schemes. Data rates may vary from a low of 62.5 bit/s when conditions are poor to 750 bit/s when conditions are good. The system constantly measures signal-to-noise ratio, frequency offset, phase dispersion and errors to select the best modulation scheme for the prevailing conditions. This correction technique is well suited for HF use where errors due to interference or fading are often short lived. For comparison, both the FEC and ARQ modes are available—as with AMTOR. CLOVER can be up to 10.5 times faster than AMTOR under ideal conditions.

PACTOR, as the name implies, is a combination of packet and AMTOR. PACTOR uses a Memory-ARQ feature, keeping copies of corrupted frames to correlate them with new data in order to correct errors. Each PACTOR cycle consists of a 0.96-second data frame, a 0.17-second CS (control signal) frame and a 0.12-second idle time for a total cycle time of 1.25 seconds. Data packets are either 96 bits long sent at 100 baud or 192 bits long sent at 200 baud. The CS frame is always sent at 100 baud. PACTOR sent with a 200-Hz shift at 200 baud will require a 600-Hz bandwidth. PACTOR is about 3.33 times faster than AMTOR.

A newer and better version of PACTOR is the German PACTOR II. It uses a 16-state phase-shift keying system to achieve a maximum of 800 bits/s at a 100 baud rate. PACTOR II uses a DSP with Nyquist waveform, Huffman and Mazrkov compression and a powerful Viterbi decoding scheme to achieve this level of throughput. All this is accomplished in approximately 500 Hz of bandwidth. PACTOR II can be up to 20 times faster than AMTOR.

G-TOR uses a Golay error correction code and can correct 3 out of 12 transferred data bits, thus increasing throughput by reducing multiple retransmissions. Each data frame is 1.92 seconds followed by a 0.48-second window for a total cycle time of 2.40 seconds. Data rates change dynamically ranging from 100 to 300 symbols/sec. Data is sent as normal ASCII or it may be Huffman encoded This is determined on a frame-by-frame basis. G-TOR uses frequency-shift keying, similar to PACTOR. At 300 characters per second with a 170 or 200-Hz shift, the spectral bandwidth is very similar to that of packet radio. When conditions are good, G-TOR increases speed automatically. To compare PACTOR and G-TOR, WØXI and WK5M sent over 1 million bytes of data on 20 meters for a month. On average G-TOR was more than 2.5 times faster than PACTOR.

Selecting the best mode to use can be difficult. The speed advantages cited are only estimates of what you might expect under average conditions. Each of the HF

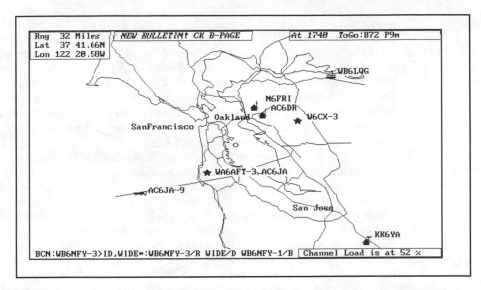

Figure 2.18—A standard APRS map screen. A built-in world map may be zoomed to any location. Call signs mark locations of participating stations. Special symbols such as houses, sailboats or cars may be individually assigned. In this example, WB6LQG is using a sailboat symbol. If a station is moving, a track of his path is visible.

digital modes degrade in a unique fashion that is highly dependent on the nature of the interference. A detailed article comparing these modes is on page 35 of the July 1996 issue of *QST*. See "A Comparison of HF Digital Protocols." Both G-TOR (Kantronics) and CLOVER (HAL Communications) are commercial products and are protected by proprietary designs. Thus, to use these modes you must buy their modems. The other modes cost a lot less to get started because you can download software (freeware and shareware) and use the HamComm interface or a simple low-cost one-chip modem. See the Resources Chapter for more information.

APRS

Bob Bruninga, WB4APR, developed the *Automatic Packet Reporting System* (APRS), which displays the location of participating packet stations on a map. APRS permits any number of stations to exchange many forms of data without the need for a point-to-point connection. Most often longitude and latitude coordinates are sent, allowing the program to locate the user on a built-in map display. APRS combines the concepts of repeaters, packet radio and the Global Positioning System (GPS) into one neat package. APRS concentrates on the graphic display of station and object location and movements. All that is needed is a packet station and the APRS shareware program.

The software will run on any computer from an 8088 to a Pentium Pro. It comes in versions for DOS, Windows and the Mac. A VGA monitor is recommended but a CGA will work. In addition to a computer you will need a TNC and a radio. APRS is widely found on 145.79 MHz in the United States and on 144.39 MHz in Canada. Mobile stations and even sailboats may be found transmitting APRS on 10.151 MHz.

APRS consists of a network of digipeating stations with each station, large or small, contributing to the relay of other stations' information. Your station must be in receiving range of at least one other APRS transmitting station. APRS uses the standardized digipeater aliases of *RELAY* and *WIDE*. The default setting is to RELAY. WIDE is used by stations that have the largest RF coverage. By using the Digipeater List feature, users can see what digipeater paths are being used by other stations. It is not uncommon to "see" stations relayed from several hundred or even thousands of miles away.

If you know the latitude and longitude of your station, you can add this information to the beacon transmissions sent by your TNC. This may be entered by hand for fixed locations or by a GPS for automatic entry. Obviously automatic entry is used when the transmitting station is moving. GPS-equipped stations have been put into balloons, cars, trains, boats, chase cars and almost anything that moves. Garmin (see the Resources Chapter) makes a popular low cost hand-held GPS unit for about $200. With a small GPS receiver, a TNC and a hand-held transceiver stuffed in a cigar box, almost any object can be tracked by packet stations running APRS software. You can place these boxes on bicycles for a marathon event, and, of course, in automobiles. Even if your station isn't the one being tracked, it's fun to monitor an APRS network and watch the activity. Figure 2.18 shows a typical MAP screen.

The APRS program reads the standardized GPS position format. You will need an interface cable to connect the GPS data output jack to the PC's serial port. Any monitoring station equipped with APRS software will translate the data and display the transmitted location on a computer-generated map.

When any person in an APRS network determines where you're located, he can move his cursor and mark your position on his map screen. This action is then transmitted to all screens in the network, so everyone gains, at a glance, the combined knowledge of all network participants. In other words, everyone knows where you are. The map screen retains this information for future reference. This means that moving objects can be dead-reckoned to their current locations with one keystroke—based on their previous positions.

APRS can also be used for triangulating the location of a hidden transmitter. A jammer command displays the intersection of bearing lines from a number of reporting stations. To use APRS in this manner, each station having a bearing on a jammer enters it into his APRS system. His station then reports its location and its bearing relative to the jammer. All stations running APRS can simply hit the J key to display the intersection of these bearing lines. Furthermore, if a direction-finding vehicle has a GPS or Loran-C receiver onboard, it can be tracked and directed to the location of the jammer.

The APRS software is distributed as shareware and may be copied for any amateur application. For additional information, see the Resources Chapter.

A Case of Mistaken Identity—Ground Loops or RF Feedback?

One of the most common and frustrating problems encountered after the receive portion of your project is working correctly, is difficulty in transmitting. If you get reports of RF feedback or distorted audio, there is a good chance that the problem is caused by a dc ground loop and *not* RF. There are two easy tests that may be made. Transmit at full power into an antenna while listening on a separate receiver. You should hear the distortion first-hand. If you are transmitting into a beam, and the distortion changes as you rotate the beam, then the problem is likely to be RF feedback. If no change is noted, substitute a shielded dummy load for the antenna, again listening to determine if the distortion has been eliminated. If it still sounds distorted, the problem is definitely caused by ground loops and the following information will be helpful.

The culprit is very likely to be a dc ground loop between the power supply and your rig. Rigs that run on a separate power supply and are connected by long leads are particularly prone to this condition. The cause of the problem is a dc voltage drop that occurs under high current conditions when transmitting. Part A of Figure A shows an example of this classic problem. For reference, point A is 0.0 V. On voice peaks, 20 A is drawn by the rig. This current produces a 0.2 V drop across the power supply leads, assuming the power supply leads have a resistance of 0.010 Ω. This is where the problem occurs, since the ground of the rig is 0.2 V higher than the power supply ground. A connection between the power supply and the computer is all that is needed to establish a ground loop. This connection is often made through the ac safety ground (green wire) or may be made through any peripheral equipment connected to the power supply or computer.

Because there is potential difference between the common of the rig and computer, a current must flow. This unwanted current, $I_{0.2V}$ is shown as a dashed line. It will add to the desired audio (I_{audio}) producing audio distortion. It often sounds like RF feedback because it occurs only on voice peaks and reducing power helps to eliminate it; however, it is not caused by RF.

The best way to eliminate $I_{0.2V}$ from flowing is to break its path with an isolation transformer. Part B of Figure A shows how this is done. A 600:600-Ω audio coupling transformer (Radio Shack no. 273-1374) mounted close to the rig does the trick. Clamping ferrite choke cores or winding the microphone cable around a core will not cure this type of problem. This technique may also stop RF feedback; however, its main purpose is to eliminate the ground loops. Any RF feedback reduction is only a side benefit. It's almost like two fixes for the price of one.

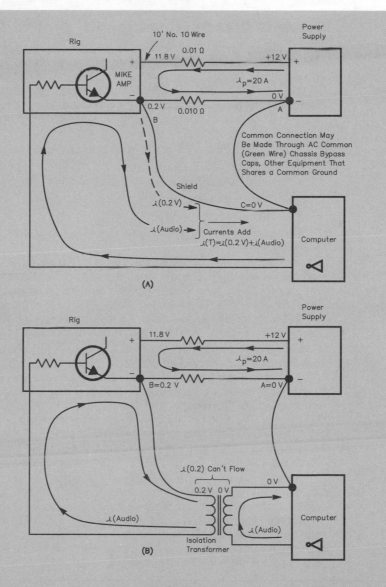

Figure A—A typical station running 100 watts connected by 10 feet of no. 10 AWG wire to an external power supply is shown in A. The resulting 20 A flows in the minus power supply leads on voice peaks, causing a 0.2 V drop between the rig and the power supply common. This 0.2-V drop will appear between any peripheral equipment connected to the power supply and the rig. The 0.2-V signal, which appears at each end of the audio shield, is effectively in series with the desired audio signal. Feedback will occur on voice peaks, and the distortion it causes is often confused with RF feedback. In B an isolation transformer (Radio Shack no. 273-1374 or similar) has been added, breaking the path of the 0.2-V current, stopping the feedback.

Correct Dial Settings for HF Digital Modes

Confusion often arises when tuning RTTY or HF packet. The problem occurs on HF because SSB rigs do not have a standardized display mode. The displayed frequency has different meanings if the rig is set to USB, LSB, CW or FSK. The MARK and SPACE audio tones depend on the VFO and sideband setting. On VHF and UHF, FM is used. Thus the audio tones can't change with a shift in operating frequency. The problem can be generalized into five basic areas.

- The audio frequency of the MARK and SPACE tones:
- Selection of USB or LSB.
- Receiver VFO offset when receiving in CW mode.
- Published frequencies.
- IF shift settings.

The following examples illustrate common tuning problems when using HF digital modes.

The usual method of modulating an HF SSB rig for RTTY or packet is to feed MARK and SPACE audio tones directly into a microphone or auxiliary audio input. These tones are generated either by a modem, a TNC or by computer emulation. In the United States, 2125 Hz is the standard for MARK and 2295 Hz for SPACE. These are considered as "high tones." In Europe "low tones" are used. They are 1275 Hz for MARK and 1445 Hz for SPACE.

Let's say you and your European friend want to have an RTTY sked and you choose a frequency of 14.100 MHz. You both have identical rigs and both select USB for transmitting and receiving. What happens? You guessed it—you can't make a contact. Figure B shows why. Each station is sending with a standard 170-Hz shift. The actual RF frequencies corresponding to the MARK and SPACE tones are 850 Hz lower for the European station, however. The US station must tune to 14.099150 MHz—850 Hz lower than 14.100000 MHz. Without retuning, both stations would be operating on different frequencies, taking up more spectrum than necessary.

Another problem occurs with some rigs when they are receiving in the CW mode. Sometimes this is necessary to permit a narrow IF filter to be selected. This alone does not cause a problem; however, the VFO display will not indicate the actual carrier frequency as it does in the sideband mode. Caution must be taken to ensure that the "CW sidetone" has been taken into account. Reading the manual is the best way to determine how your rig displays frequency when it is in the CW mode.

Figure B—A shows the actual mark and space frequencies for an AMTOR or RTTY station using the "high tone" standard of 2125 and 2295 Hz, on a carrier frequency of 14.100 MHz in USB. In B, a European station is transmitting using the "low tone" standard on the same carrier frequency. This results in a different set of mark and space frequencies. To communicate, one station will have to shift its operating frequency by 850 Hz so they will both be operating on the same frequency. C and D illustrate how the polarity of a digital signal is inverted by changing sidebands. C shows a normal polarity digital signal transmitted using LSB, and D shows how the mark tone becomes the space tone, and visa-versa, when received in USB. In each case the mark tone is always closest to the carrier frequency.

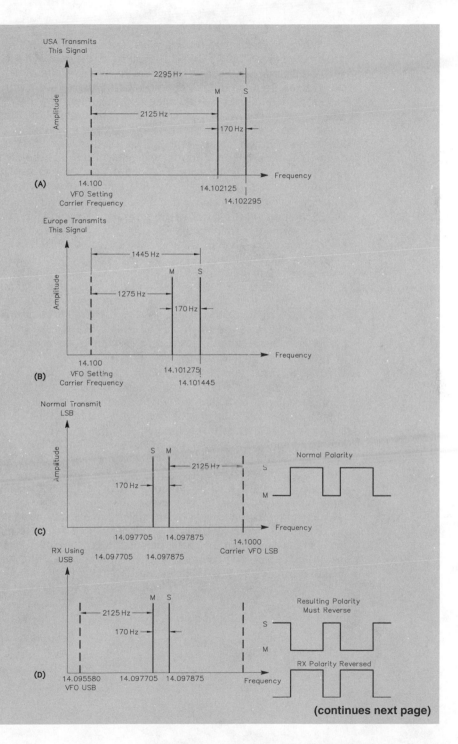

The "published" frequency is another area where there is little standard-ization. Amateur RTTY is usually specified by the MARK frequency; packet and commercial SITOR is specified by the center of the MARK and SPACE frequencies. The use of the center frequency makes more sense, since you have to keep track of only one operating frequency and a shift. Unfortu-nately, this is not the amateur convention. The roots of this problem may be found in the modulation techniques that amateurs have adopted to generate FSK. When AFSK is used, the actual carrier frequency has no effect on the demodulated signal, other than being within the IF passband. When AFSK modulates an SSB transceiver, FSK is produced. The transmitted signal is now determined by the carrier oscillator and sideband setting.

A receiving station may not know if the transmitting station is using USB or LSB. Although LSB is the de facto amateur standard, it is not uncommon to find stations transmitting on USB. The only way a receiving station can select the correct sideband is to experiment to see which of them produces good copy. As an alternative, the polarity of the demodulated signal may be reversed through software or by polarity switches on the modem. Parts C and D of Figure B show how a station transmitting a normal polarity high tone RTTY signal on 14.100 LSB can be received correctly on USB at 14.095580 MHz when the polarity is reversed. In this case the MARK and SPACE frequencies are swapped (remember MARK is always closest to the carrier frequency); therefore, the polarity of the recovered data also is swapped or "inverted."

If all this isn't complicated enough, another factor can cause problems. The setting for the IF shift must be altered to favor the high pitch of the RTTY or packet tones. This is particularly true if the demodulator is set to "high tones" (2125 and 2295 Hz). The nominal or center setting of most IF shifts is set around 1100 Hz, which is the center of the speech range. The IF shift should be shifted up to 2210 Hz (halfway between 2295 Hz and 2125 Hz) for best results. This is easy to do; simply adjust the IF shift to produce the highest S-meter reading.

Successful first-time operation on HF digital modes requires detailed information about your rig. This is something best gained by reading the instruction manual. It is not uncommon to find stations transmitting in an unconventional manner. Often, this is a result of a desire to get on these modes quickly without a clear understanding of the difficulties involved. For an in-depth study of these problems, see the articles in the August 1991 (p 28) and June 1992 (p 63) issues of *QST*.

Keeping Track of Your Station

In this chapter will we explore the many ways a computer can save you time and space by making your station faster and easier to operate. Allowing your PC to act as a *2nd op*—ready, willing and able to fill in your log, change frequencies, check a call sign, tell you what band is open and determine the correct beam heading to name a few—allows you to spend more time on the air.

Contesters and satellite operators may benefit the most from the helping hand a computer offers. A computer can fill out your log in milliseconds, whereas it could take you 10 seconds to do the same job. The time saved over the course of a weekend contest will gives the computer aided station a definite advantage. Satellite operators benefit by keeping their hands free from the rotator and receiver tuning controls, allowing them to focus on the contact.

Want a list of all the hams in your town or all a listing of the repeaters along your vacation route? The CD ROMs know all—and can tell you all they know in a flash. Trying to learn Morse code, or upgrade your license?—the computer never gets tired of teaching you, and your grade is not propagated over the local repeater. What better way is there to gain the confidence that you can pass a VEC exam—just you and your computer know the score. Fun, speed, and convenience are the reasons to give your computer *2nd op* status.

OPERATING

Logging / Contest Programs

Computer *logging* programs have become so popular and ever more sophisticated that the term *logging* has become a misnomer. They may be more aptly considered station control programs because they not only record the QSO, they also are capable of controlling your entire station. As radios with computer interfaces evolved, logging programs began to incorporate such features as frequency posting, keyboard VFO control, CW and voice messages, antenna rotator control, time and date stamps. Do not be discouraged if your radio does not have a computer interface socket on it—plenty of useful "plain vanilla" logging programs can serve your needs.

Which program you choose depends entirely on your needs. No one program is best. Contesters have been the driving force behind the development of logging programs; therefore, features that offer a competitive edge have evolved. Generally called contest programs, they can be optimized for a particular contest. We will explore some of the factors that can be used to judge if a particular program is the right one for you. First we will look at contest logging programs and then the general-purpose ones. It is difficult to compare contest programs because they are loaded with so many unique features that it would be like comparing apples to oranges. The choice of a program depends more on personal operating style than anything else. The programs all perform well; it's just a matter of knowing beforehand what you expect them to do.

Consider these factors:

⌨ The bigger and fancier programs require more horsepower. Will you need a Windows 386/486 machine to run them or will an XT style machine suffice?

⌨ What kind of support is available?—Is there a BBS, an Internet site or a 5-day-a-week telephone number?

⌨ Does the program support your favorite contests?

⌨ How many different contests will it support?

⌨ How steep is the learning curve?—Are the commands intuitive? The more powerful contest programs may take considerable time to learn how to use all the features. Perhaps a simpler program is more appropriate. If you do not use the program often, it is easy to forget the commands.

⌨ Will the program interface to your radio (this assumes of course that your transceiver has a computer interface)?

⌨ Does the program support two simultaneous radios?

⌨ How fail-safe is the program? If the Field Day generator runs out of gas, do you lose the log?

⌨ What does the program do for you after the contest?—Does it catch dupes, calculate your score, have the ability to merge its data to another logging program?

⌨ Do you have to be a computer maven to get it installed correctly?

⌨ How stable is the program?—How about bugs? The more powerful programs naturally have more to go wrong and generally have more reported bugs. This may be more a consequence of numerous revisions rather than a fundamental flaw in their design. Are the shortcomings catastrophic or inconveniences that can be put up with until another revision is available?

⌨ Cost?—Do you get your money's worth? Is the program available as freeware,

Figure 3.1—Phil, KBØNES, operates and logs Field Day at the same time! The *FD1200* is a simple Field Day logging program that is easy to set up and use.

shareware or out of your backpocket ware? How much do upgrades cost?

FD1200 is a perfect Field Day logging program. Harry Bump, KM3D, has created a simple program that will allow you to concentrate on contesting, not computing. The concept of KISS (Keep It Simple Stupid) is a must for an operation where the participants may have little or no prior experience with computerized logging. FD1200 is shareware and a donation of only $10 is asked, making it one of the best buys around. DOS based, it will even run on an 8088. It is widely available on BBSs and the web. Try (**http://oak.oakland.edu:8080/pub/hamradio/arrl/bbs/contests/**)

The Resources Chapter contains the addresses of a number of program suppliers.

General Logging Programs

Lauren Rudd, KD8PZ, has analyzed nine general-purpose logging programs. A summary of his findings, originally published in May 1995 *QST,* is given in Table 3.1. Each program has evolved by incorporating user feedback; many are updated regularly. As with most amateur software, they have been created by a single person who writes and supports them. It is usual for support hours to be limited to evenings and/or weekends. Since you will be "supported" by the programmer himself, there is no question too tough to answer. They may even take your ideas and incorporate them in a future release. All of the programs reviewed are PC-based. Six will run under DOS and three will run under Windows. A DOS or Windows platform is the first choice you must make when selecting a program. As a rule, the DOS programs are the easiest to get up and running; however, the Windows programs offer the greatest flexibility.

Table 3.1
Contest Logging Program Comparision Chart

CT-9	Log-EQF ver 8
Interfaces	
ICOM IC725 IC735 IC737 IC751 IC761 IC765 IC775 IC781	ICOM IC 706 IC725 IC735 IC737 IC738 IC751 IC761 IC765 IC775 IC781 IC970
Kenwood TS50 TS440 TS850TS94 TS950	Kenwood TS50 TS440 TS850 TS870 TS940 TS950
Yaesu FT890 FT990 FT1000 FT1000MP	Yaesu FT767 FT840 FT890 FT900 FT990 FT1000 FT1000MP
Ten-Tec OMNI-VI	Ten-Tec OMNI-VI DELTA II
	JRC 245
	PARAGON
Contests Supported	
ARRL DX (W/VE)	ARRL Sweepstakes
ARRL VHF QSO	ARRL 10-meter
ARRL Sweepstakes	ARRL 160-meter
ARRL Field Day	ARRL International DX VHF QSO Party
ARRL 10-Meter	
ARRL 160-Meter	ARRL DX (W/VE)
WAE European DX	
CQ WW DX	
CQ WPX	
CQ 160-Meter	
JARL All Asia IARU	
HFChampionship California QSO Party	
Cost of Program	
$79.95	Shareware $39.95 registration
Cost of Upgrades	
From CT-8 to CT-9 $44.95	Between $5 - $10 depending on age of previous version. Registered users receive announcements by mail, or one time $25 fee for any and all updates via BBS.
Minimum CPU Requirements	
386	8088 or higher
DOS or Windows	
DOS	DOS 3.0 or higher
Method of Support	
Free BBS access, Web Home page	Phone evenings or weekends, mail
Packet Cluster Interface?	
Yes	Yes
Special Feature	
Digital voice add-on	Powerful support features with accomplished with a simple user interface

NA-10	TR
ICOM IC725 IC735 IC737 IC751 IC761 IC765 IC781	ICOM All radios with a computer interface
Kenwood TS50 TS440 TS850 TS870 TS940 TS950	Kenwood All radios with a computer interface
Yaesu FT990 FT1000 FT1000MP	Yaesu All radios with a computer interface
Ten-Tec OMNI-VI	Ten-Tec OMNI-VI
ARRL VHF QSO ARRL Sweepstakes ARRL Field Day ARRL 10-Meter ARRL 160-Meter CQ WW DX CQ WPX CQ 160-Meter JARL All Asia IARU HFChampionship QRP Most state QSO parties ARRL DX	ARRL (10 & 160) ARRL VHF ARRL Sweepstakes CQP CQ WW CQ WPX CQ 160 County Hunter IOTA XMAS NA QSO NA Sprint ARI Field Day WAE IARU – and others
$55	$50
$35 from NA-9 to NA-10	First year free, $15 for following years
8088 or higher	286 or better, 640 Kb memory
DOS 2.0 or higher	DOS 3.0 or higher
Phone evenings or weekends, e-mail, Internet reflector	Phone TR BBS, updates via Internet e-mail or Web site Reflector
?	Yes
Easy to create a custom contest	Two-radio support, 40 CW messages

All the programs are a trade-off between ease of use and complexity. Logging programs seem to take a bit of getting used to; hands-on experience is the best way to obtain this. Six of the nine programs have made provisions for a demo copy just for this purpose. The demo copies are identical to the regular program, except that they are limited to a smaller number of QSOs. The easiest and most reliable way to get a demo version is to use the author's BBS or Web page. You are guaranteed to receive the most up-to-date version. Other sources include the ARRL Hiram Bulletin Board and the Internet.

Unlike some software that allows you to skip reading the manual and just get it going, the first step should be to print and read the manual. Otherwise, you will miss some useful features and may end up unnecessarily pestering the authors for information.

It's not easy to make a choice based on features. Hardware constraints will also limit your choices. Table 3.2 lists the minimum DOS version required. It is safe to assume that if your computer supports the DOS version given; regardless of the actual CPU, it will run the program. The programs listed for *Any* or *3.0* versions of DOS will even run on an 8088 machine. This is important if you are selecting a program for a special event like Field Day—you may want to leave the Pentium at home and use the older laptop instead.

The requirements for station hardware vary considerably because most of the programs can do much more than duplicate, in digital form, your paper log. To take full advantage of a logging program you will need a rig that is computer controllable, a packet TNC, the ability to access a Packet Cluster node, a sound card for DX voice announcements and a computer-controlled antenna rotator. At the other end of the spectrum, the minimum requirement is a computer. With just a computer many have found enjoyment by keying in QSOs previously entered in a paper log. It is fun to be able to recall past QSOs this way. Entering a few hundred QSOs this way is tedious, however, and a few thousand may be another matter entirely.

Obviously if you do not have a beam or care about DX spotting you may ignore the TNC Packet Cluster, sound card and the computer controlled antenna rotator. The key to finding the right program for you is to realize what features you want and then

Table 3.2
Comparison of Logging / Contesting Software

	DXBASE	DXLOG	Hyperlog	Logic 4	Log Master
Windows	No	No	No	Yes	No
DOS version	Any	3.0	Any	3.1	Any
BBS	No	No	Yes	No	Yes
Demo copy	Yes	Yes	Yes	Yes	Yes
Newsletter	No	No	No	Yes	Yes
Buckmaster Interface	Yes	No	Yes	Yes	Yes
Sam Interface	Yes	No	Yes	Yes	Yes
PacketCluster	Yes	Yes*	Yes	Yes	Yes

*Requires an additional software package.

select a program with just about the right amount of horsepower to get the job done. If you choose a heavy-duty program you may find yourself reading a lot more of the manual to get to the information you need. Some of the manuals can be up to 100 pages long.

Suppose you can't make up your mind which program is best for you. Your checkbook can help solve part of the problem—you can always purchase more than one program. Unfortunately, more isn't necessarily better. Logging programs can have a steep learning curve. Converting your old logs can be another of life's more challenging adventures. This is especially true if you're planning to key in your old paper logs.

The same problem arises if you and your program have a falling out. Not even the most diehard ham wants to reenter a large database of old QSOs. It is important to know if you can transfer the QSO database between programs. Vendors will often tell you it can be done, but, there have been considerable problems in this area. Data is often entered in the wrong field or entered incorrectly. This is because of terminology problems more than anything else. For example, QTH can mean city, state and ZIP code, or it can mean country. You can easily fix a converted database if it's only a few hundred QSOs. For a few thousand the problem becomes daunting. Vendors will supply a program for this purpose or offer to make the transfer for you. In the latter case, you send in a disk with copies of certain designated files, and you get back a converted database. If you are not going to transfer old QSOs into a new program, switching programs is no problem, but it defeats one of the major advantages of digital logging: The capability of retrieving previous contacts in seconds. This is particularly valuable if you want to revisit rare ones that are still unconfirmed—and it simplifies tracking awards.

The speed at which you can access a particular record in your QSO database is another factor to consider. Vendors strive to try to convince you that their package is the fastest, but, the only way to know for sure is to run each of them on the same machine and compare the results.

The user interface is where you find the greatest difference between the DOS and Windows packages. If you're already a *Windows* user, you'll probably feel right at

Log Plus!	Log View	LogWindows	WJ2O
No	Yes	Yes	No
3.3	5.0	5.0	3.0
Yes	No	No	No
Yes	No	No	No
No	No	No	Yes
Yes	No	Yes	Yes
Yes	No	Yes	Yes
Yes	Yes*	Yes	Yes

home with one of the three *Windows* packages. On the DOS side, each user interface is different, and it becomes a matter of personal preference.

Cost should play a small role in your decision. It's a competitive marketplace and you pretty much get what you pay for. None of these packages could be thought of as being expensive, especially when you consider what other ham radio accessories cost.

Here is a brief review of each of the nine programs.

DXbase

Now in its eighth year of distribution, *DXbase* claims to have been one of the first commercially available computerized logging programs. Now in release 4.6 it has kept abreast of the latest in high-performance computers and radios. The latest version is a DOS-based package but will run under *Windows 3.1* or *Win 95*.

DXbase was written originally by Dean Fredriksen, W8ZF, and Jack Lennox, AA4LU, for their own use. It not only handles logging your QSOs, but like other packages in its class, will interface with your TNC and HF transceiver. In addition to providing interfaces to a large variety of products such as call sign databases, *DXbase* is unique in that it allows you to set up interfaces to your own programs. One of the strengths of this program is its speed in data retrieval. It uses *Btrieve,* a commercial database engine

As shown in Figure 3.2, *DXbase* is menu-driven. Choices from the main menu bar at the top of the page result in drop-down menus that are clear and easy to use. The bottom half of the screen is used to report the results of a search, while the right-hand side tracks statistical information.

Function keys are incorporated into the program. For example, to toggle open the address window requires that you hit the **F6** key. If you forget which key combinations are assigned to what, a pop-up list is available by pressing **ALT-F**. Help for any field is readily available through the **F1** key.

For times when you need to log QSOs rapidly, *DXbase* uses default values for everything except the call sign. The manual warns you to test your selected default values carefully to make sure you've made the proper selections. This is excellent

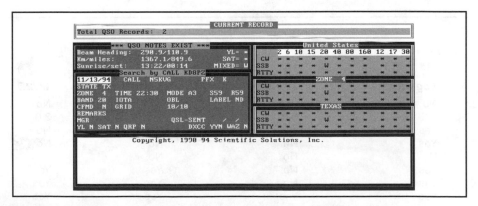

Figure 3.2—Screen shot of the *DXbase* program shows multiple drop-down menus.

advice for any logging program where you're going to rely heavily on default values.

If you aren't happy with the way other logging programs format their reports, *DXbase* has a user-definable report capability. It allows you to define nearly any kind of report with any portion of a QSO data record. You can filter QSO records on a report using as many simultaneous filter criteria as you want.

DXbase comes with a professionally printed manual that's well written and easy to use. If you find yourself needing help, there are two telephone numbers supplied. It should come as no surprise that each number gets you Dean or Jack. Support hours are 6 to 9 PM, and there's no 800 number. There's a CompuServe ID provided where you can send electronic mail. For ordering information see the Resources Chapter.

DXLOG

DXLOG is probably the oldest surviving logging program to be actively marketed. Approximately 4000 copies of the program have been shipped to customers over the past seven years. Designed and written by Drew Smith, K3PA, *DXLOG* is an easy to use, completely menu-driven logging program. Like the program, the enclosed manual is of the no-frills variety, just 20 pages in length. Length, in this case, however, is no indication of quality. The manual for *DXLOG* is clear and easy to understand.

According to Drew, *DXLOG* was designed with the objective of efficiently tracking large numbers of QSOs in conjunction with a limited, but powerful, set of capabilities for reporting, QSLing and applying for awards. If you want to operate Packet Clusters, you'll have to purchase the companion product called *ClusterLog*. Designed to work with *DXLOG*, *ClusterLog* handles the standard functions associated with using a Packet Cluster, including automatic control of HF transceivers.

Loading *DXLOG* is straightforward and takes only a few minutes. To start the program you type in the suffix of your call sign (the portion after the number), followed by the letters **LOG.** You're immediately greeted by a short menu of choices. Each choice can be highlighted using the cursor, and a brief explanation of the selection appears at the bottom of the screen. To select a choice, you type the first letter or highlight the item with the cursor and press **ENTER.** *DXLOG* then carries out the function or proceeds to the next menu screen. It's practically foolproof.

Entering information in a field automatically moves you to the next field. The screen is uncluttered and requires minimal effort to log a new contact. If the station has been worked previously, *DXLOG* offers you the opportunity to review previous contacts.

DXLOG offers what it calls a QuickLog function. Not intended for everyday logging, it's similar to the fast logging capability of other programs. You only have to enter a station's call sign. Information such as DXCC country, CQ zone and Russian oblast are determined automatically. Current date and time, frequency and mode of the last QSO, and an RST of 59 or 599 appear immediately. When a multi-country call sign is entered, the program will use a **?** for an entry, rather than distract the operator by offering a choice. You then go back and correct the record later.

The program is a basic "meat-and-potatoes" logging program that is fast and easy to use. If you want to try *DXLOG* before buying it, a demonstration copy is available for $5, which PAYL Software will credit against the purchase price if you buy *DXLOG*. The demonstration version is a fully working copy of the program and includes all documentation, but it only accepts 50 QSOs.

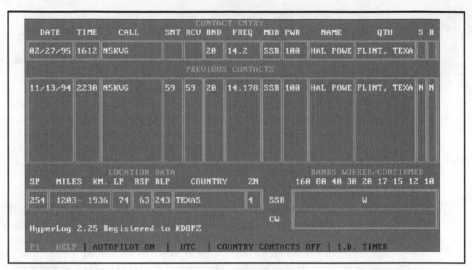

Figure 3.3—*HyperLog's* **main screen, with its simple top line commands.**

Support is available during scheduled hours, which are currently Mondays from 6 to 9 PM. If you have a question at any other time, you have to leave a number on an answering machine and someone will call you back. Further information may be found in the Resources Chapter.

HyperLog

HyperLog by HyperSoft is a full-featured DOS-based logging program with all the usual capabilities now standard in most logging programs. Written by Joe Spear, AH8B/W4, the program makes use of function keys and function keys combined with the **ALT** or **CTRL** keys to activate a particular task.

HyperLog is complex and could appear daunting to a new user. As soon as you become acquainted with the **F1** key, however, any apprehension quickly evaporates. A little practice and the program becomes one of the fastest logging programs to use when entering a new QSO.

The screen shown in Figure 3.3 is the program's primary screen and is central to the rest of the program. All data-entry and edit functions are carried out using this single screen. There are no pull-down menus. If you forget or don't know how to do a task, hit the **F1** key. Instantaneously you see a full-screen, two-column-wide listing of every command and the associated keystroke combination. After you've used the program to log a few dozen QSOs, remembering the appropriate keys becomes trivial.

The program does not require you to move down a series of nested commands to accomplish a particular task. There are a few nested commands in the utility and reporting sections, but these are minor. Furthermore, the design makes the program easy to use without a manual. There is a documentation file you can print out in place of a manual, or you may simply glance through the file using a standard word processor. From there, the list of commands under the **F1** key are all you need to happily log QSOs with *HyperLog*.

HyperLog's color scheme cannot be changed by the user, but, all the color combinations are appealing and readable. Although the program supports the standard call sign databases, it also provides for manual entry of a street address. If you don't have a call sign database, this is a feature that comes in handy if you want to print address labels or for later reference. If you're looking for a sophisticated yet easy-to-use DOS-based logging program, *HyperLog* is an excellent choice.

If you want to try a demo copy of *HyperLog*, there's a shareware copy on CompuServe and on the HyperSoft bulletin board. The program is an actual copy of *HyperLog*, but limited as to the number of QSOs you can enter. If you like the demo, a call to HyperSoft with a credit card number will get you a code that turns your demo into the full-fledged version. Details may be found in the Resources Chapter.

LOGic 4 for Windows

LOGic 4 for Windows (there's also a DOS version) written by Dennis Hevener, WN4AZY, bills itself as the most powerful and flexible system on the market, yet it claims to be easy enough for the beginning user to install and operate.

If it's not the most powerful and flexible logging program available, it's definitely in a tie for first place. The second claim requires some qualification. If you aren't experienced ham and comfortable working with *Windows*-based applications, and you are short on patience, you'll may not agree that it's easy to install and operate.

When you first bring *LOGic 4* up, you may notice that of your screen is difficult to read due to the font size or the color combinations. Changing the entire look of *LOGic 4* isn't difficult, but it does take a some patience. Clicking on the main menu item labeled FONTS enables you to set up different fonts for the main window screen, menus and data windows. The same type of procedure applies to screen-color combinations.

The power of *LOGic 4* is best illustrated by the logging screen shown in Figure 3.4. The Data window in the upper half can be used for logging new QSOs or reviewing old ones. It always shows just one record including all of that record's fields. Just below the Data window is the Browse window. It shows several records simultaneously, but only a few fields from each record. Each screen in *LOGic 4* has a Data window and Browse window.

It is possible to have other windows within a screen and to have them all open simultaneously. This is illustrated in Figure 3.4 where an Address window, Notes window and a Clock window are all open. If you find that a window isn't exactly to your liking, *LOGic 4* lets you change fields around and even add your own. You're given the power to customize the package to your own liking if you want to do so.

LOGic 4 comes set up for all the popular contests, several state QSO parties and other specialized contests. It provides on-line dupe- and multiplier-checking, packet multiplier spotting and copying information from previous QSOs.

The program claims to support files of more than two billion records. They claim one *LOGic 4* user has more than 75,000 QSOs logged into the program and it hasn't slowed down.

Report writing is just as flexible as the rest of the program. Although the program comes set up to print all the standard types of reports, these reports were all written with LOGic's report writer. You may modify them to meet your own requirements or write your own using the report writer.

Two manuals are included that together total more than 100 pages of documenta-

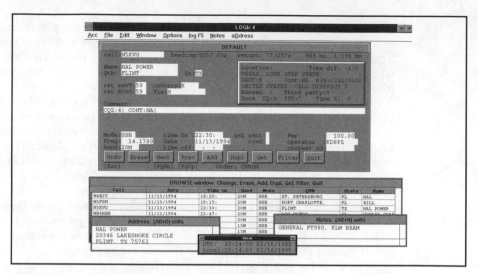

Figure 3.4—*LOGic 4* Windows screen showing multiple open windows. These would be displayed in different colors on your CRT.

tion. The first covers basic operations and the second covers more esoteric functions, such as rig interface, Packet Cluster interface, database interfaces and using the report writer. If you don't need the advanced functionality of *LOGic 4*, consider purchasing *LOGic 4* Jr. It's the same program as *LOGic 4*, without the advanced functions described in Volume 2 of the documentation.

Technical support for *LOGic 4* is available by calling the technical support telephone number or via e-mail through CompuServe or the Internet. For further information see the Resources Chapter.

Log Master Plus/Plus

Of the nine packages, *Log Master Plus/Plus* by Sensible Solutions is the easiest to install and use. Furthermore, it will work on virtually any version of DOS and on any IBM-compatible computer, even an old 8088-based machine.

The user interface is uncluttered and simple to use. Central to the program is a main screen with a horizontal menu bar across the top. There are only five possible selections on this screen: Log, View, Search, Print and Utilities. Each selection represents a functionally separate and distinct part of the program. To move from one area to another, such as from Log to Utilities, you must return to the main screen.

Selecting a main-screen function results in one or more pop-up menus, each with its own series of choices. To make a selection from any pop-up menu requires only that you move the cursor via the arrow keys or type the first letter of the selection. To make it foolproof, the first letter is always highlighted in a different color. Returning to the main menu is accomplished with the **ESCAPE** key.

QSO entry is via the screen shown in Figure 3.5. The screen is almost blank until you type in the call sign of the station you want to enter. From that point on, the program will provide as much of the remaining information as it can, prompting you only for parts you need to enter. If you have a call sign database, *Log Master* will use it to pick up the other station operator's name, city and state automatically.

Pressing the **F9** key will pop up the tag field. This field allows you to enter your own custom data that may be used as search criteria by the View and Search functions on the main menu command bar. If you want to attach a note to a record, pressing **F1** will pop up a Notepad window. Type whatever information you like, then **ESCAPE** and the information is saved.

At the bottom of Figure 3.5, you'll notice the function QBICSP, which is toggled on or off by the **F3** key. Unique to *Log Master*, QBICSP will tell you if you need a QSO by highlighting a letter in the word QBICSP. Q is a new CQ zone; B if this QSO is needed for the current frequency and mode combination qualified by CQ zone, ITU zone, country, state or prefix; I is a new ITU zone; C is a new country; S is a new state; P is a new prefix.

Other features of note in *Log Master* are a menu-driven report writer and an extremely fast search mechanism. The program can search a 20,000-QSO database in less than two seconds. With a sound card, you can receive voice announcements on Packet Cluster DX spots. Finally, user assistance is excellent. Calls are returned promptly, and they go out of their way to ensure that you're happy using the program.

If you're undecided about whether *Log Master* is for you, Alan has done something not only in keeping with the spirit of Amateur Radio, but goes beyond the proverbial "call of duty." He has available a second program called *Log Ranger. Log Ranger* is a smaller version of *Log Master*, but the user interface is identical. What's unique about *Log Ranger* is its price: It's absolutely free! And there is no obligation to ever purchase *Log Master*.

The program can be obtained from any number of bulletin boards or from Alan himself. *Log Ranger* is an excellent logging program in its own right. The program is a complete and fully functional logging program with a lot of development effort behind it. Unlike other logging programs available in demo versions, there's no limit to the number of QSOs *Log Ranger* will handle.

If you're unsure of where to start in the world of logging software or simply aren't in a position to buy software, obtain a free copy of *Log Ranger*. Alan offers *Log*

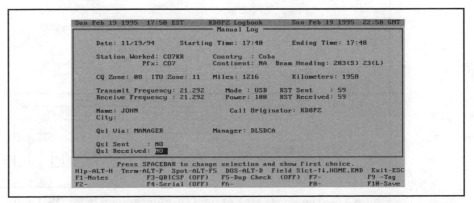

Figure 3.5—Screen display of the QSO entry mode for *Log Master* Plus/Plus program.

Ranger for free because he feels users would eventually want the enhancements found in *Log Master*. If you want to use *Log Ranger* forever, that's fine with him. He supports the program and views *Log Ranger* as his contribution to Amateur Radio. For more information see the Resources Chapter.

LOGPlus!

After starting to use *LOGPlus!* you quickly recognize that the program's subtitle "Designed for the casual operator to the serious DXer," is absolutely correct. A veteran of 19 DXpeditions, Bob Winters, KD7P, has written a program that will easily meet the needs of the casual or hard-core user. Another interesting statement appears early in the documentation. It says that if you fail to read the manual cover to cover, you're wasting your money. Clocking in at 84 pages of closely spaced text with no pictures, this manual will take you more than a few minutes to read.

The program installs easily and is straightforward in design and use. Primarily menu-driven, the main screen is divided into two distinct sections. The upper half is devoted to statistics about your logbook, including your total number of QSOs, broken down by category. You can immediately see how many DXCC countries you've worked and on what mode. The lower half is a menu window that contains all the menu selections offered in *LOGPlus!* A single-letter entry brings up the appropriate screen. Central to any logging program is the entry of QSO information. Figure 3.6 illustrates the screen used by *LOGPlus!* for on and off-the-air logging. The upper screen area has three purposes:

▫ As you log QSOs, the most recent 11 entries are listed here. When a call sign is entered, however, the log is checked for previous contacts. If any previous contacts with this call sign are found, the window is cleared and only the previous contacts are listed. In Packet Cluster mode, this portion of the screen is used to monitor the Cluster system. If you want to revert to the QSO list, pressing a single function key gets you there.

▫ The center of the screen is a data-entry window for your standard QSO information. Unlike most logging programs, the headings for some fields appear above the

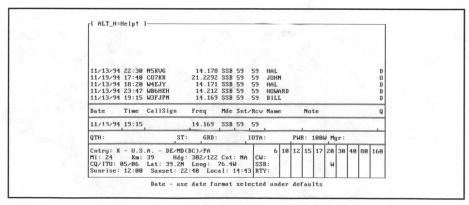

Figure 3.6—The upper area of the *LOGPlus!* screen is for QSO entry, the center for QSO information and the right bottom for DXCC statistics.

data being entered, as opposed to the left or right. This can be confusing for a few moments until you get used to it.

⊟ Finally, on the right side of the screen is a DXCC statistics window, which provides current information on band and mode breakdown for the QSO currently being entered.

If you're using *LOGPlus!* on a DXpedition or are otherwise working some sort of a pileup, you can take advantage of the program's Quick Call Saver function. Just enter the call sign of the station you're working and press the **F2** key. The QSO will be logged and the DXCC database updated.

The rest of *LOGPlus!* is just as easy to use. If you actively work DX or track awards, this is a program to look at. Although the manual is long and sometimes moves off on tangents that can be difficult to follow, it is comprehensive. Furthermore, the Table of Contents is listed first by screen choices and then by keyboard entries for that screen. As a result, looking up a particular function is particularly easy.

Two quirks of note. (1) You can't change screen colors. Although most of the screens were easy to read,, the primary logging screen is done in reverse, i.e., a black background with yellow text. (2) Putting the program in a subdirectory is discouraged and difficult to do.

Support for *LOGPlus!* is excellent. Not only does Bob provide a bulletin board, but there's a *LOGPlus!* "reflector" on the Internet. This one is dedicated to *LOGPlus!* and is run by James Reisert, AD1C. A demonstration copy of the program, limited to 100 QSOs, can be downloaded from the *LOGPlus!* bulletin board. Additional information may be found in the Resources Chapter.

LogView

LogView is a fairly straightforward *Windows*-based logging program. To use the program successfully requires that you first read the manual carefully and spend time with the demonstration log supplied with the program.

As illustrated in Figure 3.7, *LogView* has three key windows, in addition to the Main Window, which you'll always want open. As in most Windows applications, you're free to place these windows anywhere you want on the screen. In Figure 3.7, the Log Entry window is shown spread out across the top half of the screen, with the Log List window underneath to the left and the Award List window on the lower right-hand side.

The Log Entry window contains all the database fields pertinent to entering or modifying a QSO record. If space on your computer screen is tight, you can size the screen down, covering up fields that are less important. Because *LogView* assumes you're entering QSOs on a real-time basis, the date and time boxes are filled in automatically, with the time continually incrementing every second. If you're logging old QSOs, simply highlight the boxes and Delete. You can now enter whatever date and time you want. You move from field to field by means of the Tab key or your mouse. It is a good idea to always use the Tab key after entering the call sign of the station you're logging.

After entering a QSO, you'll see it appear in the Log List window, which looks like a paper log. The Log List window has been designed to allow you to browse through your database. By adjusting the borders of this window you can increase or

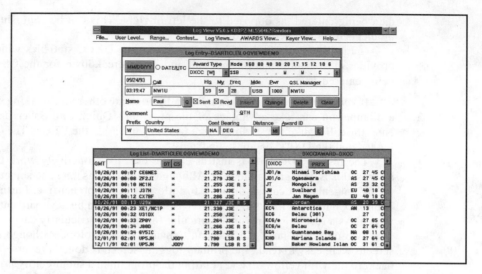

Figure 3.7—*LogView* **uses a main window with an easy to use upper command line. Inside the main window are the Log Entry (at the top), the Log List window (on the left) and the Award List window (on the right).**

decrease the amount of information shown. Clicking on the DT or CS buttons at the top of the Log List window will sort the database into date/time or call sign order. By highlighting and then double clicking on an entry in the Log List window, the QSO record will be moved back into the Log Entry window so it can be viewed, edited or removed.

Just as the Log List window is a view into your log, the Award List window is your view into the award database. Used in conjunction with the Award ID field in the Log Entry window, *LogView* will track all major awards.

Initial setup tended to be somewhat confusing. Once you have the program set up, follow the manual's advice and work through the examples using the demonstration log. If you have questions, *LogView* is distributed and supported by MFJ Enterprises Inc. Further information may be found in the Resources Chapter.

Log Windows

If you're running *Windows 3.1* (you also need DOS 5.0 or better) and you're looking for an easy to use, yet comprehensive Windows-based logging program, *Log Windows* could very well be the answer. Written by professional programmer Ira Chavis, WA1W, *Log Windows* is distributed and supported by AEA. As a result, the software is readily available from AEA's many dealers. Products with the AEA name on them are considered by many hams to be among the highest-quality products available to the amateur community. *Log Windows* keeps the tradition going strong.

Professionally packaged, *LogWindows* includes a well-written manual and a single program disk. The program installs in the same manner as any Windows-based program. You select Run from the pull-down menu of the Program Manager, type your drive designator followed by the word SETUP and the program does the rest.

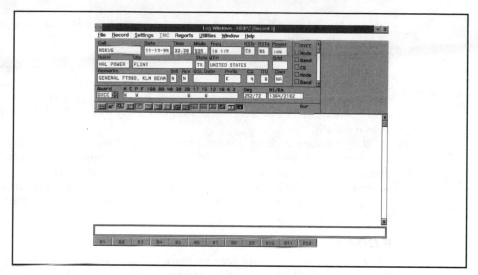

Figure 3.8— *Log Windows* **uses a simple two-part screen with logging information on the top and Packet Cluster output displayed on the lower half.**

To run the program you click on the appropriate icon just as you would to run any Windows program. The screen that comes up is shown in Figure 3.8. It's basically a two-part screen. The upper half is used to capture and display logging information, while the lower half displays local Packet Cluster output. If you don't hook up your computer to a TNC, you will not have an occasion to use the lower half of the screen.

Log Windows was designed to handle all the advanced functions you've come to expect from a state-of-the-art logging program, such as DX Packet Cluster monitoring, rig and antenna control, voice-synthesized DX announcements and so on. Needless to say, it supports interoperability with AEA's PC Pakratt for Windows, if you so desire. But if all you want to do is log your QSOs, *Log Windows* does this very well.

Looking at Figure 3.8, the command line across the top of the screen consists of pull-down menus that operate just like the pull-down menus you're accustomed to seeing in other Windows applications. For speed, instead of using a menu you can use a function key for certain tasks. For example, **F2** will open a logbook. *Log Windows* allows multiple logbooks, and they're opened in the same way you open any file in Windows. This means you can have separate logs for different awards, bands, band-modes and so on.

The data-entry fields look similar to a QSL card. Some fields are filled in automatically, and moving between fields is accomplished with the keyboard or a mouse. An award status bar shows worked and confirmed status for the current grid, prefix, state or zone. It displays and updates automatically, and you can scroll between various awards.

There's a tool bar in the center of the screen, which works in a similar fashion to tool bars in other *Windows* applications. Some functions can be carried out by clicking the appropriate button or in some cases, by using a function key.

The lower half of the screen, with the defined buttons, is used in conjunction with a TNC to show text going to or coming from the TNC, whereas the buttons can be set up to send TNC commands.

Log Windows uses special tags to indicate whether the current logbook record counts for a specific award and if it's been submitted for that award. The tags and their associated checkboxes are shown in Figure 3.8 on the upper right-hand side of the screen. Although the boxes are marked automatically by *Log Windows*, you can change them manually.

Log Windows assumes that you have some knowledge of using Windows application programs. If you do, you should have no trouble using the program. A couple of shortcomings are that the TNC window wastes screen space without a TNC and the buttons on the toolbar are somewhat cryptic. Displaying a brief description when a button was touched by the mouse pointer would be helpful. For further information see the Resources Chapter.

WJ2O Master QSO Logging Program

Officially, the program goes by the name *Master QSO Logging Program* from WJ2O Software. WJ2O is Dave Farnsworth's call sign, and as you'll quickly find out, users and competitors refer to it as the *WJ2O* program. If you have even a slight interest in logging software, do yourself a favor and at least request introductory material from Dave. The report card he'll send you is worth the telephone call. Actually a comparison chart, the card lists nearly 100 features a logging program could have. Naturally they're all in the *WJ2O* package. But the card is laid out in such a manner that you can check off the capability for other packages.

Also included in the introductory material is an eight-page reference guide to the reports possible with the *WJ2O* package. Before you ship off any of your hard-earned money, you have a fairly good idea of what the program can do. More importantly, you have some hard-copy materials to compare against other programs.

Unfortunately, Dave doesn't make available a demo copy of the software. If your questions aren't answered by his introductory material, your only other choice is to purchase a copy of the 75-page manual. Available for $5, this manual is a close second to having a demo version of the program.

According to Dave, the *Master QSO Logger* has been designed so that single keystrokes will take you through a logical sequence of events using self-explanatory menu screens. If you have questions, there's a help screen for each menu. If you happen to lose your manual during a DXpedition, no problem—you don't really need it after all.

The program is very easy to use. The main screen, which comes up after you start the program, gives you 11 possible choices in one of the following four main categories: Main Programs (two choices, logging and net operations), Sub Programs (four choices), Print Programs (two choices) and Utilities (three choices, but you normally use only one after the program is up and running).

Figure 3.9 shows what's referred to in the manual as the Master Log Program screen. It's where you add, edit or search for a particular QSO. Like most other logging programs, the *WJ2O* package will automatically fill in as much information as possible. Comments to a QSO can be added by selecting Comments where it says Enter Selection. One nice feature is the box in the upper right-hand corner, which provides local and UTC time, the total number of QSOs in the database and the order

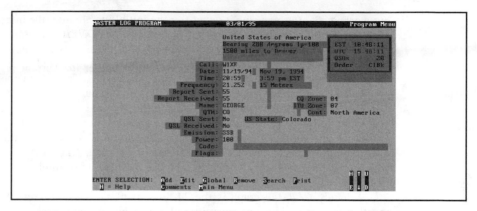

MASTER LOG PROGRAM   03/01/95   Program Menu

                          United States of America
                          Bearing 288 degress 1p-188   ┌─────────────┐
                          1588 miles to Denver   │EST 10:48:11│
                Call: W1XF   │UTC 15:48:11│
                Date: 11/19/94 Nov 19, 1994   │QSOs   28│
                Time: 28:59   3:59 pm EST   │Order   C1Bk│
           Frequency: 21.252   15 Meters   └─────────────┘
         Report Sent: 55
     Report Received: 55   CQ Zone: 84
                Name: GEORGE   ITU Zone: 87
                 QTH: CO   Cont: North America
            QSL Sent: No   US State: Colorado
        QSL Received: No
            Emission: SSB
               Power: 188
                Code:
               Flags:

ENTER SELECTION: Add Edit Global Remove Search Print   H ↑ U
        H = Help   Comments Main Menu   E ↓ D

Figure 3.9—Display of the Master Log Program screen for the *WJ2O Master Logging Program*.

they're currently being accessed.

If you're working nets and want to keep track of check-ins, this program is hard to beat. You can receive almost instant confirmation if you've worked the check-ins. If you have, their names will flash up on the screen.

WJ2O's *Master QSO Logger* is an excellent, easy to use logging program. If you're looking for a program that's particularly strong in its reporting capability and has the agility and speed to be used in contests and net operations, take a careful look at what Dave has to offer. More information may be found in the Resources Chapter.

Propagation Programs

Generally more sophisticated than logging software, propagation programs display data; they create it using sophisticated math. This places a greater burden on the computer. A 386 with a numeric coprocessor would be considered a nominal machine. There are, however, programs that will run on the older 8088 and 286 machines. The major difference between propagation and logging programs is that the propagation software is generally written for the commercial market, whereas the logging programs have been created specifically by and for amateurs. Propagation programs may not be as "ham friendly," but that is no reason to shy away from them. Some of the factors to consider in choosing one should include your planned use, computer power, DOS or *Windows* platform and cost. Serious DXers and contesters may want to consider what Dean Straw, N6BV, considers "Heavy-Duty" programs: *CAPMan, PropMan, SKYCOM 2.0, HFx* and *VOACAP*. For those of us without a real number-crunching machine *IONSOUND* and *MINIPRO PLUS* will run on an 8088 or 286 machine. Dean, a Senior Assistant Technical Editor at ARRL Headquarters, has test-driven all of these and his findings are summarized below.

CAPMan (Communications Analysis Prediction Manager), Version 3

CAPMan is a DOS-based program requiring a minimum of a 386 with a numeric coprocessor. The program is not necessarily a piece-of-cake for a beginner to install but works well after you slug it out. After the initial installation, the internal program parameters you select are saved when you run the *CCONFIG* program. One area of difficulty arises when specifying the receiver and transmitter antennas. It would be helpful to the beginner if a set of antennas similar to those used to create the *QST* "How's DX" graphs were built into *CAPMan*, as defaults. The more experienced user could still choose other more exotic forms at will, of course.

CAPMan Version 3 still creates some of the best and most useful graphs. Several graphs are tailored specifically for the radio amateur. For example, the graph of Signal-to-Noise Ratio has been augmented to plot three SNR lines simultaneously. On one graph you may see the SNR in a 250-Hz (CW) and a 3-kHz (SSB) bandwidth, as well as that in a 1-Hz bandwidth. See Figure 3.10 for an example of an SNR graph from *CAPMan*.

A handy *CAPMan* graph is the 24-hour display of signal strength (in S units) together with the dominant transmitter elevation angle (in degrees). See Figure 3.11. This graph is unique to *CAPMan* giving a tremendous amount of very useful information at a single glance.

One of the newest areas in the study of propagation is the effect that local terrain

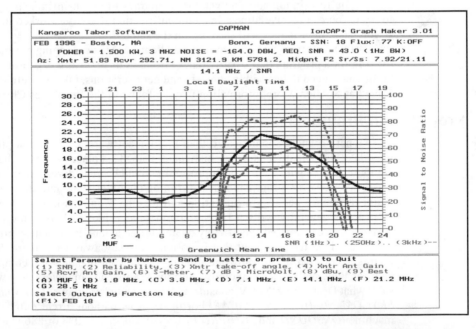

Figure 3.10—*CAPMan* **graph showing 20-meter SNR (Signal-to-Noise Ratio) for three receiver bandwidths (1 Hz, 250 Hz for CW and 3 kHz for SSB) on path from Boston to Bonn in February, for a solar flux level of 77. The transmitter power is 1500 W, into a three-element Yagi 100 feet over flat ground. The unbroken line indicates the MUF. An SNR of 10 dB in CW bandwidth is roughly equivalent to an SNR of 30 dB in a 1-Hz bandwidth. These computations were done for quiet geomagnetic conditions.**

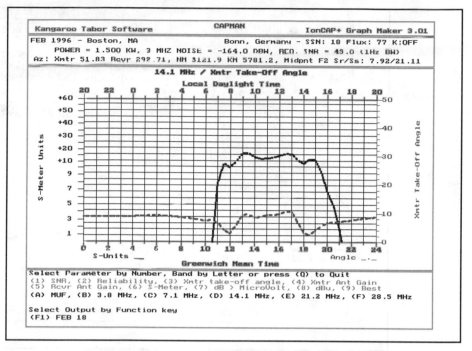

Figure 3.11—CAPMan graph showing received level in S units, together with transmitter-site elevation launch angle in degrees. This is for the same conditions as in Figure 3-10. This graph is uniquely tailored for hams, giving an intuitive picture of conditions for that level of solar activity over a 24-hour period in February. This screen shot was captured using the Windows Clipboard.

has on the launch of HF signals. N6BV wrote a simple program to manipulate elevation-response output from his *YTAD* program (Yagi Terrain Analysis, with Diffraction) to work with *MAKANT*, which is included with *CAPMan*. The final output is a special antenna file that *CAPMan* can use directly for either point-to-point or area-coverage computations. See the Resources Chapter for more information on *YTAD*.

Area-Coverage Maps

A unique feature in is area-coverage mapping, using a separate add-on program called *CAPMap*, the Contour Mapping Program. *CAPMap* is an extra-cost option. Area-coverage mapping is potentially one of the most powerful features in a propagation-prediction program. Area-mapping can display in an almost 3D-fashion communication parameters (such as signal strength, launch angle or SNR) for a wide geographic area, rather than just for a single receiving location.

At this point *CAPMap* seems to be in an early stage of development. When you print a map using the DOS Print-Screen function, the output is crude. Figure 3.12 shows an on-screen *CAPMap* map of signal strength across Europe. Contrast this with Figure 3.13, showing a map created by *VOACAP* for the same conditions. More work is definitely needed on the *CAPMap* mapping functions.

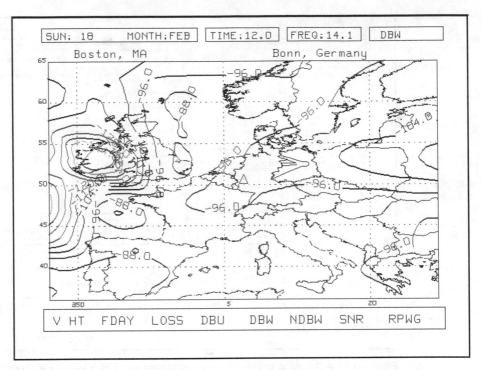

Figure 3.12—*CAPMan* area-coverage map of Europe using *CAPMap* optional add-on. This was for the 1200 UTC hour in February 1996, with a solar flux of 70—the same conditions used in Figures 3.10 and 3.11. The clutter and relatively low-resolution graphics make on-screen navigating a challenge—for example, distinguishing the various countries from the outside outline of Europe is difficult due to lack of contrast.

The K Index

CAPMan includes the ability to enter the geomagnetic K Index. The general effect of a higher K Index is to increase ionospheric absorption, especially on transpolar paths. However, you should beware—sometimes propagation between two points will actually improve as the K Index rises; more often, however, propagation gets worse.

Although the K Index is potentially useful to improve short-term prediction accuracy, a late addendum to the *CAPMan* operator's manual warns the user that a prediction made using the K Index will only be good for three hours, or until the K Index changes. It also states that short-term predictions are "anything but an exact science." N6BV has not been able to correlate Boulder K-Index readings directly with the real-time state of propagation from his QTH in New Hampshire to other parts of the world.

PropMan (Propagation Resource Manager)

PropMan by the Collins Avionics and Communications Division of Rockwell

International started out life as a military product. The manual is full of "military-speak" and there are many places throughout the program that smack of a military sort of approach. *PropMan* is definitely not custom-designed for amateurs.

PropMan is copy-protected, an antediluvian marketing technique in today's sophisticated software marketplace. It installs itself without allowing the user to override what it is doing. During installation, *PropMan* will overwrite personal *IONCAP* files—with an older version, no less! Be warned: If you already have a subdirectory called **\IONCAP** on your hard disk, you should first create a new subdirectory called **\IONCAP1** (or some such name) and move all your own files into the new subdirectory before allowing *PropMan* to do its thing.

Like *CAPMan*, *PropMan* is a specialized "shell" that shields the user from the tribulations of dealing directly with *IONCAP*. Unlike a general-purpose program like *CAPMan*, *PropMan* uses only a limited subset of the capabilities built into *IONCAP*. The ability to choose antennas is very limited as well. The whole focus of *PropMan* is on real-time, 24-hour operation, to aid relatively unsophisticated users to choose HF frequencies for communication.

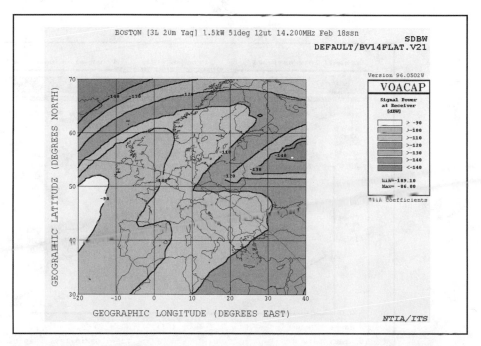

Figure 3.13—VOACAP area-coverage map of Europe for same conditions as Figure 3.12. Higher-resolution graphics produce outstanding clarity. This figure was printed directly from the program to a color Inkjet printer. The user can customize a number of parameters. For example, this map is a rectangular projection, with overlay of contours of signal strength, in dBW, chosen at 10 dB intervals. The −100 dBW contour corresponds to roughly S9 on an S meter. A matrix of 37×37 geographic points was specified. It is also possible to draw a great-circle map using VOACAP.

Figure 3.14 shows a screen-shot of *PropMan*'s only graph—a 24-hour propagation plot created for a path from Boston to London in February at a low level of solar activity. Note how the legend to the right of the graph shows "Chan ID," betraying the program's military orientation. If you chose amateur frequencies *PropMan* will use the amateur bands in meters for "channels." There is no built-in facility to print from *PropMan*—printing isn't needed for real-time operation. The operator's manual suggests using a TSR screen-capture program.

PropMan mercilessly thrashes your hard disk as it computes, rather than doing calculations for all 24 hours at one time. N6BV reports a computation that took 90 seconds of hyperactive hard-disk activity on his 100-MHz Pentium using *PropMan* was completed by *CAPMan* in three seconds. Rockwell recommends using a RAMDISK to save wear and tear on your hard disk.

In its favor, *PropMan* does have some interesting and unique features, again relating to its real-time character. You can connect it (by a 2400-baud modem) to the US-Government SESC (Space Environmental Services Center) databases in Boulder, Colorado, for updates on solar-terrestrial indices. This allows the latest three-hour Boulder K index to interact automatically with *PropMan*'s propagation predictions.

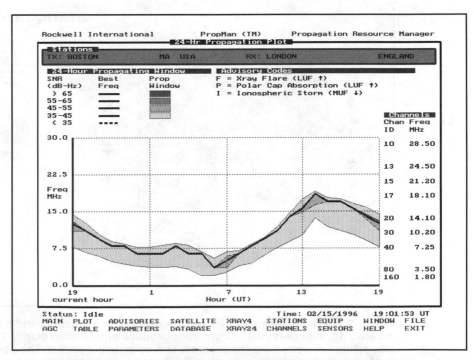

Figure 3.14—24-Hour Propagation Plot created by *PropMan*. The solid line shows the FOT (Frequency of Optimum Traffic), together with shadings indicating the range of S/R versus frequency. This image was captured to the Windows Clipboard and printed off-line. While this information is interesting and useful, it is not really tailored to the needs of an amateur operator.

The K index cannot be entered manually, only by modem. Be cautioned: the effects of the K Index in a propagation prediction are not a totally exact science.

PropMan's designers would clearly prefer to have a computer dedicated solely to it. For example, let's say that you want to plan for a contest coming up next month. *After you change the date (or the time) within PropMan, the program proceeds to change your PC's internal clock and calendar!* This is amazingly bad-mannered programming. After you quit *PropMan*, be sure to reset your computer's date and time from DOS.

PropMan can even be connected by serial port directly to a receiver AGC bus, assuming that an amateur would have access to a Collins HF-80 receiver, with a separate computer and A/D input card for interface. While it's unlikely that a ham will have such a setup, the concept certainly sounds intriguing!

In summary, Rockwell International needs to do a *lot* more work to make a suitable commercial program out of *PropMan*. For further information see the Resources Chapter.

SKYCOM 2.0

Fuentez Systems Concepts in Fairfax, Virginia, introduced *SKYCOM 2.0* to the amateur market in 1995. According to the Product Manager for this product, its main asset is that it is very easy to use. Because of its *Windows* look and feel, *SKYCOM 2.0* is indeed very easy to use. It also executes remarkably quickly, producing a plain table of numbers that can be viewed on-screen or printed. See Figure 3.15 showing an example of such an output table.

A propagation-prediction program is only as good as its core algorithms. *SKYCOM 2.0* uses as its core an enhanced version of *MINIMUF*. Unfortunately, there are some problems associated with any *MINIMUF*-derived core. *MINIMUF* was designed to compute only the Maximum Usable Frequency (MUF), and it does so with an extremely simplified model of the ionosphere, even though a recalibrated database is used in this program. Although *SKYCOM 2.0* uses other algorithms to compute the S/N at the target receiving location, it does so only at the MUF.

Amateur operators are interested in predictions for each amateur band, not the MUF. *SKYCOM 2.0* also does not compute the elevation angles at which signals are launched, an item of great interest in the DX and Contest communities to help them design antenna systems. See Figure 3.16 for a comparison of the MUF calculations from Boston to Germany generated by several programs, including *SKYCOM 2.0*. It appears to be a bit conservative predicting the 21-MHz opening that *CAPMan* predicts from about 1230 to 1530 UTC.

There is another propagation-prediction program that uses "SKYCOM" as part of its name. A Canadian company called Solar Terrestrial Dispatch in Stirling, Alberta, has been marketing a program called *SKYCOM PRO, Version 2.0*. This has recently been renamed *PROPLAB-PRO, Version 2.0*, to prevent further confusion with *SKYCOM 2.0*. *PROPLAB-PRO* is a vastly more sophisticated program, using full-blown 3-D ray-tracing techniques. It also sells for a much higher price.

In short, *SKYCOM 2.0* is a pretty face (with an admirable user interface) coupled with an anemic body. It is an ambitious undertaking that falls short of the mark, especially at the price asked for it. For further information see the Resources Chapter.

PREFIX	LOCATION	DISTANCE	BEARING
DA-DL	GERMANY/BONN	5793 (km)	52 (degrees)

SUNLIGHT STATUS		HOUR (LOCAL)	(UTC)	FOF2 (MHz)	MUF (MHz)	FOT (MHz)	S/N (dB)
NIGHT (A)	NIGHT (B)	1	6	3	8	6	(23)
NIGHT (A)	NIGHT (B)	2	7	3	8	6	(23)
NIGHT (A)	DAY (B)	3	8	3	8	6	(32)
NIGHT (A)	DAY (B)	4	9	3	8	6	(32)
DAY (A)	DAY (B)	5	10	4	12	10	(−1)
DAY (A)	DAY (B)	6	11	5	14	12	(21)
DAY (A)	DAY (B)	7	12	6	16	14	(26)
DAY (A)	DAY (B)	8	13	6	17	14	(28)
DAY (A)	DAY (B)	9	14	7	18	15	(29)
DAY (A)	DAY (B)	10	15	7	18	15	(29)
DAY (A)	DAY (B)	11	16	6	17	15	(28)
DAY (A)	DAY (B)	12	17	6	17	14	(27)
DAY (A)	DAY (B)	13	18	6	16	13	(25)
DAY (A)	DAY (B)	14	19	5	14	12	(21)
DAY (A)	DAY (B)	15	20	4	12	10	(2)
DAY (A)	NIGHT (B)	16	21	3	10	8	(4)
DAY (A)	NIGHT (B)	17	22	3	9	8	(26)
NIGHT (A)	NIGHT (B)	18	23	3	9	8	(25)
NIGHT (A)	NIGHT (B)	19	24	3	9	7	(25)
NIGHT (A)	NIGHT (B)	20	1	3	8	7	(24)
NIGHT (A)	NIGHT (B)	21	2	3	8	7	(24)
NIGHT (A)	NIGHT (B)	22	3	3	8	7	(24)
NIGHT (A)	NIGHT (B)	23	4	3	8	7	(24)
NIGHT (A)	NIGHT (B)	24	5	3	8	7	(24)

DAYLIGHT DURATION (A)= 13 HOURS
TIME OF LOCAL NOON (A)= 16 HOURS (UTC)
NOON SOLAR ZENITH ANGLE (A)= 64 (degrees)

DAYLIGHT DURATION (B)= 13 HOURS
TIME OF LOCAL NOON (B)= 14 HOURS (UTC)
NOON SOLAR ZENITH ANGEL (B)= 68 (degrees)

CONTROL LAT-LONG (degrees):
A) 50 51
(B) 54 19

Figure 3.15—Printout of *SKYCOM 2.0* table showing MUF, FOT and S/N for 24-hour period in February 1996 for solar flux of 70 on the path from Boston to Bonn, Germany.

HFx

Pacific-Sierra Research is a high-tech software and research company headquartered in Santa Monica, California. They introduced their *HFx* program to the amateur market in late 1995. Unlike most other heavy-duty propagation-prediction programs, which are based on *IONCAP*, Pacific-Sierra Research took a relatively "clean-slate" approach to *HFx* using raytracing algorithms. *HFx* predictions, especially the low-frequency ones, are claimed to be more accurate than "certain other" unidentified approaches.

HFx likes 486 or Pentium systems running Windows 3.1 with 8 Mbytes of RAM and Super VGA graphics. In addition to the usual Windows-style pull-down or pop-up menus, *HFx* includes an innovative and very appealing approach for the selection of geographic values, using an on-screen global map. See Figure 3.17. You may grab the icon for the transmitter or receiver location with your mouse and deposit it anywhere you like on the globe. That's pretty slick!

HFx includes three different prediction models. One, called the *Global MUF* model, plots the MUF, FOT (Frequency of Optimum Traffic) or HPF (Highest Pos-

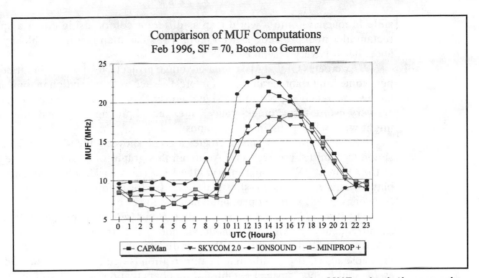

Figure 3.16—Graph showing comparisons between the MUF calculations made by four different programs. As closely as possible, each program was instructed to use the same parameters as in Figure 3-10. The line using solid rectangles is by *CAPMan* and is the standard of comparison for the others. There are significant differences among the programs, especially predicting the onset of the opening from Boston to Germany.

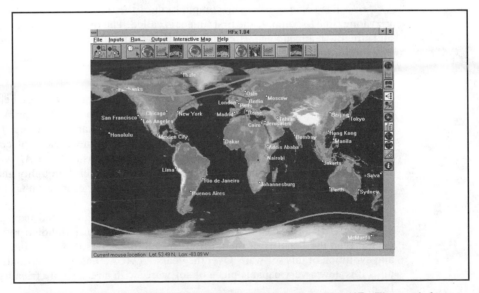

Figure 3.17—Screen shot of geographic map displayed by *HFx*. The path from the US East Coast to Berlin is shown by the curved magenta line, while the auroral ovals are shown by the curved cyan lines at top and bottom of the map.

sible Frequency) onto a world map as different colors, using either a spherical or a rectangular map projection. See Figure 3.18. The map is a little "blocky" in appearance, but it is very readable.

HFx creates Global MUF area-coverage projections quickly, but it does not compute some important parameters of interest—such as the variation in transmitter launch angles, the receiver SNR or the signal power. Nonetheless, *HFx* area-coverage maps are very useful for a "quick-glance" at expected propagation conditions, such as you might want when planning for a contest.

The *Temporal MUF* model creates a graph showing the MUF, FOT and HPF for a single transmitter-receiver pair. Although this graph looks similar to the ones shown in the "How's DX" column in *QST*, the LUF (Lowest Usable Frequency) is not displayed. This *HFx* model is thus mainly useful for predicting when one of the higher-frequency bands will be open, not when the lower bands will open.

The third *HFx* model is the so-called *Hop Mode*. This creates detailed tables for each frequency showing SNR, mode(s), mode MUF, transmitter elevation angle, ionospheric loss, field strength (in dBμV or dB/m), and mode percentage availability for the chosen UTC time. Although the information is detailed, I wish I could see the data as 24-hour graphs, instead of tables of numbers that one must scroll through using the mouse or cursor keys. The speed of computation, while decidedly slower than *CAPMan*, is not really objectionable.

HFx creates some lovely on-screen graphs. One is entitled "Hop Mode Geometry," where the number of hops each mode takes to get from the transmitter to the receiver site is shown graphically above a globe. See Figure 3.19 for an example. *HFx* also creates a nice-looking graph showing the "Hop Mode Availability." I'm just not sure how useful either of these presentations really is, but they are spectacular to look at!

HFx has some quirks. The computation of the day/night terminator line takes a *very* long time to compute the first time it is called. The on-screen result is also blotchy and streaky in appearance. Hopefully this function will be improved in later versions. For further information consult the Resources Chapter.

VOACAP

The engineers and programmers of the Voice of America who are behind the latest versions of *VOACAP* have done an admirable job, especially in the Windows version. *VOACAP* has been in the public domain for more than three years. The Voice of America started out wanting to improve on *IONCAP*—one obvious place was to improve the ungainly *IONCAP* user interface. Early versions of *VOACAP* were *different* from *IONCAP*, but not more user friendly. VOA personnel thoroughly analyzed (and documented) *IONCAP*, finding and eliminating a number of minor bugs before going on to develop *VOACAP*.

VOACAP was developed to serve the needs of designers and managers of very large VOA HF broadcast stations, but that doesn't mean individual radio amateurs cannot reap the benefits of the millions of public dollars that went into the creation and evolution of this software. Over the years, *VOACAP* has been constantly improved, until it is now a very capable piece of software, with a reasonably friendly user interface.

VOACAP still requires considerable study and a steep learning curve on the part of the user. The user Help files contain a lot of scientific jargon, and the setup of

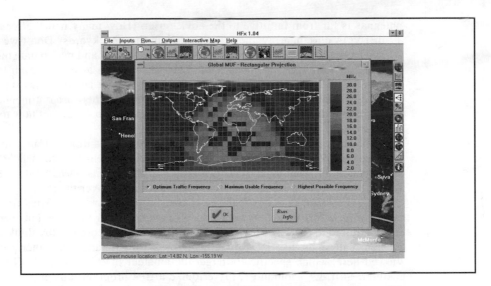

Figure 3.18—Screen-shot of "Global MUF-Rectangular Projection" by *HFx*. The distribution of FOT (Optimum Traffic Frequency) is shown. Although rather "blocky" in appearance, the display is quite usable since geographic features are readily recognizable on the global map.

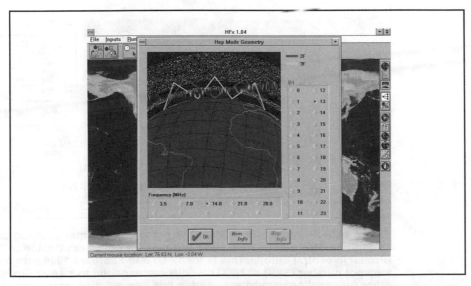

Figure 3.19—Screen-shot of "Hop Mode Geometry" by *HFx*. This is for 1300 UTC, on the path from Boston to Berlin for February 1996. While definitely eye-catching, the usefulness of the information is open to debate.

antennas is far from intuitive to the novice user. (How many hams, after all, have a 17-dBi VOA curtain array, the default value, in their backyards? Don't we wish!)

A program called *HFant* allows the operator to view and manipulate the stable of standard antenna types included with *VOACAP*. You can also use *HFant* to generate custom antenna files. As you might expect, many of the antenna files supplied with the program pertain to shortwave broadcast stations, but there are rudimentary models for Yagis and dipoles too. Carefully read the Help files to figure out how to use these types properly in *VOACAP*.

The choice of receiving antennas is more limited than that for transmitting antennas, because *VOACAP* allows only a single receiving antenna for the whole frequency range you might want to cover. This is unlike *CAPMAN*, its *IONCAP*-derived brother, which allows you to use up to three receiving antennas over the HF range.

The *VOACAP* operator may select transmitter and receiver sites from detailed tables of cities organized by continents. This is far easier than previous versions, but is not tailored to the way a ham usually thinks. We most comfortably think in terms of amateur call signs, like DL for Germany or G for England. The other programs reviewed here, which specifically target the amateur market, use the call sign-access method. Still, we shouldn't really criticize a free program too severely on this ac-

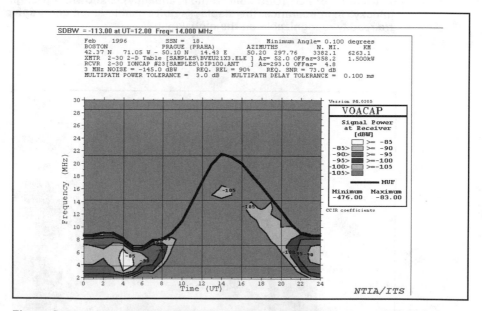

Figure 3.20—Printout from *VOACAP* direct to color printer showing signal strength in dBW versus frequency and time for path from Boston to Prague (Praha) in central Europe. This is for 12 UTC in February 1996 with a smoothed sunspot number (SSN) of 18. (This SSN corresponds to a solar flux of 70.) The other propagation parameters used in this computation were used in Figure 3.10—antenna types, receiver noise environment, etc. The cursor, presently located on 14.000 MHz at 1200 UTC, can be scrolled around the graph to show the exact signal level, time and frequency.

count. It's not all that hard to specify "Europe" then "Berlin" to pick a QTH in central Europe as a target receiving site, rather than picking "DL."

As mentioned before, the program is available in both DOS and *Windows* flavors; however, the *Windows* version is far more desirable—it's got a more intuitive user interface and it runs significantly faster than the DOS version. Keep in mind, however, that the *Windows* version takes up some 15 MB of hard-disk space—and that's before you start making your own data files. Count on reserving at least 20 MB of total disk space if you get at all serious about *VOACAP*.

Opening the *readme* file can be disconcerting for us budget-conscious amateurs. The $500 referred to in *ReadMe.TXT* is a way to try to account for future telephone support for the programs. If you really need your hand held while you learn how to use *VOACAP*, you should be prepared to hand over $500 for the privilege. This will probably not appeal much to frugal amateurs. At least for the foreseeable future, *VOACAP* will remain free and available for ftp download directly from VOA.

Point-to-Point Computations

One tricky part of using a complex program like *VOACAP* is specifying the antennas used at each end of a circuit. The graphs produced by *VOACAP Point* are useful and even rather pretty, but they are not tailored to the specific tastes of amateurs. Figure 3.20 shows a graph of SDBW (signal strength in dBW, relative to 1 W) versus UTC. The data at the cursor cross hairs is displayed at the upper left corner as −113 dBW at 12 UTC at the frequency of 14.0 MHz. The ability to query the data using the mouse cursor is pretty snazzy but many amateurs would rather see a graph showing the 24-hour performance on a single band, such as 14 MHz.

Area-Coverage Maps

This is where *VOACAP Area* really shines! The area-coverage charts it creates are spectacular; there's no other word for it. Figure 3.21 shows a special area-coverage map centered on central Europe for February, from a transmitter site in Boston during a low level of solar activity. The computed elevation angles launched at the transmitter end of the circuit are displayed.

When viewed on a computer screen, the light blue bands going from Northeast to Southwest represent launch angles between 5° to 7°. The band closest to the left edge of Figure 3.21, over central England, shows graphically the coverage of $2F_2$ hops from Boston. The next band to the right, falling over the "boot" of Italy is the range of hops, and the band falling over the Red Sea to the right of Egypt is the range of $3F_2$ hops. That is why N6BV refers to the area-coverage maps as representing "3D" data—latitude, longitude and hops, in this case.

Like *CAPMan*, *VOACAP* also allows programmers to customize data sets in exciting and interesting fashions. A small program called *MAKEVOA* takes output from *YTAD* and directly produces a *VOACAP* antenna file. Then *VOACAP* can create an area-coverage map—customized for the specific terrain in front of the transmitting antenna. See Figure 3.22, showing the area coverage predicted for a stack of three TH7DX tribanders (at 90, 60 and 30 feet) over the terrain. Carefully compare Figure 3.22 and Figure 3.13, which was computed for a three-element 20-meter Yagi 100 feet in the air, but over *flat* ground.

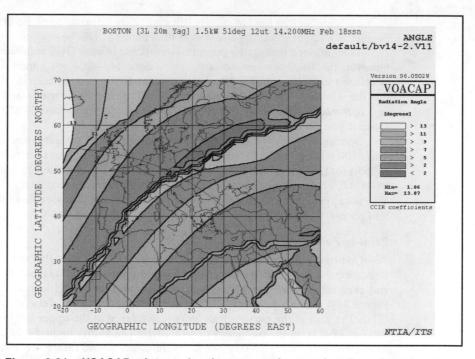

Figure 3.21—*VOACAP* printout showing range of transmitter launch angles for the path from Boston to Europe for February 1996, with SSN = 18. The same propagation parameters used in Figure 3.10 were used here. The bands correspond to the number of F$_2$-hops as the signals move across Europe, starting with two F$_2$ hops at the left side of this chart, and moving to four F$_2$ hops on the right side. This graph shows the relationship between distance and launch angle for a single hop.

You will note in Figure 3.22 that the geographic area covered for any particular signal level extends farther East than does the corresponding level for the flat-land antenna. For example, the −110 dBW contour (corresponding to about S7 on an S meter) in Figure 3.22 extends almost to 48° East longitude, while that in Figure 3.13 extends only to about 32° East longitude. This represents a distance of almost 2000 km, a significant improvement in coverage! This happens because the stack of tribanders used in this exmaple are located on a small hill, emphasizing the lower takeoff angles, and because of the gain enjoyed by the stack compared to a single Yagi.

VOACap area-coverage maps printed on a black-and-white 300-dpi laser printer are even more impressive than what shows on the video screen, since the printer resolution is better. For further information see the Resources Chapter.

Satellite Tracking Programs

The main purpose of a satellite tracking program is to tell you when a satellite

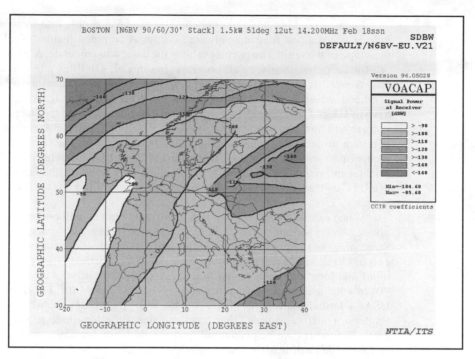

BOSTON [N6BV 90/60/30' Stack] 1.5kW 51deg 12ut 14.200MHz Feb 18ssn

SDBW
DEFAULT/N6BV-EU.V21

Version 96.0502W

VOACAP

Signal Power
at Receiver
[dBW]

> -90
>-100
>-110
>-120
>-130
>-140
<-140

Min=-184.60
Max=-85.60

CCIR coefficients

GEOGRAPHIC LATITUDE (DEGREES NORTH)

GEOGRAPHIC LONGITUDE (DEGREES EAST)

NTIA/ITS

Figure 3.22—VOACAP printout showing effect of local terrain at N6BV's station in the direction of Europe. A customized VOACAP antenna file, including computations by the YTAD program, was created for the stack of three TH7DX Yagis at 90, 60 and 30 feet. Compare this graph with that in Figure 3.13, which was computed using a single three-element Yagi 100 feet over flat ground.

will appear and where to point your antennas. They are nothing more than high power calculators, performing math to solve the orbital equations in a flash. Orbital equations are based on a fundamental law of physics. Once you put an object, a satellite for instance, into motion it will tend to stay in motion forever unless some external force is applied. The orbital equation takes into account these external forces and predicts the motion of a satellite. Fortunately NASA does most of the legwork and calculates the necessary parameters and puts them in a form that our computers can use to display a satellite's position. These parameters are called the *Keplerian Element Set*.

Before PCs were found in almost every ham shack, graphical methods were used by overlaying a ground track on a map. An early method used an OSCARLOCATOR, a clear plastic sheet pinned so that it could rotate over a map centered on the north pole. The procedure was tedious and not much fun. PCs automated this procedure and added a lot of bells and whistles. Features now include detailed earth maps showing country outlines and DX prefixes, ability to view the maps from different perspective, beam headings, RF coverage footprints and the ability to speed up time and show where the satellite will be in the future. They also print calendars, ranges and Doppler shift. Now it's fun just showing off your tracking program even if you aren't going to get on the air!

Because tracking programs are complex, and can supply information in a multitude of ways, a few fundamentals are in order. A common feature of all satellites is the shape of the orbit. The circular orbit is the easiest to calculate. A perfectly circular orbit is an impossibility, so all programs assume all satellites move in elliptical orbits. A satellite in a highly elliptical orbit appears almost stationary when it is high overhead, which facilitates antenna pointing. When you use a tracking program, you have to select a specific satellite for a given date and time, and tell the program where you are and how you would like to view the resulting data. The easiest to understand is a map projection. Tabular calendar-like outputs are also possible, however, programs often will ask for the current date and expect you to enter it as DD:MM:YY. This means you would enter *01:05:96* if it is May 1, 1996. Although most programs use UTC as their reference, many can convert displays to your local time for convenience.

When entering your location it is important to note whether the latitude and longitude should be entered as decimal numbers or in degrees, hours, seconds format. Some programs require a minus sign for latitudes south of the equator and longitudes east of Greenwich, England. For example, AMSATs *InstrantTrack* program uses latitudes and longitudes as decimal degrees and assumes latitudes are in the range of −90° to +90° and longitudes are in the range of -180° to +180°. For those of us in the USA, + latitudes are north of the equator and - longitudes are west of Greenwich, England. *Quiktrak,* on the other hand, considers the longitude to range from 0° to 360°. If numbers are being entered, you should leave out any commas. The *readme* and *help* files will usually resolve any questions.

Elevation and azimuth are also important parameters, but are not so complicated as lat and long. The elevation is simply how high up you need to point your antenna. The horizon is always 0° and directly over head is 90°. Azimuth is the compass bearing, well—almost the compass bearing. Azimuth is based on true north (as opposed to magnetic north) and is always 0°. Due east is always 90°. Magnetic north is close to true north but it varies from place to place and is not taken into account by tracking programs.

Keplerian Elements

The Keplerian elements (Keps) are a set of 7 or 8 numbers that describe the motion of the satellite. All tracking programs use them to locate the satellite in relationship to the earth. When a tracking program is installed for the first time you must input a current set of elements. The elements are calculated by NASA and are widely available. It is desirable to input new Keps often because the motion of a satellite may change in unpredictable ways. A large solar flare or sunspot can swell the atmosphere enough to effect a drag on the satellite and change its orbit. Acquiring up-to-date elements is a must for accurate tracking. Some satellites have more stable orbits than others and rarely need a correction.

The best place to obtain Keplerian elements is directly from the ARRL or AMSAT Web Page on the Internet. If you don't have web access they may be obtained weekly by e-mail from AMSAT. They also are often found on many landline and packet BBSs as well. The elements come in two flavors: user-friendly and computer-friendly. The NASA format is sent as two lines of numbers and is easily interpreted by your computer. The AMSAT format is more user-friendly and can be interpreted by a human

Where to Obtain Keps

From the ARRL www   **http://www.arrl.org/w1aw**

From the ARRL Hiram BBS 860-594-0306 look in file area 1.

From AMSAT www   **http://www.amsat.org/amsat/keps/menu.html**

From AMSAT's e-mail list server by sending an e-mail request to **listserv@amsat.org** including your call sign (if any) your e-mail address and text stating that you want to be added to the *Keplerian Elements mailing list.* Currently the list is sent once a week.

http://www.amsat.org/amsat/keps/kepmodel.html

Further information may be found in the Resources Chapter.

When you download Keps be sure to save them to a file because the tracking programs can "read" this file directly—you don't have to type in the information. If you print them out, the NASA two-line format would looks like:

```
AO-10
1 14129U 83058B   96146.12823962 -.00000065  00000-0  10000-3 0 04272
2 14129 026.1931 207.9775 6001544 018.2491 356.4172 02.05880352 97369
UO-11
1 14781U 84021B   96151.01998677  .00000071  00000-0  19728-4 0 09039
2 14781 097.7993 142.5546 0012050 142.9824 217.2216 14.69455207654988
```

The AMSAT format looks like:

Satellite: AO-10		Satellite: UO-11	
Catalog number:	14129	Catalog number:	14781
Epoch time:	96146.12823062	Epoch time:	96151.01998677
Element set:	0427	Element set:	0903
Inclination:	026.1931 deg	Inclination:	097.7993 deg
RA of node:	207.9775 deg	RA of node:	142.5546 deg
Eccentricity:	0.6001544	Eccentricity:	0.0012050
Arg of perigee:	018.2491 deg	Arg of perigee:	142.9824 deg
Mean anomaly:	356.4172 deg	Mean anomaly:	217.2216 deg
Mean motion:	02.05880352 rev/day	Mean motion:	14.69455207 rev/day
Decay rate:	6.5e-07 rev/day^2	Decay rate:	7.1e-07 rev/day^2
Epoch rev:	9736	Epoch rev:	65498
Checksum:	303	Checksum:	328

```
WinSat (Windows)                              ORBITS III (IBM PC)
APRtrak (IBM PC)                              QUIKTRAK 4.0 (IBM PC)
InstantTrack (IBM PC)                         NOVA (IBM PC)
STSOrbit Plus (IBM PC)                        QUIKTRAK (IBM PC, Text Only)
Satellite Pro (Macintosh)                     C-64 SuperTrac (Commodore 64)
C-128 Orbits (Commodore 128)                  Amiga Orbits (Commodore
Apple QUIKTRAK (Apple II)                      Amiga)
C-Track 2 (Tandy CoCo 3)                      C-Track 1 (Tandy CoCo 2 or 3)
ATARI 8-Bit Tracking Program                  TRS-80 Model 4 QUIKTRAK
ATARI ST Satellite Prediction Program
ORBIT 1 and 2 (HP-41CV programmable calculator)
```

Figure 3.23—AMSAT offers satellite tracking programs for just about any type of computer.

being. For a complete explanation of how to interpret these formats, see *The Satellite Experimenter's Handbook* by Martin Davidoff, K2UBC, or AMSAT's *Keplerian Elements Tutorial*, via the web,

Tracking software is available for most popular computers, including the PC, Commodore's C-64 and C-128, Amiga, Apples and Macs, and even the old Radio Shack TRS-80. Just about any computer may be used for tracking. Newer machines with VGA or SVGA graphics will give you a more impressive display than an old 80-column B&W display. AMSAT offers one-stop shopping for tracking software with over 18 tracking programs for just about any computer. See Figure 3.23. Two of the most popular programs are *InstantTrack* and *Nova*.

InstantTrack

InstantTrack is one of the oldest and best all around tracking programs. DOS based, it requires 512k RAM. Any type display is okay for text screens but VGA is preferred. Graphics screens require an EGA or VGA display. A math coprocessor is recommended, although, a separate program (the ncp version) is provided for machines with no coprocessor. A mouse is not required, but can be helpful. It is easy, menu-driven program to run and is ideal for both beginners and seasoned satellite operators. Figure 3.24 shows a typical map screen. Version 1.00b is current. If you have version 1.00 or 1.00a, you need Patch 2 to fix an incompatibility with recent NASA-format Keplerian element files. If you find garbage on the map screens where the text should be, Patch 4 should fix it.

Features include:

▨ Instant visibility, shows the position of your favorite satellites before your first key stroke.

▨ Real-Time displays, includes azimuth, elevation, range, Doppler shift, path loss, squint angle, subsatellite position (in latitude/longitude, grid square and nearest city), Cartesian coordinates of observer and satellite, satellite rise/set time, satellite mode, Right Ascension, Declination, sky temperature and more.

▨ Full-color high-resolution maps of the Earth, showing satellite and observer's position, two kinds of satellite footprint, gray-line, etc. You also can select either a

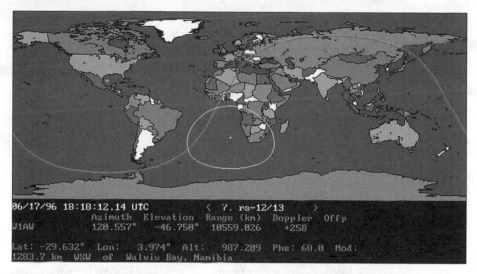

Figure 3.24—*InstantTrack* **printout showing the location of RS-12/13 over the South Atlantic. The RF footprint is depicted as the circle covering the tip of South Africa.**

diagram of the satellite's orbit showing its orientation, or a map of the sky, showing the satellite's position against a star field. Check out the screen images of the cylindrical map, the orthographic map, the star field map and the plan view diagram. (These EGA screen images will probably have a distorted aspect ratio on your display.)

 ▢ Automated Keplerian element update using AMSAT and NASA format text files.

 ▢ Schedules such as the next three weeks for a satellite or one day for 20 satellites on one screen.

 ▢ A unique background mode allows you to track satellites and control antenna rotators in real time while you run other programs.

 ▢ Tracks the Sun and Moon as well as the satellites in the database.

 ▢ Automated time setting of your computer by accessing the NIST (formerly NBS) time service via your modem.

 ▢ Supports a database of 200 satellites and 50 observer locations.

 ▢ Includes a database of 1754 cities worldwide.

 ▢ Observing stations can be specified by entering as little as their city name or their grid square.

 ▢ Shows when satellites can see each other and when they are in eclipse in real time.

 ▢ Squint (off pointing) angle shown to indicate if the satellite's antennas are pointed toward you.

 ▢ Path loss between observers and the satellite is calculated.

 ▢ Computes the time at which a satellite will rise without the delay of stepping through small time increments between *now* and *then*.

🖫 Can display the tracking parameters from both your perspective and that of another station, perhaps the one you are working.

🖫 Extensive tutorial documentation is included with the program.

🖫 On-line help can be obtained from almost any screen.

Nova

Nova by Northern Light Software is another fast, accurate and easy-to-use program. Nova is available in both DOS and Windows versions and can even run under Win95. The minimum system requirements are a 286 with a coprocessor, VGA graphics, 425 Kb memory (uses EMS if available) and 2 Mb of hard disk space. For further information see the Resources Chapter.

Features include:

🖫 Full position information (azimuth, elevation, range, height, etc.) in real time.

🖫 Includes 32 maps: Mercator projection.

🖫 Orthographic (view from space) projection with full Earth positioning and manipulation, ground tracks, footprints, and real-time orbit shapes; up to six satellites visible.

🖫 Sky temperature (3 bands: 50, 136, and 400 MHz) with current satellite and antenna positions.

🖫 Radar map showing all visible satellites and antenna position.

🖫 Grid Square maps centered anywhere in the world, with point-and-click bearing/distance display.

🖫 Autotracking via popular hardware rotor controls units, such as the SASI Sat Tracker, Kansas City Tracker and AEA ST-1.

🖫 Full control of frequency (with or without real-time Doppler compensation) and mode of all modern satellite transceivers.

🖫 Built-in logging (separate logs for each satellite if desired).

🖫 Keplerian element updating (AMSAT or NASA 2-line).

🖫 Multiple satellites/Multiple observers in real time.

🖫 Includes three TSR programs for background tracking/tuning (ICOM, Yaesu, Kenwood).

DATABASES

Probably one of the most affordable and popular accessories for the hamshack is a CD ROM-based database. If you are short on bookshelf space, they can't be beat. With over 2.5 million hams in the world, an electronic database is the only way to access an individual's personal information in a fraction of a second. Callbook databases are the most popular, but many other sources of ham radio information can also be found on CD-ROMs or floppy disks. Back issues of *QST* and the current *ARRL Handbook* are available, along with many more.

What is a database? It is simply a collection of information arranged in a structured manner so you can see it and get the information you need. This information has some common dominator to it; for example, in a callbook database all the call signs are one type of information. In computer lingo this is called a *field*. Other fields might be last names, street addresses, ZIP codes or states. To make the database useful to a human operator, a program must be used that can access and display the desired information for you. Fortunately, all of the "databases" mentioned in this chapter come with a helper program that will know how to access and display the information you request.

When you perform the installation, several files are installed, one being the actual database and the other being the program that is used to read the database. Search *filters* can look through the various fields to find entries by call, last name, first name, city, state, ZIP code, age, class of license, areas and prefixes—the list goes on. Hundreds of combinations can be used to select data. Databases are not only found on CDs or floppies; you may access them through BBSs or the Internet. See Chapter 6 for more information on databases accessible through the Internet.

Why use databases? There are fun, fast and accurate. Haven't you ever wanted to see a list of all the hams in your town? A database allows you to collect information in many different ways. For instance, you could ask the program to give you all the hams with your last name or all the hams who live on a particular street in your town. The power of a database program lies in its ability to mix and match search criteria to your own personal desires. There is even an FCC Master Frequency Database that lists every licensed radio station in the country! Ever wonder whose antenna was on the building across the street or wanted to know what frequencies your local businesses use?

The type of computer is not important. Obviously you will need a CD-ROM drive to use a CD. Many database programs are available on floppy disks, however. Be warned: These are not small programs. The SAM call sign database takes seventeen 3.5-inch floppies, for example. The speed of the search depends more on the access time of the drive rather than on the CPU clock speed. Many hams and are satisfied with the speed obtained when data is read directly from the CD drive. For fastest access take the data and transfer it from the floppy or CD to your hard drive and then read it from the hard drive. As stated earlier, these are big programs; you will need at least 24 Mb of hard disk space if you want the fastest possible access speed.

Callbooks

Callbooks are by far the most popular databases for ham use. They allow you to find hams by almost any combination of a call, city or town, ZIP code, state, street address, license class, birthday, license expiration date, call suffix and even area prefixes. The four most popular callbook database programs are:

SAM Amateur Radio Call Sign Database

Available on CD-ROM ($30) or seventeen 3.5 or 5.25-inch high-density floppies ($49.95). Note that the floppies are only the transfer media. You need to load all the floppies to your hard disk; 24 Mb of hard disk is needed. The CD-ROM may be used in four different ways:

- You may read the data directly off the CD and not use the hard drive for storage
- You may preload about 500 Kb of data to your hard drive, thus increasing access time.
- You may load the entire CD database to your hard disk for the fastest possible execution.
- You may interface them to most logging programs.

For further information see the Resources Chapter.

QRZ! Call Sign Database

This CD ROM has not only the callbook database with over 700,000 listings, but also comes with over 1000 ham radio share/freeware applications for Windows, DOS, OS/2 and UNIX. Currently Vol 7 sells for $29.95. A yearly subscription is available. Subscription disks cost $19.95 each and are sent two or three times a year.

Radio Amateur Callbooks

Radio Amateur Callbooks are supplied on CD-ROMs that run under Windows or DOS. A single CD includes both the North American and International editions. You can search by name, street, city and text string searches for clubs, and it even includes latitudes, longitudes and area codes. Output can be sent to the PC speaker in Morse code. Cost $49.95. For further information see the Resources Chapter.

HamCall CD-ROM

The *HamCall CD-ROM* uses a powerful search engine with compressed data for both DOS and Mac users. It includes beam headings and distance, grid squares and the ability to edit information. You can even add e-mail addresses. The best part of this package is the included Photo QSLs that allow you to view photos of many hams. This is a *free* service! All you have to do is send any size photo or QSL card and Buckmaster will scan it and include it free of charge. Photos will not be returned. It is updated twice a year, at the end of April and October. The program cost $50 plus $5 shipping. For further information see the Resources Chapter.

QSL Managers

A QSL Manager is a specialized form of a call sign database. Working in conjunction with both logging and call sign databases, they provide current QSL address information. They are for the serious DXer who wants fast and accurate address information. Most DX stations, and especially the rare ones, employ the services of a QSL Manager whose address is often hard to find and subject to frequent change. The *PROLOG QSL* route/manager has over 55,000 listings and is updated every two months through a subscription service. The service costs $36 a year for a set of six disks. This is important as new DX stations get on the air. Contributors submit address changes monthly to keep the database up to date. Both direct mail addresses and QSL managers' addresses are given, along with IRC and green stamp requirements. It uses a Windows-like interface and can be customized in many ways, including addresses editing and screen color selection. In additon it interfaces with the SAM, Buckmaster and Flying Horse external call sign databases. The *PROLOG QSL* route/manager will run on any system running DOS 5.0 or later and requires a minimum of 125 Kb of RAM.

Repeater Guides

Ham_DB & Open Repeater Database

Contains 700,000 licensees with all the fields from the original FCC database. You will find fields for call sign, name, address, date of birth, present and past class of license, date of issue, approximate latitude and longitude, and even special fields for club, military, RACES and alien licenses. The system is complete and runs off a CD with minimal setup and installation. If run with the *Geo-db* graphical interface package a map display will show the location of a given staton. The database also has 10,000 records devoted to repeaters. You may search by frequency or all the repeaters in a city, county or state.

Another unique aspect of this database is that it is cross-platform: It will run on either a PC under DOS or Windows or even on a Mac. Minimum requirements are a 386 with 4 Mb of RAM with a VGA display and 4 Mb of hard disk space operation under DOS 6.0 or Windows 3.1. For a Mac, a System 7.5, CD-ROM drive, mouse, 4 Mb of RAM and 4 Mb of hard disk space is the minimum requirement.

As a bonus, for those who know how to use *Dbase III+, IV* or *FoxPro,* you can manipulate the actual database records. The package costs $14.95 + shipping and handling, from PerCon Corp. For further information see the Resources Chapter.

Frequency Listings

Almost every ham at one time or another leaves the ham bands to go exploring. The mystery of what other radio stations transmit seems to have universal appeal to amateurs. If you're on the low bands, it likely your transceiver will receive non-ham frequencies. Nearly 80% of the shortwave spectrum from 1.8-30 MHz is occupied by utility stations. Utility stations provide specific services, such as time signals, marine and aviation weather forecasts, aircraft communications, military communications, and search and rescue. For example, WWV, a utility station operated by the United States National Institute of Standards and Technology, broadcasts time signals and geophysical information on several frequencies. For many years utility DXers have relied on the *Guide to Utility Radio Stations* published by Klingenfuss Publications to find and identify utility stations. This book has set the standard for the utility DXing world and is now available on a CD-ROM.

Above 30 MHz the listening is even more exciting. Fire, police and ambulances provide the heart-wrenching drama rarely found in the ham bands. Most modern 2-meter and dual-band HTs can be programmed to listen outside of the amateur bands, "Scanning" these VHF frequencies has become a hobby in itself, and a good guide to know where to tune your scanner is a must. PerCon provides two databases, one devoted to amateur licenses including repeaters and the other every possible commercial license.

FCC Master Frequency Database

The *SPECTRUM* series of CD has *everything* the scanner or SWLer could want. Listening out of band has become very popular with the advent of wide-band receive HTs . This database has over 3 million records extracted directly from the FCC Master Frequency Database. Police, Fire, Hospitals, Local Governments, Airlines, Utilities, Hotels, Theme Parks, Taxis, Phone Companies, and many more categories too numerous to mention are covered. Data can be extracted by a frequency range in a region, call sign in a state, business name, radio service code, or by all frequencies in a county or city. Powerful and easy-to-use, it has the same cross-platform requirements as the *Ham_DB & Open Repeater* program. Cost is $29.95 + $7.50 shipping and handling. For ordering information see the Resources Chapter.

Klingenfuss Super Frequency List

The *Klingenfuss Super Frequency List* on CD-ROM is invaluable to any utility enthusiast who needs accurate information fast. This single CD offers data on more than 14,000 utility stations worldwide. You can browse through the data as quickly as your drive allows, or search for specific frequencies, stations, call signs and countries.

The Super Frequency List CD contains two versions of the browser software, one in English and the other in German. The program boots up immediately and takes you directly to the main menu (see Figure 3.25). At this menu you can use the **+** buttons to step through the entire list by frequency, call sign, station name or country. Note that the **+1, +10, –1, –10** buttons do not refer to frequency steps in kHz, the way most hams are accustomed to interpreting such controls. Instead, the buttons step you through the list by individual entry (**+1** or **–1**), or in jumps of 10 entries (**+10** or **–10**). This is a little unclear in the documentation.

The Super Frequency List really shows its stuff when it's time to do a search. By clicking on Search, you're presented with a choice of searching by frequency, call sign, station name or country. If you enter a call sign, for example (see Figure 3.26), the software scans the database and shows you the results very quickly. Once you're found the information, you can use the EDIT function to copy it to Windows Notepad, to a word processing document, or wherever you desire. Additional information may be found in the Resources Chapter.

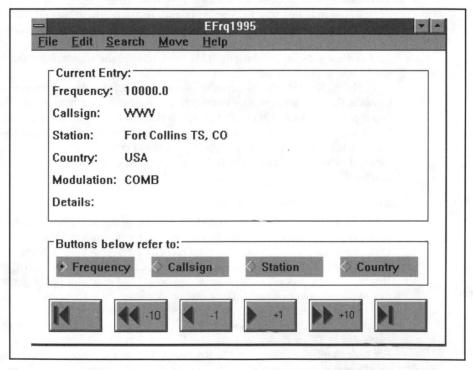

Figure 3.25—When you start the program, the Super Frequency List main menu appears immediately. From here you can step though the entire list, or search for specific stations.

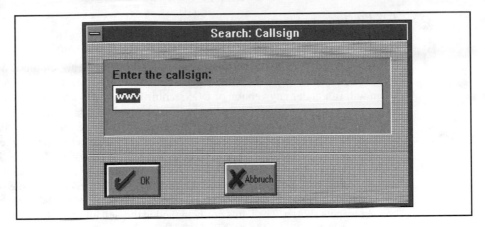

Figure 3.26—Doing a station search is as easy as entering the call sign.

Indexes

Have you ever wanted to find an article on something you may have read in *QST* and didn't want to thumb through back issues until you found it? Starting in 1995, ARRL offers a CD ROM that includes all articles from *QST*, *NCJ* and *QEX*. A powerful search engine lets you find desired information quickly by entering article titles, call signs, names or just about any other word. *Windows* printing and Clipboard support are available so you can print out articles or share them with other *Windows* applications.

The minimum requirements are a 386, 4 Mb RAM (8 Mb recommended), 10 Mb hard disk space, *Windows 3.1* and of course a mouse and CD-ROM drive. All of the drawings, tables, illustrations and photographs that accompany the article are included—even the software files that accompany an article. The *1995 QST on CD-ROM* costs $19.95 for ARRL members and $29.95 nonmembers. For further information see the Resources Chapter.

CW and Exam Review Software

We all would like bragging rights to a higher license class, and the computer can really help. Most training software is focused toward code practice, a natural for an on/off device like a computer. Code practice programs can be programmed to send any speed, and they never will embarrass you if you give the wrong answer. Learning code is more a matter of relaxing and letting it come naturally. It's amazing how fast and unknowingly one's speed increases with daily practice. A computer sending CW is interference free, keeps an honest score and reinforces weak spots—something on-the-air QSOs can't do.

There is a large choice of CW programs. It almost seems as if there was a contest to see who could make the biggest, fanciest program, and as a result many seem to be needlessly cumbersome. Learning the code is after all a fairly straightforward process, and it shouldn't take you longer to learn the program than it does to learn the code.

CW Practice

GGTE Morse Tutor and Morse Tutor Gold

GGTE Morse Tutor and *Morse Tutor Gold* are excellent, simple CW programs that can be run on any PC. That's right—even that old giveaway 8088 PC. The program will run under any version of DOS, requiring only 235 kb of memory. A calibration routine ensures that it is sending at the specified speed.

The sending speed can be selected by using either the "Standard" or "Farnsworth" method. The Standard method provides a fixed ratio of time between both the characters and the spaces. As the code speed increases the ratio remains fixed. In the Farnsworth method, this ratio is a user-adjustable variable. This feature is very desirable, since it allows you to become accustomed to the rhythm of the characters more easily. As the speed is increased the rhythm of the characters stays the same while the pause between the characters gets shorter. The Farnsworth method is the default mode for the program.

Morse Tutor Gold is ideal to use for both learning and administering CW exams. An automatic QSO generator will send every required character, punctuation mark and prosign. The sample QSO may be saved to a file, or an on-screen analysis may be performed that will give you a count of each type of character sent. This feature makes it very easy to determine your weak areas. A useful feature for VE test sessions is the ability to create and save a custom QSO; this adds a personal touch in administering a CW exam. An unformatted ASCII text file may also be used as a source. Instant code from the keyboard is useful for learning the "rhythm" of a troublesome character. You may send the character to yourself as many times as it takes until you can instantly recognize it.

Both programs offers a wide variety of practice methods and is easy to install and operate. It can be used with a "Sound Blaster" compatible card, and is available from the ARRL on either 3.5 or 5.25-inch floppy disks. *GGTE Morse Tutor* is available on a 5.25-inch disk for $20 by ordering #2081. *GGTE Morse Tutor* is available on a 3.5-inch disk for $22 (ARRL order #2936). See the Resources Chapter for address information.

Morse Academy

Morse Academy is absolutely free! A great way to getting started on the road to better CW from scratch, it is found on many ham-related software libraries. It can also be found on many ham BBSs, the web and even comes as a part of the "extras" on the *QRZ Call sign Database* CD-ROM. It is designed to help students who have no knowledge of the code or computers. Operation is simple with functions selected by a single key. Different sessions are provided to allow students to vary the way they learn the code. Testing is automated to allow the student to spend more time on learning, and less on the tedious task of checking the result of a session. The program, *ma.zip*, may be downloaded from the *vec* directory of the ARRL Hiram BBS (860) 594-0306.

Morse Academy includes:

⌨ On line HELP for each session (**F1** key).

⌨ Option settings that can be saved on diskette or disk so they are not lost when power is turned off.

⌨ The ability to edit and sequence the character set used in all sessions.

⌨ A set of sample code tests for student practice the ability to generate random Novice, General, and Extra test sessions for practice.

⌨ The ability to create, save and reload text for replay.

❏ The student can input copy via the keyboard during the Proficiency session and have it automatically compared with the generated text at the end of the session.

❏ All computer-generated text can be saved for later printing (**F10** key).

❏ You can select the frequency of occurrence of characters.

❏ Saves the history of mistakes from the last receiving game for optional use in computing character weighting.

❏ The optional ability to allow the Receiving Game to reorder the character set in worst to best sequence.

❏ The optional generation of Morse prosigns in context that helps a student understand their meaning.

❏ The ability to adjust the code sending speed for the variances of different PCs.

❏ Support for ADLIB-compatible music synthesizer cards or an external tone generator via the printer port.

Super Morse

Written by Lee Murrah, WD5CID, *Super Morse* is one of the more popular CW practice shareware programs, even though it has an overabundance of customized features. The manual is 34 pages long. It features a very realistic simulated VE exam. A simulated QSO is sent at the prescribed rate and you copy the code by whatever method you feel conformable with: by hand, on the computer or even in your head. When the test is finished the program gives you a test on the *content* of the QSO rather than on the actual characters copied. This realistically simulates an actual test session. The program includes two calibration routines and therefore can run under both Windows or DOS. The "Loop" method is nice because it takes into account TSRs that upset the timing of most other practice programs.

It is available as shareware for suggested contribution of $20 and may be found on many ham-related BBSs including the ARRL's HIRAM BBS (860) 594-0306. Look under the *vec* subdirectory for *sm415.exe*. Across the web it may be found in a zipped form or as self-expanding *exe* file.

Exam Review

Not only is code easier to learn with a computer, but the theory is also easier to learn. Because all exam questions come from a common multiple-choice question pool, a program can easily test you and even respond to wrong answers by offering an explanation. The computer is an ideal tool for tracking your progress since it can be programmed to remember your past performance and show your progress.

The *ARRL Computerized Exam Review* is the latest and easiest method to study for the written exam. The computer exam review generates VEC-type practice tests. This reduces the tension normally associated with test taking, thus increasing a newcomer's chance of success. The computerized exam is a part of the *ARRL Video Courses for Technician, General* and *Advanced Exams* and must be purchased as a package. The complete Technician Class course consists of five hours of VHS video-taped instruction and a 164-page course book. The General Class course includes four hours of video and a 96-page book. The Advanced Class course has 5.5 hours of video instruction and a 208-page book. The Technician and General Class versions are available for both Mac and PCs and the Advanced Class version is only available for PCs. Each course costs $129. For further information see the Resources Chapter.

Ham Design Software

MODELING RADIO CIRCUITS, SYSTEMS AND ANTENNAS

We use computers to do so many things that it's easy to forget that *all they ultimately do is math.* Whatever a computer does—e-mail, word processing, balancing a checkbook, stress analyzing an aircraft wing, wafting you on a cybertrip down a virtual Amazon—it does by crunching numbers. If you can represent a thing or the action of a thing numerically—that is, if you can *model* it mathematically—you can simulate it and its action with a computer.

Math can predict and analyze the actions of radio-electronic circuitry, since radio-electronic circuitry "just does math." A radio antenna "just does math," too. While receiving, it linearly sums into one electrical signal the various arriving radio energies that induce current flow in its conductors. While transmitting, the antenna emits the transmitter's energy as a composite field, phased and amplitude-shaped by the interaction of the individual fields emanating from its various conductors. Because we can describe these conductor arrangements, fields and field interactions numerically, we can use math to predict and analyze the action of radio antennas.

A computer is a powerful circuit- and antenna-simulation tool because it can *contain* math in addition to just solving it. That is, you can use a computer to determine, say, a coil's reactance (ac resistance) even if you know *absolutely nothing* about how to do it with math. All you do is run a program that contains the right equation(s) and lets you interact with them in a suitably accessible (friendly) way. You tell the computer your coil's inductance and the frequency you need to know its reactance, and the computer tells you the answer. Likewise, a computer programmed with the equations describing the production of electromagnetic fields by RF-current-carrying conductors and the reflection of electromagnetic waves by surfaces of known conductivity can model the result—the interactions of the energies emitted by an antenna's various conductors to simulate the antenna's *pattern* including interaction with the ground.

The term *CAD*—computer-aided design—is often used to describe the software and perhaps the hardware and process of using a computer to aid and improve the design process. CAD is not limited to 1000-foot suspension bridges or 50-story building designs. CAD includes any tool or process that lets you use a computer—including your personal computer at home—to replace the calculations and lists otherwise done either by hand or with hand tools such as pocket calculators. Sometimes simulation is included in the CAD program, and sometimes it is done with another program.

The greatest advantage of CAD and simulation is they can take you a long way toward predetermining the performance of a circuit or antenna design, or predetermining the effect of changes in existing circuits and antennas, *without* your having to heat up your soldering iron or spend an afternoon in the rain. Better yet, some CAD tools can even *optimize*—automatically or semi-automatically improve—a design to meet specified performance goals.

With all this computer-based capability available the first question is, of course, what do you need your ham-shack computer to do? This chapter helps you answer that question by taking you on a brief tour of what's possible with mainstream, affordable, ham-appropriate CAD tools.

Design, Analysis, Measurement

These three terms describe the kind of processes we go through to get some electronic gadget or system working:

 Design—Figure out a circuit approach (topology) that *may* meet your requirements, based on some kind of system analysis or evaluation. This process is based on your experience and input from others. Assign some values to the components, using formulas from books or of your own devising. Design is sometimes referred to as *synthesis*.

 Analysis—Simulate the gadget as accurately as possible and see if the results meet the requirements. If not, go back to the drawing board. Getting accurate and credible simulations is an acquired skill that requires experience and close attention to details. There is a lot of literature available to help with this. Analysis includes the more subtle things such as coil Q, stray R, L, C, etc, that are often not mentioned in the initial equations.

 Measurement—Buy, build or borrow the test equipment needed to verify that the gadget or antenna is working properly.

 Iteration—If the measurement shows your design is not working as you expect, look for mistakes in the previous steps. A new approach may be needed. In that case *back to the drawing board*—actually, back to your computer and the first step above, *Design*.

MATH PROGRAMS

Slide rules and mechanical adding machines were fine in their time. Pocket calculators can do quite a bit, but to really get results, see trends, generate plots of equation results and get *insight* into these results, you need a math program for your PC. There are a wide variety available, ranging in cost for a few tens of dollars to several thousand dollars.

Mathcad 6.0: A Generic Tool for the Amateur Experimenter

This section is based on an article in QST, *April 1996, pp 44-47, by William E. Sabin, WØIYH, "Mathcad 6.0: A Tool for the Amateur Experimenter."*

Mathcad 6.0 for *Windows 3.x* or later (Figure 4.1), is a low-cost mathematics program for IBM-compatible personal computers. It performs a wide variety of numerical computations very quickly and with almost no requirements for special programming skills or activity. These computations would otherwise require a complicated list of executable program statements written in some high-level language (i.e., BASIC, Pascal or a programmable-calculator language). In addition, to present useful results, the program design and the formatting of the screen and printer would require a lot of effort and debugging. What is often needed instead is a quick answer to some specific problem that can be easily stated, modified, or even completely restated. Information on obtaining software packages mentioned here is given in the Resources Chapter.

This section discusses the *Mathcad* concept. Specifically, *Mathcad* is used to solve complicated formulas (equations) that are commonly found in articles, handbooks and textbooks, or created by the user. *Mathcad* does these things in ways that the

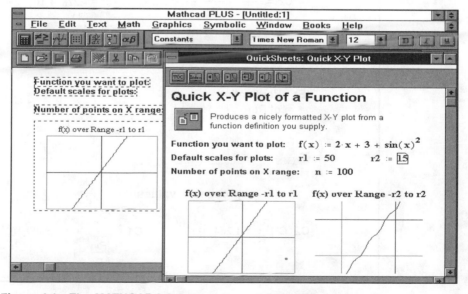

Figure 4.1—The *MATHCAD* 6.0 screen.

specific-purpose simulation programs mentioned earlier cannot perform quite as easily. *Mathcad* can get exact solutions to difficult equations rather than simplified (and perhaps dubious) estimates.

One interesting task (illustrated in the examples) is to compare an exact solution with an estimate of some kind. *Mathcad* easily and quickly plots graphs for several functions and variables. The numbers can be changed quickly and the results are almost immediately available to the screen and printer. The problem setups that you devise can be saved to disk and become part of a library of solutions to problems that interest you. The results also can be transferred to a word processor or spreadsheet. See the Resources Chapter for information on obtaining *Mathcad*.

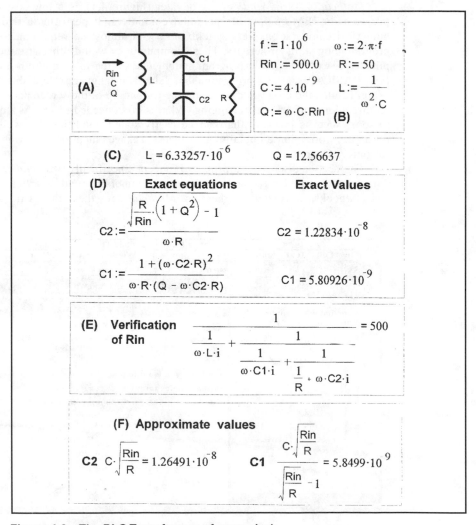

Figure 4.2—The RLC Transformer of example 1.

Mathcad is most useful during the design phase, to get the right component (starting) values and run a preliminary check to see if the approach is a good one. That's the objective of the following examples.

Example 1: A Lumped-LC Impedance Transformer

In the example of Figure 4.2, a network, resonant at frequency f, is to transform a smaller load resistance, R, to a larger input resistance, R_{in}, with a certain value of input C, resonated by L. Exact values of C1 and C2 will be calculated and compared with approximate values. The values will be verified by calculating the value of R_{in} from the network values. Numerous software packages include this network, but it is used here as a simple example to show how the problem statement and solution can be *customized* in ways that the software packages usually cannot handle. Figure 4.2 is broken up into sections; we'll analyze each section to give an overview of how *Mathcad* works.

Section A is the schematic of a commonly used network. (This picture was imported from a drawing program via the *Windows* Clipboard.) For this type of network, the impedance ratio and the loaded Q are independently adjustable.

In B, we see the *assignment* symbol (:=). For example, f is *assigned* the value 1.0 MHz, R_{in} is *assigned* 500 Ω, R is *assigned* 50 Ω and C is *assigned* 4000 pF. If any one of these values changes, the results ripple through and create a new set of values for the other components. The value of Q depends on the choice of C and is calculated as shown. The required value of L is also derived from C.

In section C, the values of L and Q are shown. These values were calculated in part B. The equal (=) symbol means that the actual values of L and Q *are to be displayed.* This is different, of course, from the assignment symbol (:=).

In D, the values of C1 and C2 are calculated, then displayed using exact equations. From the equations we see two criteria:

$$(R/R_{in})(1 + Q_2) > 1 \tag{Eq 1}$$

and

$$Q > \omega\, C_2\, R \tag{Eq 2}$$

In E, a continued-fraction evaluation is performed to verify that the required value of R_{in} has been achieved by the network. This option reassures us that we haven't made any mistakes. The continued-fraction (or ladder) method is reviewed in many text books and won't be explained here. The letter *i* is the imaginary operator used in complex algebra (the letter *j* also can be used and is usually preferred in electrical engineering). *Mathcad* performs this complex algebra with the greatest of ease.

In F, a pair of approximate equations (readily found in various handbooks) are used to compare with the exact equations. There may be times when we need to reassure ourselves that the approximations are good enough—especially if the Q is not high.

We can see that this problem sheet can be used for a wide range of values of f, C, R and R_{in}, and it can be stored on disk for future use. The appearance of the problem sheet is remarkable, too. It looks just like a scratchpad—and *Mathcad* intended it as such. We also can see that it's easy to approach the problem from a different angle. For example, the value of Q could be an input and the required value of C calculated.

The software that does the work is transparent to the user, but there are certain rules you must follow in organizing the problem setup. These instructions are easy to learn. The program is much more powerful than this simple example shows; the other capabilities come to light with experience. A second example demonstrates a few of these capabilities.

Example 2: An Audio Q-Multiplier Band-Pass Filter

Figure 4.3 shows a schematic of a narrow-band audio filter used for CW reception or tone detection. A good reference to this type of circuit is in the Resources Chapter. The circuit employs op amps and the principle of Q-multiplication. Figure 4.4 is the *Mathcad* work sheet.

In Figure 4.3, the circuit in the box is a basic band-pass amplifier. It has a Q of Qr (see Figure 4.4). The op amp to the left gets positive feedback from the output and multiplies the Q to the overall value, Qe. The gain *inside the box* is carefully set to 1.0 by resistors R1a and R1b. The *overall* gain, G, is set by the ratio of R4 to R5. R and C are set at some convenient value, and the other components are then determined relative to R and C. For most predictable results, use 1%-tolerance metal-film resistors and select the capacitors by measuring them with a capacitance meter.

Let's walk through the problem work-sheet of Figure 4.4:

Section A shows how a range of frequency values, f, from 100 to 1000 Hz in 10-Hz steps, is assigned. The peak response frequency, f_0, is 500 Hz; Qr is 3; Qe is 20; R is 10 kΩ and C is 0.1 µF.

The resistor values are calculated in B. The feedback factor, ß, is 0.85, which provides quite a bit of Q multiplication. Feedback values greater than 0.85 should be handled carefully to avoid instability.

Section C displays the values calculated in part B. At this point, look for unreasonable values. If you find any, go back to A and make changes as necessary.

Section D calculates the frequency response over the frequency range of 100 Hz to 1000 Hz. To change this range, go back to A. T(f) is in decibels and peaks at 6.0 dB (G = 2). The two vertical bars inside the brackets indicate that we're getting the *mag-*

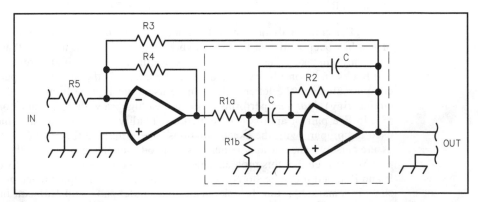

Figure 4.3—Schematic of a narrow-band audio filter used for CW reception or tone frequency detection. The circuit employs op amps and the principle of Q multiplication.

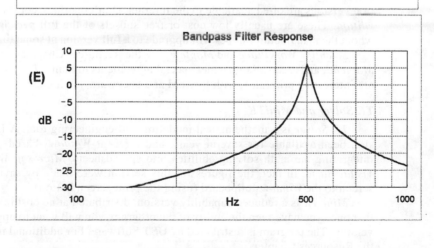

(A)
$$f := 100, 110 .. 1000 \quad fo := 500 \quad Qe := 20 \quad R := 1 \cdot 10^4$$
$$G := 2 \quad Qr := 3 \quad C := 1 \cdot 10^{-7}$$

(B)
$$R2 := \frac{Qr}{\pi \cdot fo \cdot C} \quad R1a := \frac{R2}{2} \quad R1b := \frac{R1a}{2 \cdot Qr^2 - 1}$$

$$\beta := 1 - \frac{Qr}{Qe} \quad R3 := \frac{R}{\beta} \quad R4 := R \quad R5 := \frac{R}{(1 - \beta) \cdot G}$$

(C)
$$R1a = 9.55 \cdot 10^3 \quad R1b = 561.72 \quad R2 = 1.91 \cdot 10^4$$

$$\beta = 0.85 \quad R3 = 1.18 \cdot 10^4 \quad R4 = 1 \cdot 10^4 \quad R5 = 3.33 \cdot 10^4$$

(D)
$$T(f) := 20 \cdot \log \left[\left| \frac{\frac{fo \cdot (f \cdot i)}{Qr}}{(f \cdot i)^2 + \frac{fo \cdot (1 - \beta) \cdot (f \cdot i)}{Qr} + fo^2} \right| \cdot \frac{R4}{R5} \right]$$

(E)

Bandpass Filter Response

dB (vertical axis: 10, 5, 0, -5, -10, -15, -20, -25, -30)

Hz (horizontal axis: 100, 500, 1000)

Figure 4.4—The band-pass filter for example 2.

nitude of the frequency response. The actual computation is a complex algebra problem. The phase response, or the real and imaginary parts, also can be obtained easily.

Section E shows the frequency response plot. The Qe and the gain can be verified from this plot. This instills more confidence in the equations—a good thing to do at this point, because it gives us an idea of how well the circuit is performing and we can determine if it's good enough. Generally, the 6 dB of gain is a good idea when we sharply reduce the audio bandwidth this way.

Having completed this operation, the next usual step is to set up the circuit in *ARRL Radio Designer* (discussed in the next section) for a more detailed study. We can then do the following things:

Configure *ARD*'s op-amp (OPA) element with parameter appropriate to a low-noise real-world op-amp (such as the OP27E or, more availably, an NE5534 or LM833).

Perform sensitivity studies to see what values are critical.

Perform Monte Carlo statistical studies of component values.

Model other parts of the system that are connected to the input and output of this circuit.

MATHCAD Summary

These two simple examples show how design and simulation work together to help us get projects to perform the way we want them to. *Mathcad* is a very powerful program. As you browse through the Amateur Radio literature, you'll see many opportunities to put *Mathcad* to work in interesting and useful ways. *Mathcad* also is *fun* to work with—that's important, too! Mathematical skills are becoming more and more important in electronic technology and software of this kind can make it easier.

Other Math Programs

Several companies offer math packages similar in purpose to *MATHCAD*. They are usually available with several levels of capability (and cost), and 30-day evaluation versions are often available in the Internet. Don't overlook copies labeled *student edition*. These are usually low cost or free subsets of the full package for students, whom the manufacturer hopes will upgrade to a full version at some time in the future.

Scientific WorkPlace and *Maple V* (see the Resources Chapter) are alternatives to *Mathcad*, and are available under special agreements to hams. *TK Solver* and *MiniTK* are interesting programs, with forward and backward solving capabilities.

TK Solver and MiniTK

TK Solver is a mathematical modeling and engineering tool. A DOS-based version been available for several years, and a recent *Windows*-based version permits integrating the math-solving abilities into spreadsheets, *Microsoft Word*, *Excel* and *Visual Basic*. In fact, the figures for this section were made by saving the *MiniTK* screen to the *Windows* clipboard (using the print screen button).

Mini-TK is a reduced capability version, distributed at no cost in the expectation that once you have seen the ability of the program, you will want to upgrade to the full version. The program is distributed by UST Software. For additional information, see the Resources Chapter.

The user interface is *sheet-based*. All entries are made on a sheet, with the analogy to a sheet of paper. The min-version, which was used for this example, is limited

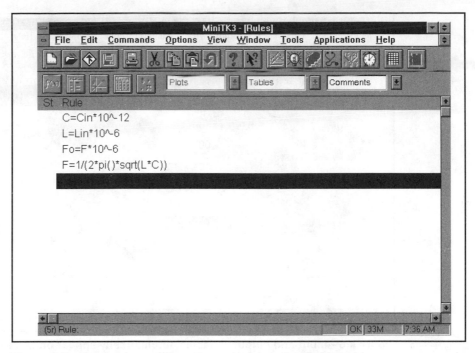

Figure 4.5—The basic equations are entered on the *Rule* sheet.

to only six simultaneous equations and 10 variables. Figure 4.5 is the common starting point, the *rule sheet*.

For this example, the standard equation for resonant frequency was used. To make the example realistic, the first two lines entered define Cin and Lin so they are entered directly in pF and µH. The third line takes the resulting frequency and scales it to appear in MHz. The final line defines frequency as a function of L and C.

TK has many built-in functions, including Pi. In the fourth line Pi is represented by **pi**(). When entering equations, the built-in parser checks for grammar and consistency. Omit one of the multiplication symbols (an asterisk), and it will warn you and place a cursor where the omitted symbol is needed. If there is problem with the logic—variables are defined incompletely or redundantly—the program warns you.

After entering the equations on the rule sheet, the program automatically generates the *Variables* sheet (Figure 4.6). Any variable can be designated an input, and a solution made of one or more remaining variables as outputs. If you pick too many inputs, or not enough, the program flags the inconsistency. Here the input values (Cin and Lin) were entered as 10 µH and 100 pF. By highlighting either Fo or F in the output column, you select them as outputs. Press **F9** and there is a solution—values appear for all remaining variables.

The program has the ability to *backsolve*—that is, given a set of results, if you want other results, pick the output value you want, place it in the input column, delete one of the previous inputs, and tell the program to solve. You can see the result of

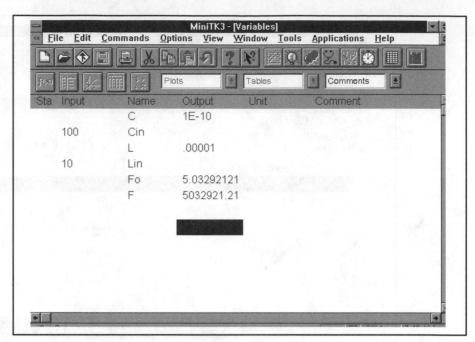

Figure 4.6—Input and output variables automatically appear on the *Variables* sheet. Lin and Cin are inputs, and F and Fo are outputs.

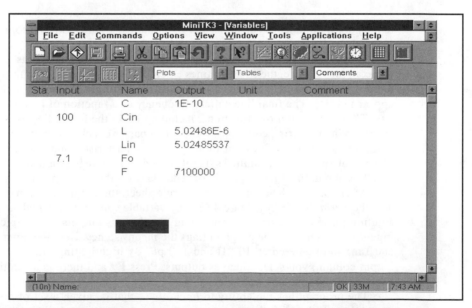

Figure 4.7—Fo was set as an input at 7.1 MHz. C was kept as an input, and L changed to an output. *Backwards* solving gave a required value of L=5 mH.

backsolving in Figure 4.7. In the previous example, the output was 5.03 MHz. To change this to 7.1 MHz, Fo was made into an input by entering 7.1 in the left (input) column. The previous input, Lin, was deleted and the *Output* column next to Lin was highlighted. After pressing **F9** (or using the a menu command) the result is a new value of Lin, a bit over 5 μH, for the frequency selected (7.1 MHz).

Results can be chained easily. By entering the equation for an air wound inductor, the output of that equation can be made equal to Lin, and you can see the direct result of varying the inductor diameter, turns and length on resonant frequency.

The program comes with a full help file, and a context-sensitive help ability. Whenever the result on the screen has a symbol whose meaning is not obvious, highlight the symbol with the cursor, go the to the help menu, and select context-sensitive help. Specific information explaining the symbol will appear on the screen.

Spreadsheets

Excel, Lotus and other widely available spreadsheets are valuable math tools you might already own. They can calculate the result of chained formulas, vary the inputs and give you a range of results, plot inputs against outputs, calculate statistical values and many other functions. You can write macros to do repetitive jobs automatically.

The mathematical problem solving ability of these spread sheet programs should not be dismissed, just because they don't come with a *mathematics, engineering* or *ham radio* label. They are all capable of solving basic arithmetic, contain statistical functions, can handle chained equations and multiple variables.

Each allows formatting the inputs in many convenient ways, setting ranges of input variables with just a few keystrokes and taking the results to a plot or graph. The newer versions of these programs will import data from almost any file format, and export results to word processors and other application programs. If speed is not a consideration, you can take the results and use them for real time control of interfaces.

If you do not own one of these spread sheet programs, check out local book sales. Often, *obsolete*—actually completely functional, but earlier releases—of these programs are available for a few dollars, complete with disk and original instruction book. Many computer bulletin boards and shareware internet sites have shareware or freeware clones of Lotus, which also are worth trying.

CIRCUIT DESIGN TOOLS

A few years ago, if you started to design a circuit from scratch, you knew how much work was ahead of you. A single amplifier stage might mean solving several equations, taking the results and plugging them into several other equations (or blurry curves in book), and then—back to the first set of equations. Back and forth, iteration after iteration, since the change of one component resulted in the change of several stage parameters—gain, bandwidth, power dissipation, impedance and others.

Today, once you are familiar with a circuit design program, there is a lot less to worry about. Each change is automatically reflected in all applicable design equations. The total result of that change is immediately available—or at least after the computer, and not you, grinds for a few seconds or minutes. No wonder circuit design tools have made a major impact on designers. These tools range in price up to $10,000 or more. The trick is to pick one that covers your needs, at an affordable price.

ARRL Radio Designer: Excellent Small-Signal Circuit Analysis and Optimization at a Get-Yourself-a-Present Price

For almost two years, David Newkirk, W9VES (formerly WJ1Z), wrote a monthly column for QST *titled "RF Design." This section is based on several of these columns.*

Since its introduction in November 1994, this tailored-for-Amateur Radio version of Compact Software's industry-standard Super-Compact simulator has been winning ever-increasing praise from experimentally minded hams and professional RF engineers alike. A full-color article in October 1994 *QST* described it, and you can find much more, including Adobe Portable Document File versions of the subsequent *QST* Exploring RF columns that dealt with it, through *ARRL Radio Designer*'s World Wide Web page (http://www .arrl.org/ard), a subset of the American Radio Relay League's site at (http://www .arrl.org/). Here are two examples of ARD: one that investigates a direct-conversion receiver's audio chain, and another that brings ARD to bear on the fascinating subject of oscillation.

Modeling a Direct-Conversion Receiver's Audio Response and Gain with ARRL Radio Designer

This example is the simulation of the audio channel of a heterodyne direct-conversion. Many of us have built heterodyne direct-conversion receivers, so we know what they do: They heterodyne RF signals to AF, amplify the resulting audio, and drive headphones or speakers.

Although *ARRL Radio Designer* can't model frequency conversion or transducer action, it can make itself pretty useful in helping us understand, design and modify the linear subsystems in a direct-conversion radio. Roger Hayward's "Ugly Weekender" receiver (see the Resources Chapter), a sound, friendly direct-conversion design for 7 MHz, is a good example for study because most of its active devices are easily modelable discrete transistors. The Ugly Weekender is a popular design because it's easy to build, uses no hard-to-get parts, and sounds like a real radio.

The entire Ugly Weekender Receiver (UWR) schematic covered a full *QST* page. Our *ARD*ized UWR schematic (Figure 4.8) takes less space because we need to model only four of the original's 11 transistors—just those that amplify and band-limit the UWR's audio. Table 4.1 shows Figure 4.8 in *ARRL Radio Designer* netlist form.

Netlist Structure

How we structure an *ARRL Radio Designer* netlist for a particular circuit depends somewhat on what we want to know about the circuit we're modeling. We know, for instance, that a direct-conversion receiver containing little or no RF amplification— the UWR uses none—must be capable of something like 80 to 100 dB of audio gain. We also know (by carefully reading citation trails through several articles' worth of footnotes) that the UWR's first audio preamp was designed to terminate the receiver's double-balanced diode mixer in something reasonably close to 50 Ω, resistive, at least in the audio range. Since we're out to see whether *ARRL Radio Designer* can correctly tell us things we already know, what we already know is what we want to find out.

Accordingly, the Table 4.1 netlist represents the Ugly Weekender Receiver in three circuit blocks—MIXER, Q8-9-10 and Q12 —so we can zero in on the radio's

Table 4.1

Simulating the Ugly Weekender Receiver's Audio Amplifier with *ARRL Radio Designer*

```
BLK ; this is MIXER (Figure 4.8A)
 RES 1 0 R=150
 RES 1 2 R=36
 RES 2 0 R=150
MIXER:2POR 1 2
END
BLK ; this is Q8-9-10 (Figure 4.8B)
 CAP 10 0 C=0.1UF          ; C30
 CAP 10 11 C=10UF          ; C27
 BIP 13 12 11 A=0.99 RE=(26/0.636); Q8
 RES 12 0 R=10KOH          ; R30
 CAP 13 0 C=10UF           ; C28
 RES 13 0 R=22KOH          ; R33
 RES 13 0 R=100KOH         ; R32
 CAP 12 0 C=0.1UF          ; C31
 BIP 12 14 15 A=0.99 RE=(26/0.5); Q9
 RES 15 0 R=10KOH          ; R36
 CAP 15 0 C=10UF           ; C32
 RES 14 18 R=4.7KOH        ; R35
 RES 18 0 R=1KOH           ; R34
 CAP 18 0 C=10UF           ; C33
 CAP 14 0 C=0.1UF          ; C34
 BIP 14 18 16 A=0.99 RE=(26/0.886); Q10
 RES 16 0 R=10KOH          ; R37
 CAP 16 17 C=10UF          ; C38
Q8-9-10:2POR 10 17
END
BLK ; this is Q12 (Figure 4.8C)
 RES 40 0 R=5KOH           ; R38 (GAIN control at max)
 CAP 40 41 C=10UF          ; C39
 RES 41 42 R=1KOH          ; R39
 RES 42 0 R=10KOH          ; R40
 RES 42 44 R=10KOH         ; R41
 CAP 44 0 C=0.1UF          ; C40
 RES 44 43 R=47KOH         ; R42
 BIP 42 43 0 A=0.99 RE=(26/1.919); Q12
 RES 43 0 R=3.3KOH         ; R43
 CAP 43 45 C=10UF          ; C41
 CAP 45 0 C=0.01UF         ; C42
Q12:2POR 40 45
END
BLK ; this block chains MIXER, Q8-9-10 and Q12
 MIXER 10 20
 Q8-9-10 20 30
 Q12 30 40
 SYSVGAIN:2POR 10 40
END
FREQ
 ESTP 20HZ 20KHZ 500
END
```

subsystems. To model how these blocks work together as one big system, we chain them end to end (using a new set of arbitrary node numbers that happen not to duplicate those of the constituent blocks) in a fourth netlist block:

```
BLK
MIXER1020
Q8-9-102030
Q123040
SYSVGAIN:2POR1040
END
```

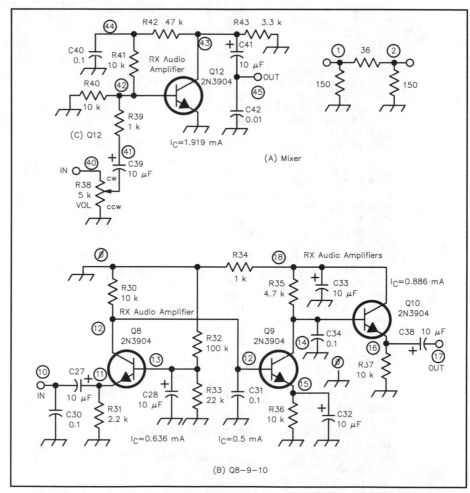

Figure 4.8—We need concern ourselves with only four of the Ugly Weekender Receiver's 11 transistors in modeling its basic performance with *ARRL Radio Designer.* The circled *node numbers* were added as the circuit was coded into a *ARD* netlist (Table 4.1).

ARRL Radio Designer will use this block to calculate the Ugly Weekender's overall audio voltage gain, so we'll name it **SYSVGAIN**. Finally, we tell *ARD* to calculate these four circuits' performance at 500 exponentially stepped frequencies from 20 Hz to 20 kHz:

```
FREQ
ESTP20HZ20KHZ500
END
```

Transistor Modeling

The Table 4.1 netlist models the Ugly Weekender's four 2N3904 bipolar junction transistors (BJTs) with ARD's **BIP** element. Because our modeling goals are simple— we're pretty much after just gain and impedance, and at audio frequencies to boot— we can get away without specifying any more than the transistors' alphas and emitter resistances, which happen to be the only two **BIP** parameters *ARD* absolutely can't live without.

An alpha of 0.99—corresponding to a beta of 100— is a safe assumption for a garden-variety small-signal transistor like the 2N3904. For emitter resistance (RE), we insert a formula (26 [*as in 26 millivolts*, the room-temperature value of the quantity V_T, which is the thermal equivalent of voltage in the transistor's semiconductor material.] ÷ collector current in milliamperes) that comes from the well-established transistor model developed by Ebers and Moll. Yanked out of Table 4.1 and grouped, the Gang of 3904s looks like this:

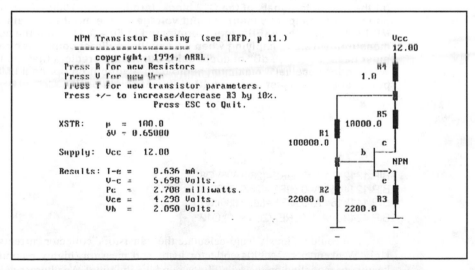

Figure 4.9—Wes Hayward's *NPNBIAS.EXE*, one of over 20 utilities on the software disk shipped with ARRL's reissue of his *Introduction to Radio Frequency Design*, provided the collector currents coded into the BIP netlist lines in Table 4.1.

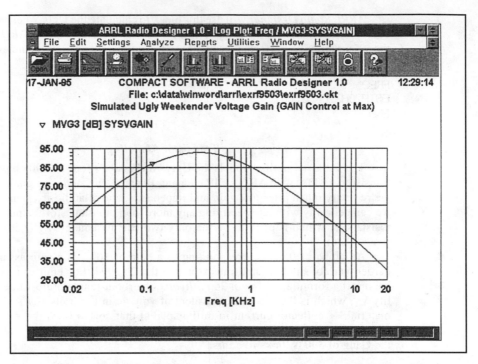

Figure 4.10—*ARRL Radio Designer* can evaluate voltage gain in several ways. This graph merely expresses in decibels the ratio of the UWR's output voltage (at the output terminals of the Q12 block, terminated in 2000 + *j*0 Ω, the circuit's anticipated headphone load) to input voltage (at the input terminals of the MIXER block, with MIXER's input terminated in 50 + *j*0 Ω)—just the sort of measurement we're implying when we say that a direct conversion receiver must have "80 to 100 dB" of audio gain. Our model predicts that the Ugly Weekender Receiver's maximum audio gain—without its optional LM386 audio power amp IC—is just under 94 dB at its passband peak.

```
BIP 13121  1 A=0.99RE=(26/0.636);Q8
BIP 121415   A=0.99RE=(26/0.5);Q9
BIP 141816   A=0.99RE=(26/0.886);Q10
BIP 42430   A=0.99RE=(26/1.919);Q12
```

You could tediously hand-calculate the transistors' collector currents, or snip the Ugly Weekender's 2N3904 collector leads and measure (highly recommendable to keep your modeling on the rails, if you can take the time). An alternative method is to use *NPNBIAS.EXE* (Figure 4.9), one of the 20+ highly useful utility programs included on the software disk shipped with the *Introduction to Radio Frequency Design* book (see later in this chapter), to give ballpark collector-current numbers.

Modeling Results

Figures 4.10, 4.11 and 4.12 tell the rest of the story. Our Ugly Weekender Receiver model predicts realistic audio gain—just below 94 dB, maximum—and a useful degree of AF bandwidth limiting. And Q8, the UWR's post-mixer preamp, does indeed exhibit a reasonably resistive input impedance that's reasonably close to 50 Ω across the audio range of interest.

Using ARRL Radio Designer to Enhance an Oscillator

ARRL Radio Designer can indicate the possibility of instability—instability that may well result in oscillation rather than dependable amplification— in electronic circuits intended to be stable. Even though a desired sustained, stable oscillation is a large-signal, nonlinear phenomenon, *ARD* can indicate the possibility or likelihood of oscillation because oscillation begins under *small*-signal conditions. To put it very roughly, large-signal operation occurs when the signal level handled by a circuit is high enough to cause a dc shift in the operating point of the circuit's active device(s).

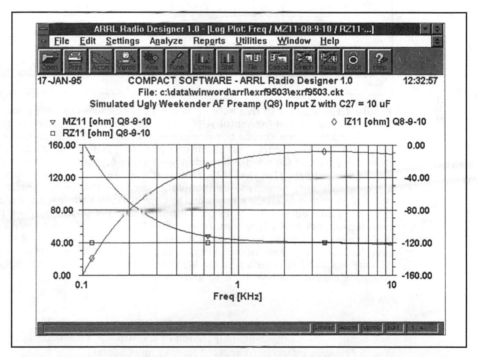

Figure 4.11—The Ugly Weekender's first audio preamp, Q8, is biased to terminate the radio's mixer with a resistive load reasonably close to 50 Ω across the span of common CW receiving pitches. *ARRL Radio Designer* can complex impedances in magnitude and R + jX (that is, real-imaginary) form, so this graph shows Q8's input impedance in terms of magnitude (MZ$_{11}$, triangular marker, 0 to 160-Ω scale), resistive component (RZ$_{11}$, square marker, 0 to 160-Ω scale) and imaginary (reactive) component (IZ$_{11}$, diamond marker, 0 to -160-Ω scale.

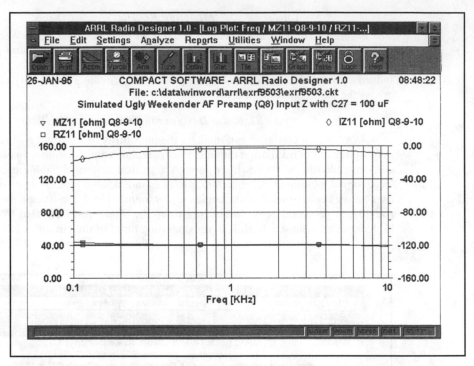

Figure 4.12—Finally, in five acts, a "what if?" detective vignette from the tattered casebook of Inspector *ARD*: (1) If Q8's input impedance is supposed to be flat and resistive across our audio range of interest, how come its magnitude (Figure 4.11's MZ_{11} curve) takes off so noticeably below 1 kHz? (2) Hey, the imaginary part of Q8's input impedance—Figure 4.11's IZ_{11} curve pretty much tracks the *reciprocal* of that MZ_{11} rise over the same range! (3) Hmm, that IZ_{11} curve shows only negative—capacitively reactive—values. By convention, we ascribe negative reactance numbers to capacitive reactance, so the culprit must be a capacitor between the circuit's input terminal and Q8's emitter. (4) That would probably be C27, shown as 10 mF in Figure 4.8. Come to think of it, 10 mF *does* seem a bit small for a part that's supposed to act as a low-Z series element down to a few hundred hertz. So what would happen if we made C27 100 mF instead? (5) Answer: a Q8 input impedance that's almost purely resistive across the 100 Hz to 10 kHz range.

See Section 1.4, Large-Signal Operation of the Bipolar Transistor, in *Introduction to Radio Frequency Design* (discussed later in this chapter).

The return-loss (MS_{11}) and stability factor (K) analyses are just the ticket for circuits we intend to be stable. In this section, we bring *ARD* to bear on predicting useful things about oscillators—circuits we *want* to oscillate. As is true of circuits we intend will be stable, if we know what conditions to look for in an oscillator, we can use *ARD* to confirm or even enhance those conditions. Instead of the MS_{11} and K approach, we'll evaluate a circuit's tendency to oscillate in terms of *negative resistance*.

Table 4.2

An Oscillator as a Negative Resistance Generator

```
* SIEMENS BFQ74 BJT:
* Analysis of an NPN bipolar model.
* Bias network is set for Ie=10 mA. ************Cf:10pF ;
Feedback network
IE:10mA ; Emitter current
FT:6000e6 ; Device ft in Hz
Rd:(26mV/IE) Cte:(1/(2*PI*FT*Rd))
**************************************************
BLK
  BIP 1 2 3 A=0.98 RB1=4 CE=Cte RE=Rd
* Feedback network
  CAP 1 11 C=Cf
  CAP 11 0 C=Cf
  RES 3 11 R=15
* Emitter feedback network
  SRL 3 0 R=220 L=1UH
* Tank Circuit
  CAP 1 4 C=2.8PF
  IND 4 31 L=5NH F=800MHZ Q1=120
  CAP 4 0 C=7PF
* Collector decoupling
  CAP 2 0 C=1NF
  RES 2 0 R=100
* DC bias network
  RES 1 0 R=2000
  RES 1 0 R=3000
  OSC:1POR 31
END
FREQ
  STEP 500MHZ 1000MHZ 10MHZ STEP 700MHZ 850MHZ 2MHZ END
```

Another Oscillator Model

Generally, an oscillator consists of an amplifier, a resonator (filter) and positive feedback. It's also possible to view an oscillator as a resonator and a negative-resistance generator (Figure 4.13). At start-up in this model, the resonator and oscillator reactances must be equal in value and opposite in sign. In a 1994 *QEX* article (see the Resources Chapter), Ulrich L. Rohde, KA2WEU, showed how *ARRL Radio Designer* can be used in evaluating an oscillator's performance in terms of this negative-resistance-generator model. The following is extracted from his work:

Figure 4.14A shows a simple oscillator circuit. This 800-MHz oscillator uses a Siemens BFQ74 bipolar transistor. Looking at this circuit from the standpoint of the negative-resistance generator of Figure 4.14A, we analyze the net resistance of the resonator (5 nH) and the oscillator circuit. The resistance should be 0 or slightly negative. We most easily view this by breaking the circuit at the ground connection of the

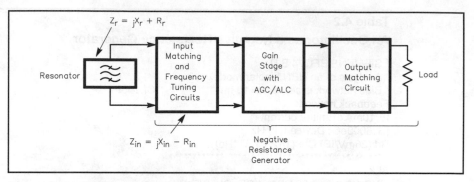

Figure 4.13—An oscillator viewed as a resonator and a negative-resistance generator. At start-up, the resonator and oscillator reactances must be equal in value and opposite in sign, while the sum of the resonator and oscillator resistances must be less than 0. For sustained oscillation, the sum of the resistances must not become positive.

coil and treating that point and ground as the terminals of a 1-port circuit, so we can investigate its impedance.

The circuit model is shown in Figure 4.14B. We want to select a bias current that is as small as possible, without reducing it to the point where the oscillator output power is too small to give a useful ultimate signal-to-noise ratio. In this case, we selected a bias emitter current of 10 mA. Now we have to find the appropriate feedback network, consisting of C1 and C2. Varying these capacitance values will vary the feedback and thus the loading of the resonator by the oscillator circuit. Finding the point at which the net resistance of the modeled circuit is just negative enough gives us the proper feedback; at this point, the loading is the least that will sustain oscillation, and the loaded Q is therefore the highest available with the selected bias.

Table 4.2 shows the circuit netlist used with *ARRL Radio Designer* to simulate the circuit of Figure 4.14B, and Figure 4.15 shows the port resistance (RZ_{11}) and reactance (IZ_{11}) calculated by the simulation. The trace labeled 1 corresponds to values of C1 and C2 of 5 pF. Trace 2 is with C1 and C2 at 10 pF, and trace 3 is at 25 pF. What we are looking for here is the resistance at resonance, where the reactance the zero. For trace 3, this occurs at about 735 MHz. Here, the resistance is almost exactly zero. This allows no room for component tolerances or for adjusting the frequency upward, either of which may inhibit oscillation.

Trace 2 shows a better result. At resonance, about 760 MHz, the resistance is negative, and it stays negative up through about 1 GHz. Small variations in component values, or adjusting the frequency upward, should not keep the circuit from oscillating. Trace 1 might seem to be even better because the resistance is more negative, but now we are loading the resonator—and lowering the loaded Q—more than we need to.

This is shown in Figure 4.16, which shows the magnitude of the impedance for the same three cases. Even though the resistive part of the impedance is negative, we can use the magnitude of the impedance to determine the loaded Q. From Figure 4.16 we can find the impedance at resonance, then find the 3-dB points on the curve, by multiplying the resonant impedance by 1.414. The loaded Q is then the resonance frequency divided by

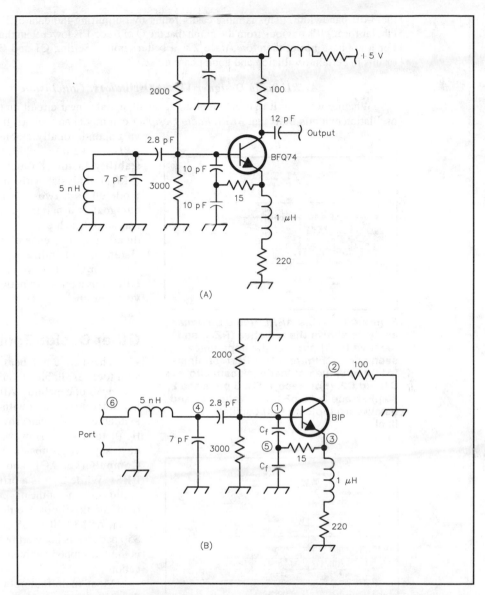

Figure 4.14—Even though *ARRL Radio Designer* is a small-signal linear simulator, and the active device in an oscillator (A, a simple 800-MHz circuit) operates in a large-signal, nonlinear way, *ARD* can help us determine component values that make oscillation likely, and how close to the edge of nonoscillation an oscillator circuit may be. B shows the same circuit redrawn for *ARRL Radio Designer* modeling. The model treats the circuit as a one-port device so we can investigate the impedance seen looking into the oscillator's ungrounded resonator (coil) and common. If the resistive part of this impedance is zero or negative, the circuit will likely oscillate.

the 3-dB bandwidth. (This is more easily found by outputting the data of Figure 4.4 in tabular form.) It's obvious from the graph that the Q of trace 1 is lower than that of trace 2. For low phase noise, therefore, trace 2 is a better choice. Setting C1 and C2 to 10 pF results in certain oscillation and good phase noise.

ARRL Radio Designer Versus Oscillators: Conclusion

Whether we want it to oscillate or not, a small-signal, linear circuit on the brink of oscillation exhibits traits that *ARRL Radio Designer* can model and report. If our goal is an unconditionally stable amplifier, *ARD* can help us achieve it through stability factor (K) and return-loss (MS_{11}) analysis, with the amplifier modeled as a two-port network. If our goal is a better oscillator, *ARD* can help us achieve it by directly indicating the presence of negative resistance, and indirectly indicating resonator Q, when we model the oscillator as a one-port network and investigate the impedance of its resonator.

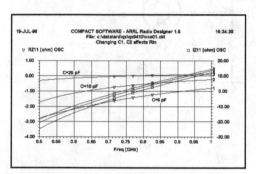

Figure 4.15—This *ARRL Radio Designer* analysis shows the resistive (RZ_{11}) and reactive (IZ_{11}) parts of the impedance seen across Figure 4.14's Port terminals for three values of feedback capacitors C1 and C2. (For trace 1, C = 5 pF; trace 2, 10 pF; trace 3, 25 pF.) RZ_{11} values of and below zero indicate that oscillation is likely.

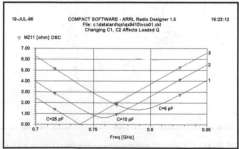

Figure 4.16—Graphing the magnitude (MZ_{11}) of the impedances plotted in Figure 4.15 reflects a dramatic Q reduction as the feedback capacitors are decreased in value. (For trace 1, C = 5 pF; trace 2, 10 pF; trace 3, 25 pF.) The more rounded the trace corner, the lower the Q.

Other Design Tools

There are a number of other design tools available at various prices and levels of capability. All have steep learning curves, and without readily available support can prove to be difficult to master. However, most do have support groups on the Internet, CompuServe, AOL and electronic BBSs. While cost is a prime consideration—some of the packages examined for this book would require a check of $3,000 to $5,000—even a $50 package is not worthwhile if there is limited support for ham radio applications.

Most manufacturers recognize the difficulty in picking a circuit design tool, and offer either a free or low cost trial, student or *demo* version for you to try. Often, this trial version is enough for many purposes. You will not find the ability of *ARRL Radio Designer* in any free or trial package, however. For the mail addresses, telephone numbers and Web site addresses of the suppliers discussed in the following paragraphs, please see the Resources Chapter. Each of the following programs are either derived from or related to versions of *SPICE*. Each manufacturer has their own proprietary spelling variation.

MicroSim Design Lab

MicroSim Corporation sells Design Lab, a heavy-duty *Windows*-based design and analysis package. An evaluation version can be requested by telephone or from their Web site. The evaluation version is fully capable within certain limits, such as only 50 components and one-page schematics. MicroSim recommends a 486DX or Pentium, with 16 Mb of memory. A CD-ROM drive is needed to run the evaluation version, and you **must** be using either *Windows 95* or *Windows NT*. Before calling them, read the material on their Web site, to see if you can utilize the evaluation version.

ICAP5

Intusoft has a set of SPICE based design tools. *ICAP/4Students* is a $40-class package specifically for college students. It has both analog and digital capability and performs dc, frequency response, transient analysis and various other simulations. A *Windows* operating system (3.X, 95 or NT) is required with 8 Mb of memory. Intusoft has a full line of products with prices of the non-student versions starting at $95.

MICRO-CAP V

This *Windows*-based software begins, as do most others, with a schematic entry screen and permits you to see the results of full-up simulations in both the time and frequency domains. You can probe the schematic for the waveforms at any point, and see the performance with a Monte Carlo analysis. A working demo (and student version) can be downloaded from their Web site.

Included in the free package is a scripted demo program. It carries you through schematic entry, component selection and assignment of values, analyses and some data manipulation.

A large number of engineering schools used an earlier (DOS) based version of *MICRO-CAP* for many years, and may have packages in stock in their bookstores. This earlier release (*MICRO-CAP IV*) was considered a standard tool for students, and may be enough for your needs. It came with a book, which many people still feel is needed for them to take full advantage of any program's capabilities. The new (*Windows*-based) version contains built-in help.

Introduction to Radio Frequency Design

Rather than being a design program, *Introduction to Radio Frequency Design* is a classic book accompanied by a disk full of handy programs. It is included here because many serious designers point to it as a source of needed information, and the disk qualifies it as a PC-based design tool. Written by Wes Hayward, W7ZOI, the book has its origins in the 1980s. Because of its importance to the ham community, it is now available from the ARRL (see the rear of this book for ordering information). It is written at a college level, which is appropriate to the complexity of some of the topics and material that should be understood to carry RF design past a certain point.

The programs are keyed to topics in the text, where Hayward was able to provide design programs in place of having the calculations done by hand. Most of the programs are .EXE (executable) files, and require minimum computer capabilities.

MODELING ANTENNA SYSTEMS, ANTENNAS, TRANSMISSION LINES AND TUNERS

An antenna is just part of the radiating system. To have a really effective design, you have to consider the effect of the feed line, the tuner (if any), the antenna's height and the surrounding terrain. Pay attention to just the antenna design, and you may have a good antenna. Pay attention to the feed and antenna positioning, and you will optimize your *total system*—you will send the maximum signal towards where you want it to go, whether you are a DX big gun or a Saturday evening QRPer. To say you want a big antenna to work DX is not quite enough; you also have to go though several steps to optimize your antenna system. The first step is a look at propagation.

Chapter 3 of this book contains a discussion and comparison of propagation-prediction programs. Each of them can be run on your PC. Thus, given the path, time of day, time of year and status of the sun spot cycle, you can calculate the range of *possibilities*—which band, where it is open to and what elevation angle maximizes your chance of getting through.

Table 4.3 is taken from Chapter 23 of *The ARRL Antenna Book*. It compares the primary features of six popular propagation-prediction programs—*ASAPS, IONCAP, IONSOUND, MINIMUF, MINIPROP* and *CAPMAN*.

Propagation Data

The disk accompanying the 17th Edition of *The ARRL Antenna Book* has a directory called **\ELEVAT**, containing data calculated with *IONCAP*. One such file is in Figure 4.17. Calculated for the W3 area to Europe, it allows a comparison of launch elevation angle vs band.

The numbers given were calculated from a large data base, containing only those cases where the band *was open*. Two modes are apparent for 40/30 meters and up—5° to 6° and 9°. A better choice for your antenna beam center on 80 meters is about 18°. Thus, you would want to optimize your antenna designs around these launch elevation angles—while aware of all the caveats surrounding these calculations that appear in the *Antenna Book*.

The same disk contains the *ION_HDX* program, which is used to produce the predictions curves appearing monthly in the *How's DX?* column of *QST* magazine. This program enables you to make your own predictions from your location to various areas of the world.

Antenna Modeling Software

During the 1990s, many, if not most, antenna articles in the amateur literature have sported detailed azimuth and elevation plots created by *ELNEC* or *NEC/Wires*, *MN, AO* or *YO*. This section covers several recent antenna-modeling programs, based on *NEC* (the Numerical Electromagnetics Code, originally developed by the US government), plus a description of a program that provides the effects of surrounding terrain and antenna height on the vertical launch angle of the beam. With this combi-

```
W3-EUROP.PRN
W3-EUROP.PRN Rx QTH: Western and
Eastern Europe
```

Elev	80m	40m	30m	20m	17m	15m	12m	10m
1	0.0	0.0	0.4	0.5	0.0	0.0	0.0	0.0
2	0.0	0.0	0.4	1.9	3.1	0.0	1.5	0.0
3	0.0	0.5	0.9	5.3	14.0	6.5	18.2	24.5
4	0.0	6.7	2.7	3.8	16.3	13.0	21.2	15.1
5	0.0	3.8	4.9	9.1	10.9	12.0	9.1	17.0
6	0.0	3.3	10.6	5.7	10.1	5.4	12.1	7.5
7	0.0	0.0	9.3	2.4	1.6	2.2	6.1	17.0
8	0.0	3.3	8.4	4.3	3.9	5.4	3.0	3.8
9	0.0	1.0	11.9	19.6	20.2	17.4	6.1	7.5
10	0.0	2.4	14.6	25.8	14.7	14.1	10.6	7.5
11	0.0	1.9	8.0	13.9	3.9	13.0	12.1	0.0
12	0.0	3.3	6.6	4.3	1.6	7.6	0.0	0.0
13	0.0	15.8	3.1	1.0	0.0	3.3	0.0	0.0
14	0.7	14.8	8.0	1.0	0.0	0.0	0.0	0.0
15	2.2	12.9	7.5	0.0	0.0	0.0	0.0	0.0
16	14.4	7.7	2.2	1.4	0.0	0.0	0.0	0.0
17	15.1	6.7	0.4	0.0	0.0	0.0	0.0	0.0
18	19.4	4.3	0.0	0.0	0.0	0.0	0.0	0.0
19	18.7	2.9	0.0	0.0	0.0	0.0	0.0	0.0
20	14.4	6.2	0.0	0.0	0.0	0.0	0.0	0.0
21	2.2	2.4	0.0	0.0	0.0	0.0	0.0	0.0
22	1.4	0.0	0.0	0.0	0.0	0.0	0.0	0.0
23	0.7	0.0	0.0	0.0	0.0	0.0	0.0	0.0
24	2.3	0.0	0.0	0.0	0.0	0.0	0.0	0.0
25	0.7	0.0	0.0	0.0	0.0	0.0	0.0	0.0
26	0.7	0.0	0.0	0.0	0.0	0.0	0.0	0.0
27	2.2	0.0	0.0	0.0	0.0	0.0	0.0	0.0
28	1.4	0.0	0.0	0.0	0.0	0.0	0.0	0.0
29	1.4	0.0	0.0	0.0	0.0	0.0	0.0	0.0
30	0.7	0.0	0.0	0.0	0.0	0.0	0.0	0.0
31	0.0	0.0	0.0	0.0	0.0	0.0	0.0	0.0
32	0.0	0.0	0.0	0.0	0.0	0.0	0.0	0.0
33	0.0	0.0	0.0	0.0	0.0	0.0	0.0	0.0
34	0.0	0.0	0.0	0.0	0.0	0.0	0.0	0.0
35	1.4	0.0	0.0	0.0	0.0	0.0	0.0	0.0

Figure 4.17—For the path from the mid-eastern US coast (W3-land) to Europe the 30 to 10-meter bands seem to show two modes—around 5° and around 10°. The 80-meter band seems to peak around 18°.

Table 4.3

Features and Attributes of Propagation Prediction Programs

	ASAPS V. 2.2	IONCAP PC.27	IONSOUND PRO	MINIMUF	MINIPROP PLUS 2.0	CAPMAN
User friendliness	Good	Poor	Fair/Good	Good	Good	Good
Review data	Yes	No	No	No	Yes	Yes
User library of QTHs	Yes	No	Yes	No	Yes	Yes
Bearings, distances	Yes	Yes	Yes	No	Yes	Yes
MUF calculation	Yes	Yes	Yes	Yes	Yes	Yes
LUF calculation	Yes	Yes	Yes	No	No	Yes
Wave angle calculation	Yes	Yes	Yes	No	Yes	Yes
Vary minimum wave angle	Yes	Yes	Yes	No	Yes	Yes
Path regions and hops	Yes	Yes	Yes	No	Yes	Yes
Multipath effects	No	Yes	Yes	No	No	Yes
Path probability	Yes	Yes	Yes	No	Yes	Yes
Signal strengths	Yes	Yes	Yes	No	Yes	Yes
S/N ratios	Yes	Yes	Yes	No	No	Yes
Long path calculation	Yes	Yes	Yes	No	Yes	Yes
Antenna selection	Yes	Yes	Yes	No	No	Yes
Vary antenna height	Indirectly	Yes	No	No	No	Yes
Vary ground characteristics	Indirectly	Yes	No	No	No	Yes
Vary transmit power	Yes	Yes	Yes	No	Yes	Yes
Graphic displays	Herc/VGA	ASCII	Herc/VGA	No	Herc/VGA	Herc/VGA
UT-day graphs	Yes	Yes	Yes	No	Yes	Yes
Color monitor support	Yes	No	Yes	No	Yes	Yes
Hard disk required	Yes	Yes	No	No	No	Yes
Save data to disk	Yes	Yes	No	No	No	Yes
Documentation	48 p	226 p	52 p	QST art.	56 p	Yes
Price class	Aus. $350†	$128 fee	$75*	——	$60	$89

"Review data" indicates ability to review previous program display screens.
Herc = Hercules/compatible; CGA is also compatible with EGA/VGA systems. ASCII uses characters such as .... and xxxx, no graphics card is required.
Price classes are for early 1994 and subject to change.
*STD version, with reduced features, available for $35. Version tailored for "How's DX?" column from QST available for $15.
†Australian dollars, equivalent to about $280 US at early-1994 exchange rates.

nation of programs, you are able to design an antenna, predict its operating characteristics and determine how it will operate when mounted at a height you pick over real terrain.

The following section is based on a product review by R. Dean Straw, N6BV, "QST Compares: Antenna Modeling Software," QST, October 1995, pages 72-74.

Why NEC?

MININEC and its variations, such as *ELNEC* or *MN*, have been the standard computer-based tools hams have used to model and design antennas. With the appearance of several new *NEC*-based modeling programs, such as *EZNEC*, *NEC/Wires* or *NEC/Yagis*, we have a new ability to look in more detail, with great ease, at antenna designs. *MININEC* is fine for many antenna-modeling problems but it has serious limitations when analyzing a number of real, practical antennas. If a horizontally polarized antenna is located less than about 0.2 wavelengths above the ground, *MININEC*-derived programs will report that the gain is higher, sometimes substantially higher, than it should be.

Users have reported that *MININEC* has built-in frequency offsets, most often noted on multielement VHF Yagis. It also has difficulties with certain wire geometries, such as that of a quad antenna. There are workarounds for some of these problems, but these can cause the programs to run more slowly, often substantially. *NEC*-based programs do not suffer from these problems and they often run significantly faster. In addition, *NEC*-based programs can directly model lossless transmision lines, an important factor in phased arrays and log-periodic antennas. Therefore, for increased accuracy, speed and enhanced modeling capability the new *NEC*-based programs are the tools of choice. In this section we will look at one program by Roy Lewallen, W7EL, *EZNEC* and three programs by Brian Beezley, K6STI: *Antenna Optimizer (AO) 6.5*, *NEC/Wires 2.0* and *Terrain Analyzer (TA) 1.0*. The Resources Chapter has details on purchasing these tools.

EZNEC

If you're already an *ELNEC* user, you'll be comfortable with *EZNEC*, introduced in July 1995 *QST*. For those new to the world of antenna modeling, *EZNEC* lives up to the reputation for "reasonably friendly" operation established by its little brother. That said, please consider this warning about antenna modeling: *It's not all that easy, no matter what program you use.* The user must be able to visualize antennas as objects in three-dimensional space, something not all people are comfortable doing.

Antenna modeling programs require the user to look at an antenna as a set of straight-line "wires," with x, y and z coordinates for the end of each wire. W7EL's on-disk *EZNEC.DOC* documentation is clear and well written, guiding the neophyte user through the intricacies of modeling. You should read it several times, even if you are an experienced modeler. There also are sample files on disk, with a detailed description of the subtleties in each design. *EZNEC*'s main menu is laid out in a logical, if somewhat busy, fashion. See Figure 4.18. The operator uses two-letter abbreviations

```
                      EZNEC  ver. 1.0
              (c) 1995-6 by Roy Lewallen, W7EL

    TI   TITLE:                 Dipole w/arms rotated down
    FR   FREQUENCY:             14 MHz. (wavelength = 70.25509 ft.)

    WI   WIRES:                 3 Wires          WL   WIRE LOSS: Copper
    SO   SOURCES:               1 Source         UN   UNITS:     Feet
    LO   LOADS:                 0 Loads
    TL   TRANSMISSION LINES:    0 Lines
    GT   GROUND TYPE:           Real/Hi Accuracy Anal    LAST FILE SUD/RCLD:
    GD   GND DESCRIPTION:       1 Medium              LAST.EZ

    PT   PLOT TYPE:             Azimuth          RF   REFERENCE: 0 dBi
    PA   ELEVATION ANGLE:       20 Deg.          SZ   SWR Z0:    50 ohms
    PR   PLOT/TABLE RANGE:      0 - 360 Deg. (full)   FI   PLOT FLDS: Tot fld only
    SS   STEP SIZE:             1 Deg.
    OR   OUTER RING OF PLOT:    Automatic scaling

    <BR>owse file   <DE>lete, <RE>call, <SA>ve desc   <Freq S>wp   <RET> = Plot
    <AN>alyze  <CU>rrents  <Guideline C>k  <Load D>ata  <OP>tions  <Print D>esc
    <Src D>ata  <TA>ble  <View A>nt  <EX>it pgm without saving desc  <QU>it  _
```

Figure 4.18—Main menu for *EZNEC*. A simple inverted-V dipole is being analyzed, over real high-accuracy (Sommerfeld/Norton) ground.

to enter any submenu. For example, keying in "GT" will take you instantly to the "Ground Type" submenu, where you may define the type of ground over which an antenna is situated. More complicated functions take you to other full-size screens to enter data. For example, keying in "LO" will take you to the LOad screen, where you may specify the placement and types of various loads, such as parallel-tuned traps, series inductors, capacitors, resistors, etc.

One of the very nice, intuitive features of *EZNEC* is that you may specify a "load" or "source" generator in terms of the percentage from one end of a particular wire. For example, to put a source in the center of wire number five, you would specify 50% from End 1 of Wire 5. *EZNEC* figures out the best segment placement automatically.

Since the process of specifying wires is often a complex, tedious and error-prone task, you should draw a picture, on paper, of the desired antenna before starting on the computer. Then, you can use *EZNEC*'s "View Antenna" function to see a detailed geometric picture of the antenna you are entering, wire by wire. You may rotate, scale, zoom in or zoom out the picture to inspect minute details.

A particularly endearing feature, unique to W7EL's software, is the "Highlight" function in View Antenna. You use the arrow keys to highlight each wire on-screen, one by one. The numeric values (x, y, z, diameter, and length) for that wire are shown in detail. With Highlight, you can sort out a complicated model made up of many wires. See Figure 4.19, showing a two-element quad, with segment 2 highlighted on the View Antenna screen.

Once you have specified, inspected and then saved your model to disk, you next press the **ENTER** key. The program computes for a while and then displays either an azimuth or elevation plot, your choice, showing how your antenna performs. *EZNEC* must recalculate when changing between an azimuth or an elevation plot. In K6STI's programs, both elevation and azimuth plots are computed at the same time and are alternately displayed by hitting the **ENTER** key.

EZNEC's unique ability to recall and overlay multiple *traces* (W7EL's terminology for an elevation or azimuth plot pattern saved to disk), is a plus. (Beezley's programs allow for only two patterns to be displayed on one plot.) In *EZNEC*, you may overlay as many as five trace patterns on one plot, each with different color legends. Actually, you can overlay even more, if you don't mind the confusion trying to figure out which trace is which!

Where such a multiple-trace capability becomes really useful is if you do a detailed frequency sweep. For example, consider a sweep from 21.0 to 21.5 MHz, in steps of 50 kHz, for a 2-element quad. The resulting 11 traces on one plot can easily be distinguished despite the limitation of only five different on-screen colors, since the trend of how the patterns changed with frequency is smooth and obvious to the eye. Modeling an antenna over a range of frequencies, not just at a single spot frequency, where you might miss the progress of a trend entirely, is recommended. Remember the story of the blind men trying to describe an elephant?

Another *really* neat feature of *EZNEC* (and *ELNEC*) is that once either an elevation or an azimuth pattern has been generated, it may be overlaid on the View Antenna plot. This reveals the relationship between the wire geometry, the currents on each wire, and the resulting pattern. See Figure 4.20 for an example of this.

EZNEC produces user-customizable tables stored to disk for later use, including antenna currents. By contrast, K6STI's *NEC/Wires* saves only a limited set of param-

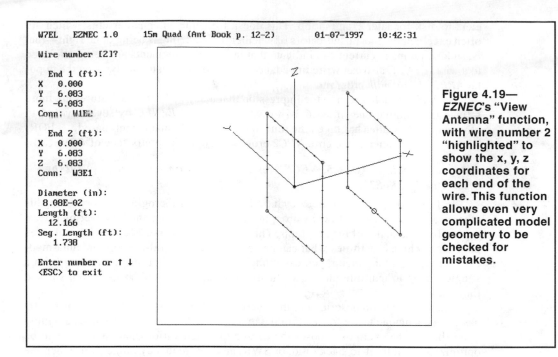

Wire number [2]?

End 1 (ft):
X   0.000
Y   6.083
Z   -6.083
Conn: W1E2

End 2 (ft):
X   0.000
Y   6.083
Z   6.083
Conn: W3E1

Diameter (in):
 8.08E-02
Length (ft):
  12.166
Seg. Length (ft):
   1.738

Enter number or ↑ ↓
<ESC> to exit

Figure 4.19—
EZNEC's "View
Antenna" function,
with wire number 2
"highlighted" to
show the x, y, z
coordinates for
each end of the
wire. This function
allows even very
complicated model
geometry to be
checked for
mistakes.

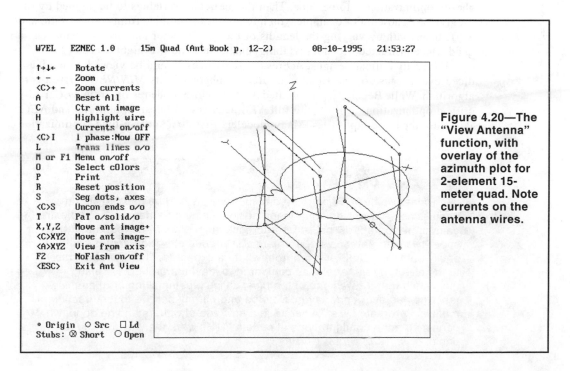

↑→↓←   Rotate
+ -   Zoom
<C>+ -   Zoom currents
A   Reset All
C   Ctr ant image
H   Highlight wire
I   Currents on/off
<C>I   1 phase:Now OFF
L   Trans lines o/o
M or F1   Menu on/off
O   Select cOlors
P   Print
R   Reset position
S   Seg dots, axes
<C>S   Uncon ends o/o
T   PaT o/solid/o
X,Y,Z   Move ant image+
<C>XYZ   Move ant image-
<A>XYZ   View from axis
F2   NoFlash on/off
<ESC>   Exit Ant View

• Origin ○ Src □ Ld
Stubs: ⊗ Short ○ Open

Figure 4.20—The
"View Antenna"
function, with
overlay of the
azimuth plot for
2-element 15-
meter quad. Note
currents on the
antenna wires.

eters to disk for later examination. This doesn't include antenna currents, which are often excellent diagnostic indicators of whether the modeling is being done right—that is, sudden jumps in current can indicate that insufficient segments are being allocated to a wire. *EZNEC* also can write impedance files to disk for later analysis by the popular *ARRL MicroSmith* program.

Such nice touches lead to the impression that many of *EZNEC's* features are more refined than similar ones in *NEC/Wires*, which predated *EZNEC* by several years. In other words, Lewallen has taken the time to really hide the mainframe-based, FORTRAN-like character of the core *NEC2* program behind the pretty face of *EZNEC*.

Antenna Optimizer (AO) 6.5, NEC/Wires 2.0 and Terrain Analyzer (TA) 1.0 (by Brian Beezley, K6STI)

In July 1995 *QST*, Brian Beezley introduced the *TA 1.0* program, repositioning his other products at the same time by dropping all copy protection and by lowering prices, especially for bundles of his programs. This discussion covers a $120 package of three programs, which constitutes what can be considered a general-purpose antenna-modeling suite. With this lineup, you can model, perhaps even optimize, anything from a simple dipole to multiple phased verticals, Beverages, stacked Yagis—even stacked rhombics.

The first program described in this section is *AO 6.5*, the Antenna Optimizer. *AO* has carved a unique niche for itself in the modeling world; nobody else does anything quite like it. The operator chooses the degree to which various parameters are to be optimized: gain, front-to-back ratio, or SWR, and the frequency range over which the chosen optimization is to be done. Then the particular variables to be juggled by the program are chosen. For example, you might want to optimize front-to-back ratio and SWR bandwidth by varying the lengths of the first director and driven element in a quad. Once instructed, *AO* does its thing, unattended and overnight if need be.

For really critical designs, *AO* results sometimes should be viewed with a jaundiced eye, because of the small inaccuracies inherent in its *MININEC*-derived core algorithm. While Beezley has calibrated *AO* to be close to the results from *NEC*, really critical optimizations still require full *NEC* accuracy. By design, both *AO* and *NEC/Wires* use the same input files. Many modelers first do a "coarse-tune" optimization

Beezley on TA

Rather wistfully, Brian related to me recently that he used to spend endless hours tweaking an antenna design, gaining perhaps 0.1 dB of extra gain, or maybe a 2 dB better front-to-back ratio. With *TA* he found that his super-tweaked antenna's performance at various elevation angles could easily be down 10 dB or more from what he expected. This was due solely to the effect of real terrain, as compared to ideal flat ground. He also mentioned that *TA* was one of the most difficult, painstaking programming tasks he had ever undertaken. Both he and I firmly believe that diffraction-modeling programs like *TA* herald in a new age of understanding about why certain antenna configurations at certain QTHs work the way they do (or don't). —*R. Dean Straw, N6BV*

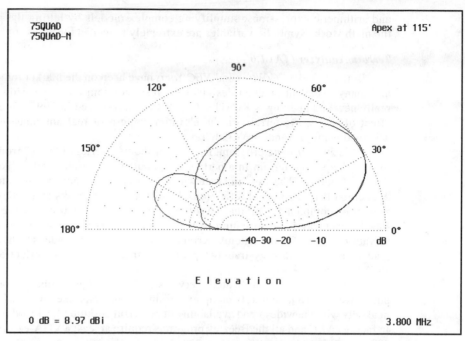

Figure 4.21—Overlay of two elevation plots of N6BV 75-m quad. The plot with more than 20 dB F/B is by *NEC/Wires*, while the other is by *AO*. This illustrates the frequency shift inherent in *MININEC*-derived programs for critically tuned models—the *AO* model peaked 15 kHz higher in frequency.

with *AO* and then manually "fine-tune" with the big brother program, *NEC/Wires*.

NEC/Wires modeling of the performance of a 75/80-meter quad designed according to this procedure was accurate to within 2 kHz on 3.8 MHz; *AO* modeling, to within about 15 kHz for this critical, narrow-band design. See Figure 4.21 for an elevation plot from *AO* for this quad, overlaid with the pattern generated by *NEC/Wires*.

AO is faster than other *MININEC*-type programs, since many routines were written in speedy assembly language. (*YO*, Beezley's Yagi Optimizer, is blazingly fast, because it's streamlined for modeling only Yagis and uses custom assembly-language routines.)

For *NEC/Wires* and *NEC/Yagis*, Beezley tweaked his FORTRAN compiler's math libraries for speed, using assembly-language routines. The result is a noticeably faster program compared with other implementations of *NEC2*, including the original. For example, a two-element 15-meter quad (with 154 total segments) took about 17% less time to complete using *NEC/Wires* (79 seconds total) than did *EZNEC* (95 seconds total) on a 486DX-33 computer.

An input file for either *AO* or *NEC/Wires* is created using an ASCII text processor, outside of the programs. At first glance, this seems like a disadvantage compared to *EZNEC* with its smooth, integrated environment. However, the advantage of the Beezley strategy is that the user can define data as *symbolic variables*, rather than as fixed numbers. In fact, antennas may even be defined incorporating trigonometric functions and arithmetic expressions, simplifying complex models by letting the programs do the math work. Symbolic variables are extremely powerful tools.

Terrain Analyzer (TA) 1.0

Both *AO* and *NEC/Wires* and *NEC/Yagis* have been on the market for several years and many excellent antenna designs have resulted from their use. However, what's really new and exciting is K6STI's *TA* software, introduced in 1995. *TA* evaluates the effect of real-world terrain on the elevation pattern of real antennas, perhaps ones designed using *AO* and/or *NEC/Wires*.

TA is a *ray-tracing* program. In effect, it shoots a series of "rays" from an antenna toward the ground terrain in a particular azimuthal direction—rather like shooting a bunch of bullets. The rays interact with the ground in many complicated ways: by bouncing off it in classical reflections, by diffracting off peaks and valleys in the terrain, or by compound combinations of reflections and diffractions. At the end of their travels, each ray is vector-summed with all the others to create an overall far-field elevation pattern for the antenna/terrain combination. The reader might also want to read the article on this ray-tracing technique with diffraction and reflection in the July 1995 issue of *QEX*.

Things get very complicated, very fast, when a large number of rays are computed over even a moderately complex terrain. An analysis like *TA*'s has become practical only with the widespread availability of powerful desktop PC's in today's hamshack. In fact, *EZNEC* and all the Beezley programs require at least a VGA-equipped 386DX/387-coprocessor computer to run.

To use *TA*, you first generate a terrain file by carefully taking multiple range/elevation data points off a USGS topographic ("topo") chart for your QTH. This is a painstaking task that must be done for each azimuth direction of interest (toward Europe, Japan, South America, etc.), for more than a mile out from your tower base. You'll also need a data file for the antenna you want to evaluate over your terrain. Beezley has included with *TA* more than 40 sample *.PF plot files. Each contains the free-space elevation amplitude and phase data for one antenna, ranging from a simple dipole to a monster 13-element 20-meter Yagi on a 320-foot boom. He also includes the terrain profiles for a number of prominent US contest stations, for fun and comparison.

Figure 4.22 shows the *TA* output for the N6BV QTH towards Japan, using a single 60-foot high four-element Yagi at 14.0 MHz. The elevation response of the antenna is shown at the top, with a picture of the terrain at the bottom. *TA* is mouse-oriented. Figure 4.22 is the result of clicking on the elevation response at 6.25° to show the various reflection and diffraction components associated with this exit angle as they interacted with the terrain.

With *TA* you can even identify which terrain points affect the elevation pattern. You do this by "grabbing" a terrain point with the mouse and moving it up, down or sideways. When you release the mouse button, the elevation response is computed and displayed. This could be dubbed the "bulldozer" analysis mode—wouldn't it be great if our neighbors actually did allow us to sculpt their landscapes with a bulldozer to optimize our antenna patterns?

YTAD—Propagation Prediction Combined with Terrain Effects

According to its author, N6BV, "*YTAD* (Yagi Terrain Analysis, with Diffraction)

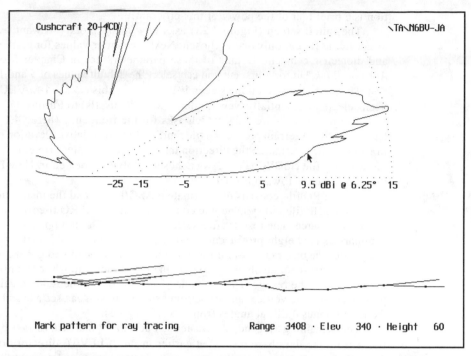

Cushcraft 20-4CD   \TA\N6BV-JA

-25 -15   -5   5   9.5 dBi @ 6.25° 15

Mark pattern for ray tracing   Range 3408 · Elev   340 · Height   60

Figure 4.22—Output screen from *TA* program, showing elevation pattern and terrain at N6BV QTH toward Japan, with a 60-foot high 4-element Yagi on 14.0 MHz. At 6.25° the response is 9.5 dBi, with numerous components of reflection, diffraction and reflection-diffraction shown interacting with the terrain at this elevation angle.

is a ray-tracing program designed to evaluate the effect of foreground terrain on the elevation pattern of up to four HF Yagis in a stack. This is an experimental program, still a *work in progress.*"

YTAD is a *systems approach* to HF station design, in which you need to know the following:

- ▣ The range of elevation angles necessary to get from point A to point B
- ▣ The elevation patterns for various types and configurations of antennas
- ▣ The effect of local terrain on antenna elevation patterns.

The program is based on the same extensive data base discussed previously, available in the directory \ELEV AT on the disk accompanying the 17th edition of *The ARRL Antenna Book.* This provides the first needed item—the elevation angles. Internal to the program are the pattern computations for one to four stacked four-element Yagi antennas, thus providing the second needed item. Finally, the program accepts a data file representing the local terrain in front of the antenna, and calculates the diffraction patterns and resulting beam pattern—the final item above.

A full history, description and examples of the program can be found in *QEX,* July 1995, page 3—*The Effect of Local Terrain on HF Launch Angles.* The following section is a brief tour of the power of this program.

The initial screen (Figure 4.23) asks how many plots you want overlay, up to three. In the figure, only one is chosen. Next, you enter values for earth conductivity and dielectric constant. Details of these parameters are in Chapter 3 of *The ARRL Antenna Book*, but for a first cut you can select the default values of 5 and 13 as shown.

The next selection on the screen is the path. In this case W1-MA-EU.PRN has been selected—essentially New England (Massachusetts) to Europe.

The result is Figure 4.24, which asks for the frequency (here 14.1 MHz) and a terrain profile. A terrain profile is a file representing the relative elevation of the ground in front of the antenna, in the direction the antenna is pointed. Here, to be consistent, the existing file **N6BV-EU.PRO** was chosen. N6BV is located in New England, and the -EU indicates toward Europe.

Each .PRO file consists of a formatted ASCII text, and the instructions found in the source .ZIP file tells you how to construct your own .PRO file from a topo map or other data source. The result, after selecting a .PRO file, is Figure 4.25. This screen summarizes the height profile data, and asks for the number of stacked antennas. Finally, after the program asks for the antenna height, it begins to generate results.

A color screen, much easier to read than the black and white rendition in Figure 4.26, provides the results. The top (smooth) curve shows the relative gain (left axis), plotted against the vertical angle (bottom axis). Here you can see a broad set of peaks, from 0 to minus 4 dB, at angles from 3 to 12 degrees.

The remaining (jagged, with asterisks at data points) curve is a plot of points taken from the data base discussed earlier in the **/ELEVAT** directory of *The ARRL Antenna Book*. It represents what you want—in this case a peak around 11 degrees and perhaps another around 4 degrees.

In this case the results are not too bad—what you have is close to what you want.

```
             YTAD, Yagi Terrain Analysis, with Diffraction
           Ver. 3.51, Sep 17, 1996, Copyright 1995-96 ARRL, by N6BV
     Ray Tracing, With Refl., Direct Diff., Diff.-Refl., and NO Diff.-Refl.-Diff.
             No Terrain Pre-Smoothing; With No Output Post-Smoothing.

   You may overlay up to three plots. How many plots [Default = 1]? 1

   Enter frequency (MHz): 14.1

   Enter earth conductivity (Default=[Enter] = 5 mS/m): 5
   Enter dielectric constant for earth (Default=[Enter] = 13): 13

   Volume in drive C is DISK1_VOL1
   Directory of C:\ARRL\YTAD

 W1-MA-AF.PRN    W1-MA-AS.PRN    W1-MA-EU.PRN    W1-MA-JA.PRN    W1-MA-OC.PRN
 W1-MA-SA.PRN    W6-SF-AF.PRN    W6-SF-AS.PRN    W6-SF-EU.PRN    W6-SF-JA.PRN
 W6-SF-OC.PRN    W6-SF-SA.PRN
        12 file(s)           29,184 bytes
                        653,983,744 bytes free


   Enter name of elevation statistical file [Default = None]: w1-ma-eu.prn ▮
```

Figure 4.23—The first screen of Y*TAD* asks for the number of plots to be overlaid (here 1), the earth conductivity and the dielectric constant. It places default values into the last two if you press the [Enter] key. A frequency of 14.1 MHz was chosen with a path from New England to Europe.

```
        Volume in drive C is DISK1_VOL1
        Directory of C:\ARRL\YTAD

    W1-MA-AF.PRN      W1-MA-AS.PRN       W1-MA-EU.PRN      W1-MA-JA.PRN      W1-MA-OC.PRN
    W1-MA-SA.PRN      W6-SF-AF.PRN       W6-SF-AS.PRN      W6-SF EU.PRN      W6-SF-JA.PRN
    W6-SF-OC.PRN      W6-SF-SA.PRN
            12 file(s)             29,184 bytes
                          653,983,744 bytes free


        Enter name of elevation statistical file [Default = None]: w1-ma-eu.prn
    Invalid switch

        Volume in drive C is DISK1_VOL1
        Directory of C:\ARRL\YTAD

    K1DG-EU.PRO      K1DG-JA.PRO        K1KI-330.PRO      K1KI-40.PRO       K1KI-45.PRO
    K1KI-50.PRO      K1ZZ-EU.PRO        K1ZZ-JA.PRO       K5ZD-45.PRO       KM1H-EU.PRO
    KM1H-JA.PRO      N1MM-EU.PRO        N1MM-JA.PRO       N1MM-SA.PRO       N1MM-W6.PRO
    N6BV-EU.PRO      N6BV-JA.PRO        FLAT.PRO
            18 file(s)              6,144 bytes
                          653,950,976 bytes free

    Frequency =    14.100 MHz, statistical file = W1-MA-EU.PRN
    Filename for terrain profile data: n6bv-eu.pro█
```

Figure 4.24—Since New England to Europe was selected for the path, the elevation profile in this direction, at the tower of N6BV/1, was chosen for a *.PRO* file.

If there was a large discrepancy, however, you have the choice of using more antennas (up to four), lowering them, raising them, and perhaps relocating the tower. The ability to do terraforming or transformation, with a bulldozer, is an alternative for very few people.

YTAD is available at no cost on the ARRL HIRAM BBS system, and on the Internet at several sites that echo files on HIRAM. Start with the address of the ARRL home page (**http://www.arrl.org/**) and look for a link to ARRL files.

As N6BV states in his introduction, this program is constantly evolving. When a new version is available, it will be announced in *QST* and on the Internet.

Feed Line and Tuner Analysis

TL—Instant Answers to Antenna Feed Questions

Recent editions of *The ARRL Handbook For Radio Amateurs* and *The ARRL Antenna Book* include *TL*, another program written by R. Dean Straw, N6BV. It contains the equations to give you considerable insight on the operations of antennas with real feed lines and tuners. The program allows you to pick a commercial feed line type (and length) or specify your own. A comprehensive instruction sheet is included with the software.

To illustrate this software, look at the common problem of the operation of a short dipole. In the back of the *TL* documentation, the feed -oint impedance of a 100-foot dipole is given for various frequencies (Figure 4.27). At 1.8 MHz, this dipole would appear as 4.8–j1673 Ω, a highly reactive load. The first screen of TL (Figure 4.28) allows selection of the type of feed line. After picking 100 feet of 450-Ω window line as the transmission line, the second screen of *TL* appears as in Figure 4.29. *TL* gives us the SWR at the input to the line as 86.3. Even with low loss (at these frequencies) line, the total loss is calculated to be slightly over 12 dB—not a good situation! With 1.5

```
      18 file(s)            6,144 bytes
                      653,950,976 bytes free

  Frequency =    14.100 MHz, statistical file = W1-MA-EU.PRN
   Filename for terrain profile data: n6bv-eu.pro
Distance(  1) =      .0  Height(  1) =      430.0
Distance(  2) =    200.0  Height(  2) =      420.0
Distance(  3) =    500.0  Height(  3) =      410.0
Distance(  4) =    700.0  Height(  4) =      400.0
Distance(  5) =    800.0  Height(  5) =      380.0
Distance(  6) =    900.0  Height(  6) =      360.0
Distance(  7) =   1000.0  Height(  7) =      340.0
Distance(  8) =   1500.0  Height(  8) =      340.0
Distance(  9) =   1550.0  Height(  9) =      360.0
Distance( 10) =   1800.0  Height( 10) =      360.0
Distance( 11) =   1900.0  Height( 11) =      340.0
Distance( 12) =   2200.0  Height( 12) =      340.0
Distance( 13) =   4800.0  Height( 13) =      340.0
Distance( 14) =   5000.0  Height( 14) =      360.0
Distance( 15) =   5200.0  Height( 15) =      380.0
Distance( 16) =   5450.0  Height( 16) =      400.0
Distance( 17) =   5700.0  Height( 17) =      420.0
Distance( 18) =   7600.0  Height( 18) =      440.0

  Enter number of antennas in a stack (4 max): 1
```

Figure 4.25—The contents of N6BV-EU.PRO show a slight dip from Distance (5) to Distance (15), followed by a slight rise.

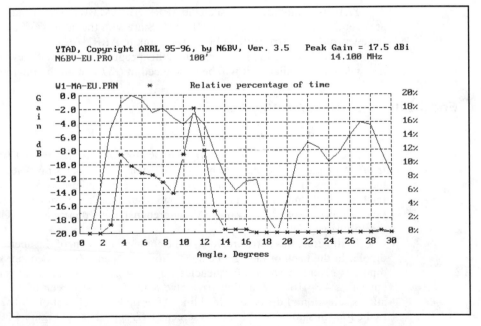

Figure 4.26—The result is a gain peak broadly over 3 to 13°, including the needed angle of 11°. This helps N6BV have a very big signal in Europe.

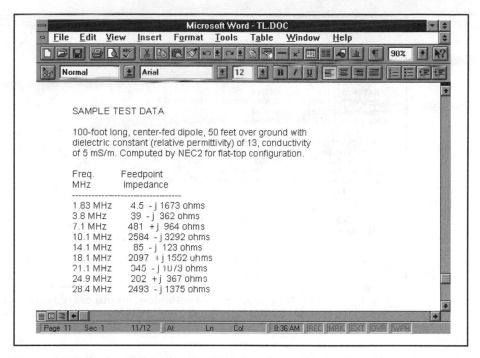

Figure 4.27—As input data for *TL*, this table shows the feedpoint impedance of a 100-foot dipole on various frequencies.

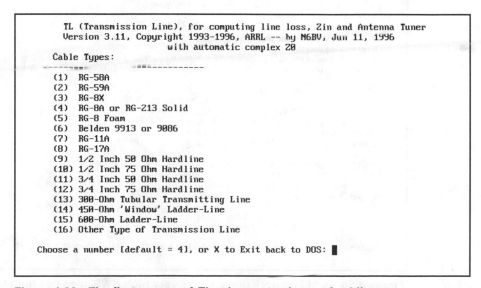

Figure 4.28—The first screen of *TL* asks you to chose a feed line.

```
           TL (Transmission Line), Copyright 1993-1996, ARRL -- by N6BV
                      Version 3.11, Jun 11, 1996
   Length of line:  100.00 ft.
   Frequency:      1.800 MHz
   450-Ohm Window Ladder Line
   Transmission line characteristic impedance:  450.0 - j  3.34 Ohms
   Matched-line loss, dB per 100 ft.:   0.078 dB
   Velocity factor of transmission line: 0.950
   Maximum voltage rating of transmission line: 10000.0 V
   Matched-line attenuation =    0.078 dB

   Resistive part of load impedance at antenna (ohms):  4.5
   Reactive part of  load impedance (- cap., + induct., ohms):  -1673
   SWR at load:       393.83
   SWR at line input:      86.67
   Additional line loss due to SWR:  11.97 dB
   Total line loss:  12.05 dB

   At line input, Zin = 4.91 - j 44.12 Ω = 44.39 Ω at -83.64°
   At 1,500 W, max. rms voltage on line:  7640.4 volts
   Distance from load for peak voltage =    1.9 ft.
   Maximum rms voltage rating of cable: 10000 volts estimated

   Impedance (Z), Frequency (F), Main Menu (M), Antenna Tuner ([T]), Exit (X): ▌
```

Figure 4.29—At a glance, you can see a 100-foot length of ladder line does not do too well when the SWR is very high. The 12 dB loss almost insures very few people will hear you!

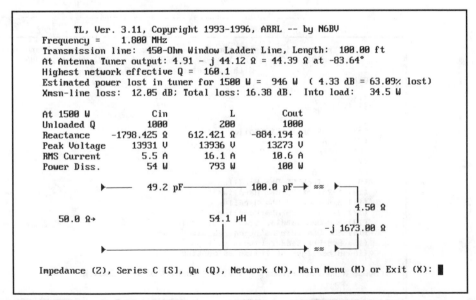

Figure 4.30—A "T" network tuner, under very high SWR, also has high losses. *TL* **allows you to see the effect of changing the feed line on the tuner losses.**

kW applied, the RMS voltage on the line is 7570 V, a rather important situation if someone can get in contact with the line or if you are concerned about the line arcing.

If you are willing to accept this loss, *TL* will go even further by looking at a matching network design. Figure 4.30 is the screen resulting from picking a "T" network tuner (series input cap, an inductance to ground, and a series output cap). The situation here looks even worse, with over 4 dB lost in the tuner. This results in 780 W dissipated in the inductance (for 1500-W input).

Now the real value of TL becomes evident! You can play "What If?" Suppose you think your selection of 450-Ω ladder line is the real problem, and IF you go to "real" open wire line, the losses will come way down. After all, "everyone knows" at HF the losses in open wire line are very low.

Figure 4.31 gives you the answer. Selecting 100 feet of open wire line brings the swr up at both load and line input, and the losses in the line are less. But with the increased SWR the total loss goes down to 6.63 dB—half the loss before, but still not a very good situation.

The net result? In a few minutes, you can really get the message—it is not a good idea to feed a very (electrically) short antenna with a long transmission line, at least for the line type, line length and wavelength tested here. As your antenna *system* design, you may have decided to put up this dipole as high as you can. *TL* tells you not very much power will ever reach your dipole.

TL has several nice features. Most erroneous key presses are trapped, so if you hit a letter or a function key when the program is expecting a number, you don't go off into never-never land. In addition, most inputs have a default value. The default may not be anything close to what you want, but again you don't find yourself into the

```
        TL (Transmission Line), Copyright 1993-1996, ARRL -- by N6BV
                     Version 3.11, Jun 11, 1996
    Length of line:  100.00 ft.
    Frequency:    1.800 MHz
    600-Ohm Open-Wire Ladder Line
    Transmission line characteristic impedance:  600 R - j 1.27 Ohms
    Matched-line loss, dB per 100 ft :  0.022 dB
    Velocity factor of transmission line: 0.970
    Maximum voltage rating of transmission line: 12000.0 V
    Matched-line attenuation =    0.022 dB

    Resistive part of load impedance at antenna (ohms):  4.5
    Reactive part of load impedance (- cap., + induct., ohms):  -1673
    SWR at load:     655.17
    SWR at line input:    247.99
    Additional line loss due to SWR:   6.62 dB
    Total line loss:   6.64 dB

    At line input, Zin = 2.37 - j 24.63 Ω = 24.75 Ω at -84.50°
    At 1,500 W, max. rms voltage on line: 14216.1 volts
    Distance from load for peak voltage =    0.0 ft.
    Maximum rms voltage rating of cable: 12000 volts estimated

    Impedance (Z), Frequency (F), Main Menu (M), Antenna Tuner ([T]), Exit (X): █
```

Figure 4.31—For comparison with Figure 4.29, a slightly better feed line helps, but not very much.

situation of having to close down, re-boot and start over. The current version is a DOS text program, so it should work on most machines. An older machine will simply take longer. Since the program is heavy on number crunching, a *DX* chip or numeric coprocessor is desirable on any older machine.

Other Antenna Design Resources

The ARRL Antenna Book

This is the primary publication for Amateur Radio antenna design and antenna analysis. A disk of software and files is provided, including *YA*—an interactive Yagi analyzer written by Brian Beezley, K6STI. An explanatory .DOC file discuses a number of design points, and approximately 80 design files, optimized for performance, are given to illustrate the use of *YA*. The utility program *SCALE* makes the 80 files even more useful, by allowing you to change the file formats to be compatible with *NEC2, MN* or *AO*.

Many commercial and home-brewed Yagis are made of telescoping tubing. Most designs are based on a constant element diameter, and lengths must be adjusted for the taper encountered with telescoping elements. *TAPER.BAS* provides the information needed to adjust element lengths. Design help for gamma matching is included on the same disk, with the program *GAMMA.BAS*.

Where to Find More Programs

There are quite a number of PC-based antenna design and simulation programs. Many of them are quite specialized and others general and broad. VE3ERP's time-saving freeware programs contain several antenna related programs; most of them are simply implementations in *BASIC* of the equations found in the *ARRL Handbook* and *Antenna Book*. *MicroSmith* and *Physical Design of Yagi Antennas* have companion disks with specialized software (see Appendix C).

The ARRL Antenna Compendium (Volumes 2 and 3) disks contain several programs written in *BASIC*. A number are stored as ASCII files so that you can examine them with any text editor. These sets of programs are good places to start if you want to "roll your own" programs—they will let you see what was being done a few years ago. The disk for Volume 4 of this series has a number of design examples in the form of files for *NEC2, NM, NEC/WIRES, AO* and *ELNEC* programs. Thus the design examples in the book are illustrated by the disk files. The actual NEC2 or other software is not supplied, but if you own one of these, or a compatible successor, you can use the author's files as a starting point for your own antenna design. Volume 5 is the latest of this series. Note the books do not succeed each other—each contains a set of articles and disk programs on a variety of topics considered worth saving for future use in one convenient place. For more information on these books and matching programs, see Appendix C.

One of the best sources for locating the most recent antenna design software is by selectively searching the Internet. Start with the ARRL home page (**http://www.arrl.org/**). Recent ARRL and *QST* offerings will be listed on the Oakland server, and pointers to other sites including extensive ham radio related sites are shown at the ARRL Web page with hot links. See Chapter 6 of this book for more information on the Internet.

Controlling and Calculating

When PCs were new—and relatively expensive—the idea of electrically connecting to this rare and wondrous device was considered very scary. After all, what would happen if you made a mistake and damaged something? What if you actually blew up the entire computer? Repair services were expensive and not readily available. Further, the internal workings were still a mystery to most people, so do-it-yourself repair was not possible.

Today, this mystery is gone. It is very difficult to "blow the whole thing up," and most mistakes are minor and forgiven by the computer. In addition, most interfacing is done through plug-in cards, so if anything is damaged it is usually on an easily replaced card. Books on the internal working of PCs, while expensive—$39.95 to $59.95 is the most common price range—are readily available.

Since PCs are electrically forgiving and flexible—in fact programs are called *soft*ware—there is no reason for hams to avoid directly interfacing with their own PCs. This chapter contains the information you will need on the various *ports*, or I/O (input/output), to allow electrical interconnection. How many times have you said: "I'll bet a computer can do this, and faster than I can by hand." Now you can make your computer do it. The projects included here will give you some ideas to start, and then you can put together your own computer-based ham station, test equipment or accessories.

PORTS, INPUTS AND OUTPUTS

You have probably heard, in one form or another, the story of the origin of the Apple computer. One of the most significant developments associated with this machine was the popularization of the concept of *open architecture*. This meant there was an opportunity for anyone who wanted to build hardware, since the details of the computer were readily available. Everyone knew how their hardware would operate with the computer.

Just think what would happen if the computer details and interfaces were not available to everyone. You would be limited to buying only printers, modems and monitors made specifically for your model computer, and probably only by the manufacturer of your computer. Fortunately, connector standards are so widespread that we can talk about the electrical connections or *interfaces* to a PC and be confident it applies to *all* PCs.

Occasionally there will be an "improvement" or slight change to an existing standard that will not apply to all machines. For example, some parallel printer ports are *bidirectional*—not only do they send out 8 bits of information in parallel, but they can be used to read into the computer an 8-bit input word. Previous generations of computers did not have this feature. In this chapter, only the most common (to both older and newer PCs) interface features are used.

The PC provides a wide choice of connectors and interface possibilities. In Figure 5.1, a PC is drawn to highlight the most commonly available I/O connectors. *LPT1* and *LPT2* are the usual labels for the parallel ports. Typically, one of these ports is connected to a printer. A description of this port and several examples of interface circuits are included later in this chapter.

Older computers contained only two serial ports, *COM1* and *COM2*. Newer machines contain four serial ports. At least one of them is usually devoted to a telephone modem. A special chip that formats the output data to a specific form drives the COM port. The format is called the *RS-232 serial data format*. This means the actual "data out" line on this port may be a bit difficult to use, yet the COM port is widely used for ham applications. This is due to the direct accessibility of the control lines on these ports for both input and output information. As described later in this chapter, these lines are generally used for interfacing.

The game port is also available to external circuits. Since it is connected to several unique timing circuits, it is often used to measure resistance—a game joystick, as plugged into this port, consists of several variable resistors and push-button switches. It was thus one of the earliest ports used by hams to interface with their computers. Some examples are shown in this chapter.

A sound card, often included in a computer package with a CD-ROM player, is specifically designed as an audio I/O device. There is usually a stereo audio input and two speaker output connectors. Newer sound cards are based on *DSP* (digital signal processor) chips, whose function is to analyze audio coming in and synthesize audio to be sent out. The trend described in this chapter is to use this device for ham radio interconnections. Although programming this device can be complex, there is a great deal of information available on the Internet. This fills in the gap left by what the sound card manufacturer does not tell you.

The final common port shown in Figure 5.1 is the telephone modem. The tones used by these common devices are not generally transmitted on the ham bands, due to the mark/space tones used on landline service. Since hams rarely, if ever, use them on the air, they are not covered in this chapter. They are included in the figure to perhaps give you some ideas!

Where Can You Go With PC Control

Since your PC can be used for both calculations and control, applications that require calculating values and then controlling external units can be built. In the March 1995 issue of *QST,* Craig Lee, AA3HM, described a Radio Interface Unit he built to take advantage of his PC (Figure 5.2). Notice he used two COM ports and an LPT port to control a wide variety of HF and VHF station units. His controller is described later in this chapter.

You can use either commercial or shareware software to control your station with a PC. One program, *VisualRadio 2*, is both a control program and database for over a dozen transceivers and receivers. It includes scanning, spectrum analysis and automatic recording into *.WAV* files (see the Resources Chapter for further information).

Robert Schetgen, KU7G (see the Resources Chapter) described a repeater based on a PC in the 1994 edition of *The ARRL Handbook for Radio Amateurs.* Included are 9 flow charts, outlining the software routines needed to control and operate the repeater. The I/O used on the computer is not detailed, since it will depend on the capabilities of the actual computer used.

Figure 5.3 is a flow chart of the main program of this repeater. Most of the terms

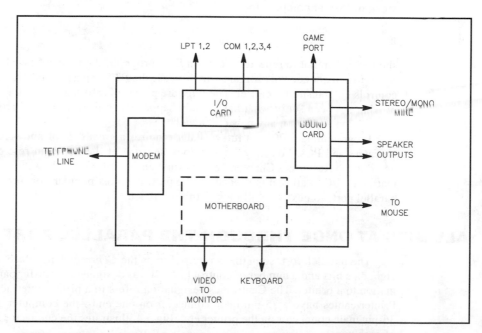

Figure 5.1—Most PCs have these output and input connections. The game port may be connected to the sound card, I/O card or its own bus card.

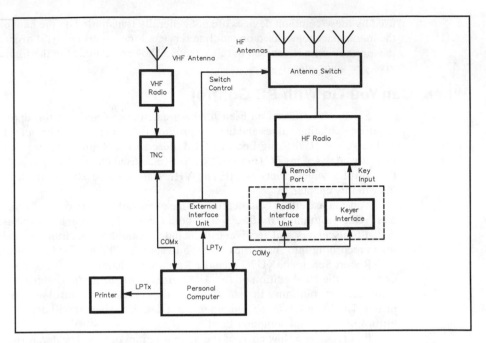

Figure 5.2—A block diagram of a fully automated station. Your setup may be more or less encompassing.

shown are familiar to repeater users. An *Exec* program, shown in a flow chart, usually refers to a major control program—in this case the *PTT* or push-to-talk program—that controls the transmitter carrier. The *flags* are pieces of information used to keep track of what has been set or what has already happened, so the repeater controller knows what action to take on any new command.

Programming a PC as a full repeater requires a great deal of knowledge of both repeaters and PCs. You may want to look at some of the non-ham reference books noted in the Resources Chapter. To perform many simpler tasks, however, some information on I/O is all that is needed. In the past, the most popular port for I/O was the parallel port, so next we will look at this approach.

ALL BITS AT ONCE THROUGH THE PARALLEL PORT

The parallel port, sometimes referred to as the *Centronics* interface, consists of eight data bits and a number of control lines. It was designed to transfer parallel information to a printer. The Centronics designation refers to a printer interface standard. Printer cables have a 25-pin male connector on one end—the computer end—and a 36-pin male connector on the printer end. Fig 5.4 illustrates the connector and the use of each wire.

The data bits are numbered 0 through 7. Pins 18 though 25 are grounds. For most

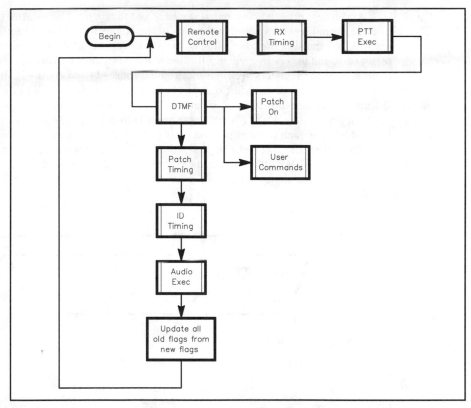

Figure 5.3—Before writing the actual software for any major function, most programmers draw a flow chart. This chart includes the main program flow for the PC-based repeater.

ham radio use, only one of these wires is needed, since they carry low level signal returns. The other wires carry control signals that are used to transfer information— some out of the computer and some in.

Signals listed with an overscore, such as $\overline{A}$, are inverted for use in a printer interface. These are *logical* inversions, and do not affect our use of the signal. *Electrically* inverted signals are discussed later in the text.

The Parallel Port In Electronic Space

All computer ports and most other computer devices have an address on the internal computer data bus. By looking at this address, and often adjacent addresses, the ports and devices may be controlled and monitored. These addresses may be given either in decimal notation or in hex (hexadecimal). Since many programming languages require hex notation, this chapter will refer to many addresses in hex. Standard notation uses a simple number, such as 345, as a decimal address. When a lower-case *h* follows the number, such as 232h, it is a hex number.

An address often has two parts, the *base* and the *offset*. The parallel port consists of three digital registers wired to the pins of the connector. The first register, the *data resister,* is located at the base address, the *status* register at the base address with an offset of 1, and the *control* register located at the base address with an offset of 2. The addresses of the registers are therefore (base), (base+1) and (base+2). If the base is given in hex notation, the addition must be in hex. For example, 7h+4h = Bh. See the sidebar for more information on binary and hex number systems.

Gary Sutcliffe, W9XT, wrote a program called *FINDLPT* to help you find the base address of each parallel port on your computer. A copy of *FINDLPT.BAS* is on the ARRL BBS and Internet file sites, in the *QEX* directory. Older computers, with older versions of DOS, normally had only two LPT ports. Newer computers and operating systems can support four LPT ports, numbered consecutively as LPT1, LPT2, LPT3 and LPT4.

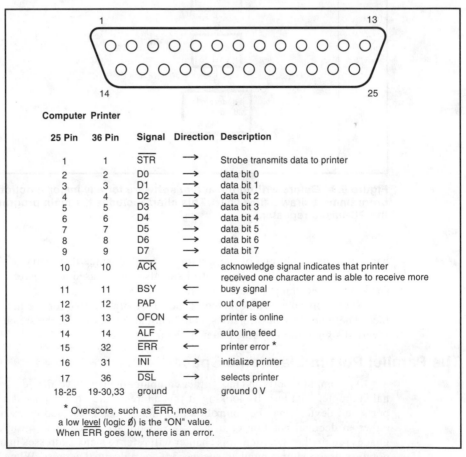

Computer	Printer			
25 Pin	36 Pin	Signal	Direction	Description
1	1	$\overline{STR}$	→	Strobe transmits data to printer
2	2	D0	→	data bit 0
3	3	D1	→	data bit 1
4	4	D2	→	data bit 2
5	5	D3	→	data bit 3
6	6	D4	→	data bit 4
7	7	D5	→	data bit 5
8	8	D6	→	data bit 6
9	9	D7	→	data bit 7
10	10	$\overline{ACK}$	←	acknowledge signal indicates that printer received one character and is able to receive more
11	11	BSY	←	busy signal
12	12	PAP	←	out of paper
13	13	OFON	←	printer is online
14	14	$\overline{ALF}$	→	auto line feed
15	32	$\overline{ERR}$	←	printer error *
16	31	$\overline{INI}$	→	initialize printer
17	36	$\overline{DSL}$	→	selects printer
18-25	19-30,33	ground		ground 0 V

* Overscore, such as $\overline{ERR}$, means a low level (logic Ø) is the "ON" value. When ERR goes low, there is an error.

Figure 5.4—A parallel or printer port usually has a 25-pin connector. When connected to a printer, the other end of the cable has a 36-pin connector.

Number Systems

Personal computers are based on a number system that can be derived from having only two values, 0 and 1, in each column (digit) of the number. Compare this with the normal decimal number system (base 10) we use daily. Each digit in a decimal numbering system has a value from 0 to 9 (a total of 10 possible values), and it is multiplied by the power of 10 corresponding to the column of the number. As an example, the number 723 has a 3 in the rightmost column. Therefore the number contains 3 multiplied by 10^0. The expression 10^0 is equal to 1, so a 3 in the right most column has a value of $3 \times 1 = 3$. For the number 723, we have:

$3 \times 10^0 = 3 \times 1 = 3$ (right hand column)   72**3**

$2 \times 10^1 = 2 \times 10 = 20$ (next column)   7**2**3

$7 \times 10^2 = 7 \times 100 = 700$ (left column)   **7**23

The total number is therefore 700+20+3=723

Each column, starting from the left, has a value corresponding to a power of the *base* of the number system— in our example a power of 10. For an octal base system, powers of 8 are used. The right hand column would be a multiple of $8^0 = 1$, the next column $8^1 = 8$, the third column $8^2 = 64$ and so on. In a decimal system, the numbers ranged from 0 to 9, a total of 10 possible numbers. In the octal system, the numbers range from 0 through 7, a total of 8 possible numbers. The number 723 in octal, translated to decimal, would be worth:

$3 \times 8^0 = 3 \times 1 = 3$ (right hand column)   72**3**

$2 \times 8^1 = 2 \times 8 = 16$ (next column)   7**2**3

$7 \times 8^2 = 7 \times 64 = 448$ (left column)   **7**23

The total number is therefore 448+16+3=467 in decimal.

In a binary system, only two values are possible, 0 and 1. A binary number would consist of a string of digits such as 1101. Translated in decimal, 1101 is

$1 \times 2^0 = 1 \times 1 = 1$ (right hand column)   110**1**

$0 \times 2^1 = 0 \times 2 = 0$ (next column)   11**0**1

$1 \times 2^2 = 1 \times 4 = 4$ (next column)   1**1**01

$1 \times 2^3 = 1 \times 8 = 8$ (left most column)   **1**101

The total number is therefore 8+4+0+1=13 in decimal.

In place of using long strings of 1's and 0's, the *hex* (hexadecimal) system is often used. A single hex digit is 4 digital bits long. These four bits (one *nibble*) can stand for any number from 0 to 15. Since we want to represent any of these values in just one column, the 16 possible digits, 0,1,2,3,...9,A,B,C,D,E,F are used to represent the values from 0 to 15.

Since one hex digit is one nibble, two hex digits would be eight bits (two nibbles) or one byte. Hex values are often used to express memory locations or ASCII character values in a PC, and are normally are written in a form such as *3Dh*. The characters *3* and *D* are the hex digits. The *h* does not have a value, but just indicates this is a hex number.

Parallel Port Addresses

Data Register—Located at the Base Address

Bit 0	Output at connector pin 2
Bit 1	Output at connector pin 3
Bit 2	Output at connector pin 4
Bit 3	Output at connector pin 5
Bit 4	Output at connector pin 6
Bit 5	Output at connector pin 7
Bit 6	Output at connector pin 8
Bit 7	Output at connector pin 9

Status Register—Located at the Base Address + 1

Bit 0	Undefined
Bit 1	Undefined
Bit 2	Undefined
Bit 3	ERROR-Input at connector pin 15
Bit 4	SLCT -Input at connector pin 13
Bit 5	PE-Input at connector pin 12
Bit 6	ACK-Input at connector pin 10
Bit 7	BUSY-Input at connector pin 11

Control Register—Located at the Base Address + 2

Bit 0	STROBE-Output at connector pin 1
Bit 1	AUTOLF-Output at connector pin 14
Bit 2	INIT-Output at connector pin 16
Bit 3	SCLTIN-Output at connector pin 17
Bit 4	Interrupt enable, internal connection
Bit 5	undefined
Bit 6	undefined
Bit 7	undefined

Typical LPT port addresses are 3BCh, 2BCh, 378h and 278h. Each register consists of the individual bits of an 8-bit binary number. The bit values for each wire of the parallel port are shown in the sidebar. Thus, if you sent the binary equivalent of decimal 3—00000011—to the register located at the base address, data bits 0 and 1 will be set high, and data bits 2 though 7 set low. The binary word printed above consists of the data bits 7 thorough 0, with bit 7 on the left and bit 0 on the right.

By changing the value of the word you send this register, you can make the individual bits go high and low, and thus place either +5 V or 0 V on the individual pins. For the previous example, pins 2 and 3 will have +5 V on them, and pins 4 through 9 have 0 V or ground.

The register at the address of (base+1)—the status register—is used to look at external information. Thus, you can place +5 V or 0 V from your external circuit on a pin, read the register values, and decode the voltage on the pin. Normally only bits 3 through 7 of this register are used. Bit 7 of this register is wired inverted. A 0 on this pin will decode as a logical 1.

Since the register is an 8-bit register, the values of each bit are 1, 2, 4, 8, 16, 32, 64 and 128. If the register was a normal binary register, the first three bits would have a cumulative value of 1+2+4=7. Since these pins are meaningless, and not used, any value taken from the register must ignore these three lower bits.

Figure 5.5A illustrates one example. If bit 7 was not inverted, the connector wired as shown would result in a logical 1 on pin 11 (bit 7, or 2^7=128). Since bits 0 through 2 are undefined, any value from 128 to 128+7 = 135 would tell you the connector is wired as shown, with +5 only on bit 7.

Since bit 7 is inverted, it acts opposite to the normal convention. As shown, when bit 7 is tied to +5 (logical one), it acts in the register as a logical 0. Wired as shown, the connector will result in a value in the register of 0 to 7. To generate a value of 128 (to 128+7), the connector port must be connected as shown in Figure 5.5B.

Bit 6 of this register has a special interrupt function. It may be sagely used, without any interrupt problems, as long as the value sent to the final register, the control register, is limited to 15 or less—allowing use of only the 4 lower bits of the control register.

The control register, located at the address (base +2), provides additional output pins. Bits 0, 1 and 3 are wired inverted. Writing a decimal value of 1 to this register

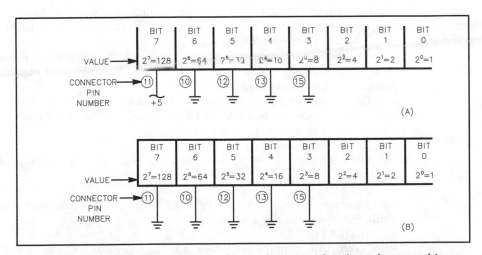

Figure 5.5—In A, this status register for a printer port has been jumpered to an input of 1000XXX, where X is no connection. Since the most significant bit is inverted, B gives a real value of 0000XXX. For the result of these inputs, see the text.

will result in keeping the bit 0 low. To place +5 V on pin 1 (bit 0), you must write a value of 0 (or any even number) to the register.

Bit 4 is a special bit, tied to the interrupt system and controlled by pin 6 of the status register. It is best to avoid this bit, unless you mean to control an interrupt. To avoid generating an interrupt, never send a value of more than 1+2+4+8=15 to the register.

In total, the data register plus the control register provide a total of 8+4 or 12 individually addressable output pins on the LPT connector. The status register provides 5 addressable input pins. This port operates on nominal +5/0 V dc or TTL levels. You can connect directly with the pins and external TTL circuits, or you can use an interface unit such as that designed by W9XT (see the Resources Chapter for more information). Generally, the LPT port will drive about 10 feet of cable without needing buffer amplifiers.

Interface Programming

Most common computer languages can be used to address the parallel port directly. Each language has its own syntax, its own tools for writing and debugging a program and its own advantages and disadvantages. Some, such as *assembly language* and *C*, are generally credited with allowing very fast computer operations.

One of the older computer languages is *BASIC*. It was distributed in many varieties, and often was included with new releases of the Microsoft or IBM DOS (disk operating system). In its plain vanilla form it is an *interpreted* language—the computer reads the English-like program statements and converts them to machine operations on the spot.

The oldest IBM PCs reverted to a variety of BASIC—often referred to as *IBM BASIC* or *BASICA*—when certain system failures occurred. *GWBASIC, QBASIC* and *QUICK BASIC* are other popular BASIC packages.

In this book, for many programming examples, a vanilla BASIC will be used. This allows explanation of the program to non-programmers in an English-like language. Since so many BASIC packages are readily available at no cost, it also allows experimentation without investing in a language package. If you like to use *C, C+++*, or any other language to duplicate the programs, feel free—just observe the usual precautions in using correct syntax.

The addresses given here are in hex. Most BASIC programs accept hex notation in their commands, but be cautious. For example, the *GWBASIC* command to write information to an address takes the form of:

OUT *address, data*

where the address may be in hex form. For example, you might think the command

OUT 278h, 100

would write the decimal value 100 the hex address 278. Unfortunately, this statement would result in the dreaded message:

SYNTAX ERROR

since GWBASIC requires hex numbers in the form **&H278**. The correct command would be:

OUT &H278, 100

Interface Testing

If you have never connected your own circuit to a PC port, the breadboard adapter in Figure 5.6 is a good starting point. It consists of a male DB-25 connector wired to a terminal strip. Pins 1 to 17 are connected to the terminal strip. Pins 18 through 25 are all grounds, so only one of them—pin 25—is connected to the strip. The male DB-25 was selected to mate with a printer extension cable, which in turn plugs into the female 25-pin printer port connector on the computer.

Often flea markets will provide a printer extension cable for the same or less money than the cost of a new DB-25 connector. You can choose to cut off the female connector and replace it with a terminal strip. The male connector remaining will then plug directly into the parallel port on your computer.

The tutorials for most computer languages usually begin with showing you how to write "HELLO WORLD" on your monitor. The equivalent, for a first step in interfacing to a PC, is to wire the two LEDs and resistors as shown in Figure 5.7. Connect the resistors to pins 2 and 3 and the common connection of the LEDs to pin 25. You now can monitor bits 0 and 1 of the data word from the parallel port.

Figure 5.6—If you are going to experiment with interfacing to the parallel port, you probably will want to make a connector-to-terminal strip adapter. It will save you a great deal of time later, wiring and rewiring a cable connector!

The first step requires you to determine the address of your parallel port. Fire up your copy of *BASIC, GWBASIC* or what ever you have and then run *FINDLPT.BAS*. This will tell you the address of your port. If you wish, you can use *MSD.EXE*, the Microsoft systems analysis program that comes with later versions of DOS, or any commercial equivalent, such as *CheckIt*, to determine these addresses.

For this example, the address used for the parallel port is 378h. Just substitute the correct address for your machine when you run your test.

The LEDs are wired to the lowest two bits of the data register. Therefore, with

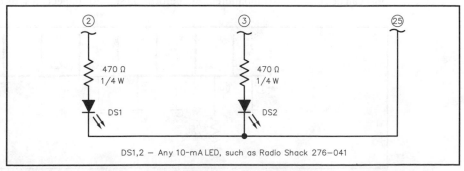

Figure 5.7—Two LEDs and two resistors are all you need to run a quick check on your parallel port interfacing hardware and program.

BASIC running, the command:

OUT &H378,0

will place 0s on all bits, including the lower two—so neither LED will be on.

OUT &H378,1

will set only the lower or 0 bit, so the LED wired to pin 2 will come on. Sending out a 2 will set the second bit, so the LED wired to pin 3 will be on, and finally sending out a 3 will turn both LEDs on. Congratulations—you have now done the equivalent of writing "HELLO WORLD" in a new language!

To access the bits of the third register, the control register, you must change the address. This register has an offset of 2 so add 2 (in hex) to the data register address. For this example, 378h+2h = 37Ah. The command would then be

OUT &H37A, 1

to set the lowest bit of this register to a value of +5 V.

The remaining register, the status register, has an offset of 1 so its address is 378h +1h = 379h. It is an input register, used to test the value of the signal connected to its last 5 bits. For a first experiment with this register, connect pin 11 (bit 7 of the status register) to ground (remember it is wired internally inverted). The decimal value of this pin is 2^7 or 128. Connect a 470-Ω resistor from pin 10 (2^6 or 64) to +5 V, and pins 12, 13 and 15 (Figure 5.8) to ground (pin 25).

As described earlier, the lower 3 bits of this register are indeterminate, giving an ambiguity of decimal 7 for each time you read the value of this register. Wired as shown, bits 7 and 6 are enabled (logical 1s), with a total value of 128+64=192—plus a possible addition of 7 for the lower 3 bits. To examine the contents of the register, the command:

PRINT INP(&H379)

will print the decimal value on the screen—in this case a number between 192 and 192+7.

A little hint might be in order—since very little current will be drawn by the resistor connected to pin 11, you can get +5 V from this connector.

OUT &H378,1

will set only the lower bit, so pin 2 will have +5 V on it.

By changing the connections of the 5 pins wired to this register, you can see the effect on the decimal value printed on your monitor. Thus the state or voltage on each of these 5 pins can be continuously monitored. But before you start to connect all sorts of switches to

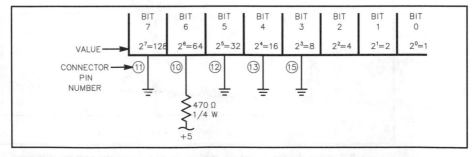

Figure 5.8—These connections to the status register will set the register to a decimal value of 192 to 199.

these pins, read the balance of this chapter on voltages, switch bounce and isolating your computer. For one approach to using a parallel port as a general purpose input/output device, see the reference to the material written by W9XT in the Resources Chapter.

The Weekend DigiVFO—a Parallel Port Application

James Craswell, WBØVNE, owned a 1980-vintage HF transceiver. Its analog VFO has always drifted noticeably during warm-up. To eliminate the drift and to allow working "split"—transmitting on one frequency and receiving on another—he designed this *direct digital synthesis* (DDS) VFO. It was first described in the May 1995 issue of *QST*.

Unused Bits and Signal Purity

What about those four unused bits? How can we get away with just ignoring them? A true sine wave contains energy at only one frequency, but the DigiVFO's DAC puts out some weak, unwanted (spurious) signals besides the strong, single-frequency signal desired. (Analog VFOs are not perfect, either, by the way.) The more bits of the HSP45102's output you use, the more closely the DAC's output can approach sine-wave purity. (Depending on your application, some additional output filtering might also be needed. In this case, none is needed, which simplifies the design.) In other words, the more bits of U1's output data you use, the weaker U2's spurious outputs will generally be relative to the single-frequency output signal desired. A 10-bit DAC would provide somewhat cleaner output and a 12-bit DAC would generate a sine wave even closer to a true sine wave. In this application, finer data resolution would have been overkill. Filtering in a typical transceiver's circuitry pretty much does away with the DigiVFO's weak spurs in the 5-MHz region and entirely does away with the circuit's higher-frequency spurs.

The DigiVFO can be commanded to put out RF at any frequency up to 20 MHz. This makes it attractive as a general-purpose signal source for experimentation and testing. If you're interested in using the DigiVFO to drive a transmitter or receiver mixer directly, you'll probably need to filter its output. In addition to various weak spurs—whose numbers and absolute frequencies vary as the DigiVFO's output frequency varies—the unfiltered output of the DigiVFO's DAC includes energy at these frequencies:

- the desired signal (fundamental) and its harmonics
- the clock (40 MHz) and its harmonics
- aliases of the fundamental (the clock plus and minus the fundamental)
- clock harmonics plus and minus the fundamental
- intermodulation products generated within the DAC's linear circuitry

In short, the DigiVFO should not be fed right into an antenna! At output frequencies up 10 MHz or so, filtering no more complex than what you need to make a Class C amplifier comply with Part 97's purity-of-emissions rules will probably be enough for transmission purposes. (See *The ARRL Handbook for Radio Amateurs,* Filters and Projects chapter, for the filter designs and component values needed to comply with the FCC requirements. The CA3338's output impedance is about 160 Ω for filter design purposes.)

The closer the DigiVFO's output signal gets to 20 MHz (half the clock frequency), the closer its lowest alias (an unavoidable artifact of DDS) approaches 20 MHz from the high side. If, for example, you tell the DigiVFO to output 19.1 MHz, the alias comes out at 20.9 MHz, and is almost as strong as the fundamental. Simple low-pass filtering won't be able to eliminate one of two signals this close together.

Figure 5.9 shows the DigiVFO's entire schematic. It is based on a DDS IC, fed by a stable crystal-controlled clock signal (40 MHz in this circuit). By programming a few control pins through the parallel port of a PC, you can select whatever frequency you want up to 20 MHz! The steps can be as small as 0.009 Hz, and there are no circuits to tune or PLL problems.[1]

The DDS chip (U1, a Harris HSP45102PC-40) generates a stream of data words describing how the amplitude and phase of the DigiVFO's output signal should change

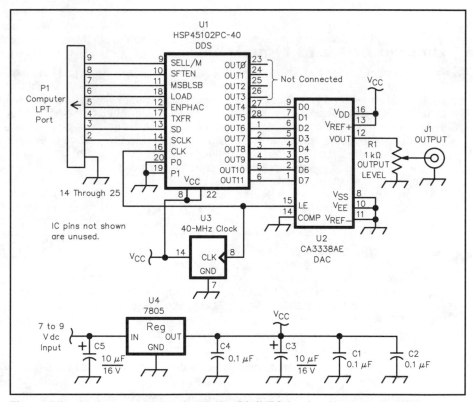

Figure 5.9—At the component level, the DigiVFO is simpler than the analog external VFO it replaces. The 0.1-μF capacitors are 50-V monolithic ceramics, and the polarized capacitors are tantalum electrolytics. (Connect C1 between common and pin 8 of U1; C2 between common and pin 16 of U2.) A complete kit of parts is available; see Note 4.

P1—PC-mount male DB-25 connector.
R1—1-kΩ, 10-turn trimmer potentiometer.
U1—HSP45102PC-40 12-bit numerically controlled oscillator IC (Harris Semiconductor).
U2—CA3338AE 8-bit video DAC IC with voltage output (Harris Semiconductor).
U3—40-MHz, TTL-output clock module, 14-pin DIP.
U4—7805 5-V, 1-A voltage-regulator IC (equip this part with a heat sink).

over time. U2, a CA3338AE digital-to-analog converter (DAC), translates these digital words into a stepped-dc signal that closely approximates a sine wave.

The HSP45102PC-40's output consists of 12-bit data words, so the '45102 has 12 data output pins (OUT0 through OUT11). The DigiVFO circuit uses an 8-bit DAC, and its eight input pins (D0 through D7) connect to the eight U1 output pins (OUT4 through OUT11) that convey the eight most significant bits of U1's output data. See the sidebar for a discussion of the unused bits.

Control Software

Two programs, *SIG_GEN* and *DigiVFO*, to control the DigiVFO through an IBM-PC compatible's line-printer (LPT) port, as well as several supplementary files, can be downloaded from the ARRL BBS (*QST* directory) and Internet sites. *SIG_GEN* is written in Microsoft *QBASIC*. Its primary purpose is control of the DigiVFO as a general-purpose signal generator.

SIG_GEN includes a routine to control the DigiVFO as a sweep generator, but at relatively slow sweep rates. Inspecting the *QBASIC* source code can help you understand how to make the DDS play in your application.

You can use *SIG_GEN* to control the DigiVFO as substitute for remote VFOs of various types. Doing so requires some thought, though, because the frequencies you enter will probably be only indirectly related to the operating frequency you want. For example, the TR-7A's VFO tunes from 5.05 to 5.55 MHz as the radio's actual operating frequency moves from x.000 to x.500, or x.500 to x.000 MHz. Using *SIG_GEN* would therefore require entering 5.253000 MHz if you want to tune the TR-7A to 7.203 MHz—not the sort of mental arithmetic that makes for fast frequency changes! The second program, *DigiVFO*, solves this problem (for the TR-7A) by taking this arithmetic into account.

Construction

The prototype of this project was built on perfboard, and therefore can be duplicated using this simple method of construction. Ground-plane or wire-wrap construction also can be used. An etched, drilled PC board is available by itself or as part of a kit of DigiVFO components. The completed board is shown in Figure 5.10.

The DigiVFO should be placed in a metal enclosure and connected to your radio and computer with shielded cables. Any digital device including a 40-MHz clock and a digital IC with over 32 kilo transistors produces significant RF noise if it's not well shielded!

For information on printed circuit boards and the needed software, see the References Chapter.

Figure 5.10—One board—and not an inductor in sight—produced a modern, PC-controlled VFO.

Operation

R1 is the OUTPUT LEVEL control. To set it to the center of its range for initial tests, turn it 10 turns in one direction and then 5 turns back. It should be adjusted to

Another Application

WJ1Z has successfully used the DigiVFO to drive a Kenwood TS-130V transceiver, whose VFO tunes from 5.500 to 6.000 MHz as the radio's operating frequency moves from x.500 to x.000 or from x.000 to x.500 MHz. (Program and/or DigiVFO hardware changes would be necessary to meet the TS-130V's need for an 800-Hz VFO shift during CW transmission, however.) The VFO-frequency-to-operating-frequency relationship is even more complicated for radios with VFOs that move *up* as the operating frequency moves *down*. You can contact the author, WBØVNE, to discuss this project and software questions. See the Resources Chapter for contact information.

A New Golden Age of Equipment Design

This project is typical of many newer equipment designs that either take advantage of PCs in the ham shack or use embedded microcontrollers. The result is a large amount of functionality with very few parts.

Compare this direct digital synthesizer's schematic with that of any "normal" VFO, and you'll see the DigiVFO is easily the simpler design. Best of all, there are no nasty inductors to wind! Yet, some readers may say that the circuit's simplicity is deceptive because its ICs' internal workings are so complex. Who's right?

Perhaps "Whose view is more useful?" might be a better question. I remember the good old days when it seemed like everyone was complaining how the newfangled ICs were too complex, and no one could work on their rigs any more. I can also remember insisting on seeing the schematic of what was inside some "big" linear IC before I could imagine working with it. When I eventually saw the full circuit—thirty or forty transistors!—it boggled my mind. It made no sense to me at all because I allowed its complexity to overwhelm me. What I should have done was *take the IC's overall operation at face value and start building something with it!*

I honestly believe we are in a new golden age of equipment design. But getting in on the action takes a willingness to use new tools, such as the personal computer. With a program called *CIRCAD*, for instance, I can use my computer to draw schematics, make mechanical drawings and lay out PC boards. With another program called *TASM*, I can program little microprocessors—and a program called *PLD* lets me design new glue (gate array logic—GAL) parts. Then there are programs like *SPICE* and *ARRL Radio Designer*—programs that let you prototype, simulate and optimize the performance of *entire circuits* in your computer before you ever pick up a soldering iron.

So let's put to rest the idea that 1990s gear is too hard to design, and that 1990s parts are too hard to design with. Parts like the Harris HSP45102 allow us to design big sections of our gear with simple building blocks. (Did you know you can get a superhet receiver minus the audio stage and a few miscellaneous parts on *one* chip? Troubleshooting a radio like that has to be pretty simple.)

I must admit that this Harris *numerically controlled oscillator* (what a mouthful) overwhelmed me at first. According to its spec sheet, the HSP45102 contains 32,528 transistors! But after I prototyped the DigiVFO circuit on perfboard and got it to generate output, I forgot the '45102's internal complexity and put it to work!—*WBØVNE* give the same output as the VFO being replaced. With R1 set to maximum, the DigiVFO's peak output is just a few tens of millivolts less than 5 V, with a strong dc component. In some applications, a blocking capacitor may be required to remove the dc component.

The *DigiVFO* software commands are quite simple. Up arrow increases the frequency; down arrow decreases the frequency. The keyboard's numeric-keypad + and – keys change the DigiVFO's step size. The smaller steps sound so smooth you may think you've built an analog VFO! With larger steps (100 Hz and greater), the radio's tuning steps musically through the band.

DigiVFO also lets you directly enter an operating frequency. Hit the **D** key and type in the digits from the right of the decimal point of your target frequency in megahertz. For example, let's say you want to go to 14.1798 MHz. Type **D 1 7 9 8 0 0 0 0** and you're on frequency!

The *DigiVFO* system includes memory storage. Each frequency is saved by hitting the S (for Save) key and pressing one of the keyboard's function keys (**F1** through **F10**). Then, hitting the same function key again immediately moves the rig to that frequency.

Other Parallel Port Applications

Another parallel port VFO design was described by Peter Anderson, KC1HR, in the January 1996 issue of *QEX*. For information on this publication, see the Resources Chapter.

The parallel port is a natural connection for PC-based test equipment, and commercial manufacturers widely advertise their products to connected to this port. For a view of a two-chip adapter to turn the port into a 1-Hz to 5-MHz frequency counter, see the 1995 article in *EDN Magazine* listed in the Resources Chapter.

PICK A NUMBER FROM 1 TO 4—COM1, COM2, COM3, COM4

The *COM ports,* or serial ports, is an area of a PC where the inability to stay *backwards compatible* is a constraint on the PC's usefulness. Backwards compatible refers to the ability of old software to work on the new machine, and the ability of some new software to work on old ones. COM ports, just as parallel ports, have an address, and the most common COM port addresses are listed in the sidebar. (In this chapter, the terms *COM port* and *serial port* are used interchangeably.)

Figure 5.11 illustrates the wiring of a serial connector, and gives a good view of the operation of a COM port. In this book the focus will be on what we can do with these signals. If you are interested in the functions as a standard computer serial port, connected to a matching serial device, one of the references in the Resources Chapter will introduce you to the ins and outs of *DTR, DSR, DCD* and the entire control concept of a serial port.

Both the older connection system (a 25-pin connector) and the newer (a 9-pin connector) contain wires labeled *Receive Data (RX)* and *Transmit Data (TX)*. These are the primary data wires for the serial port. Unfortunately, they are connected to a preprogrammed chip that formats the data one specific way, and most programming information for this port provides instructions for loading and unloading this preformatted data. There is little, if any, choice on the use of these two wires unless you are using the port as a direct serial port, conforming to an industry standard known as RS-232 or EIA-232. Whenever you see a similar number—RS-232, 232A, B, C or D, EIA-232, EIA/RS-232—they refer to one or another version of the serial data transmission standard used on the COM port of all PCs.

In a PC, this I/O ability is constructed using a *UART*—a universal asynchronous receiver transmitter—with the 8250, 16450 and 16550 the most popular chips used.

Programmable Wires on a COM Port

The COM port does give a capability similar to that of the parallel port. There is an address, also called the base address, and two registers with offsets from the base address. By addressing these two registers, you can use two pins on the conn- ector for output from the port and four pins for output from the port and four pins for inputs.

The sidebar lists the *modem control register* at the base address (assuming COM1) 3F8h plus the offset (04h). Therefore, writing information to the sum of these two numbers, 3FCh, will direct the information to this register. Pin 4 is the lowest bit and pin 7 the next bit, allowing you to control these two output wires in 4 possible combinations—00, 01, 10 and 11. Similarly, the *modem status register* is at 3F8h + 06h or 3FEh, and bits 4,5,6 and 7 may be decoded.

You can repeat the HELLO WORLD test, described in the section on the parallel port, by changing a few addresses. To make this test on your PC, increase the series resistor for the test LED to about 1k, to limit the current through the LED. For COM1 and the outputs on the modem control register:

OUT &H3FC, 1

sets the lowest bit of this register to a logical 1. An LED (with its series resistor) connected between pin 4 (bit 0) and pin 5 (ground), will turn on. A second LED resistor combination, connected between pin 7 (bit 1) and pin 5 will show the state of the second bit. You can cycle the four possible values of 00, 01, 10 and 11 by changing the value of the **OUT** command—the **1** after the comma—to 0,1,2 or 3.

The modem status register has an offset of 06h, so its address is 3FEh. Since it is an input register, you can use it to test the value of the signals connected to its last 4 bits. Just as with the parallel port, this input register has its lower bits undefined for our purposes, so in this case there is an ambiguity of $2^0+2^1+2^2+2^3=15$. Thus, any number read from this register must be rounded off by a value less than 16.

The command:

PRINT INP(&H3FE)

COM Port Base Addresses

COM Port addresses are usually assigned paired with an interrupt. Although variations are common, the following pairs are good starting points:

Com	Address	Interrupt
1	3F8h	IRQ4
2	2F8h	IRQ3
3	3E8h	IRQ4
4	2E8h	IRQ3

COM Port Addressable Registers

Modem Control Register at offset 04h			Modem Status Register at offset 06h		
Pin	*Bit*	*Name*	*Pin*	*Bit*	*Name*
7	1	RTS	8	4	CTS
4	0	DTR	6	5	DSR
			9	6	RI
			1	7	DCD

will print the decimal value of the register contents on the screen. You can test it by connecting a series resistor of 1 kW from ground or +12 to the pins in various combinations and reading the value on the screen.

For example, grounding the resistors connected to pins 8, 6 and 9 and connecting the resistor on pin 1 (bit 7 or 2^7) to +12 will produce a value of 128 in the register—plus a possible addition of a number of 15 or less. Thus by making these connections, you can see a number from 128 to 128+15 printed on the screen.

The same hint is in order here, if you are looking for a source of +12 V. Again, since very little current will be drawn by the resistor connected to pin 1, you can get +12 V from this connector by using the **OUT** command to make pin 4 or 7 a logical *1*.

The Electrical Interface of the COM Port

Unlike the parallel port, the serial port is not compatible with 5-volt TTL logic. The value of a logical *1* is a positive voltage greater than +5 V, and the value of a logical *0* is not ground but a negative voltage. Older serial ports allowed voltage swings as large as +25 V and −25 V. Under a later industry specification, RS-232C, a *1* for outputs can be any value from +5 to +15 V, and a *0* for outputs −5 to −15 V. The port must respond to input signals as low as +3 V for a *1* and −3 V for a *0*. **Warning: Voltages as high as ±25 V may appear, even on newer computers that are supposed to follow the latest EIA-232 standard!** Still other computers, while claiming -232 performance, are built with 0/+5V serial ports.

To use the COM port as a general control port, you must provide an interface to convert the RS-232 voltages to those your external circuitry can use. In addition, you may have to convert your 25-pin serial connector to a 9-pin equivalent, or your 9-pin to a 25-pin. Figure 5.11 is a schematic of the wiring needed to assemble a converting cable from a 25-pin serial connector to a 9-pin serial connector. Unlike the parallel port, which is limited to cable lengths of about 10 feet, the serial port is normally okay with cable lengths up to 50 feet.

A Single-Chip COM Port Converter

Often, external commercial equipment can be connected to a serial port, but they need TTL levels rather than +15 to −15-V signals. Several microcircuit manufacturers have recognized this need, and produce chips specifically for this purpose. TI pro-

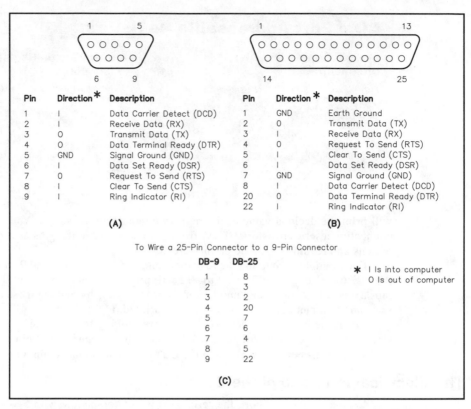

Figure 5.11—Newer PCs generally use a 9-pin connector, and older PCs a 25-pin connector. Wiring for a 9 to 25-pin converter is given in C.

duces the SN75C188 quad line driver chip, which accepts TTL signals and converts them to EIA-232. The complementary chip, the SN75C189, converts the EIA-232 bipolar signal it receives to TTL. Maxim Corporation offers its MAX232 and MAX233 interface chips. These chips and others are available from most electronic supply houses. See the Resources Chapter for suggested sources.

The controller built by Craig Lee, AA3HM (*QST*, March 1995), uses a Maxim Corporation MAX231CPD chip. To monitor and control his HF radio, an interface translator converts the RS-232 output of the PC serial port to the TTL level required by the radio. This is a simple device, easily constructed in a couple of evenings for less than $10. The interface works perfectly with the ICOM rigs and should work well with others—and it replaces controllers available commercially for $50 to $100!

One Chip Does Most of The Work

The interface schematic is shown in Figure 5.12. It makes use of a Maxim dual RS-232 receiver/driver IC, and operates from supply voltages of +5 V dc, and +7 to +15 V dc. It all fits within a 25-pin D-subminiature shell that attaches to the PC serial

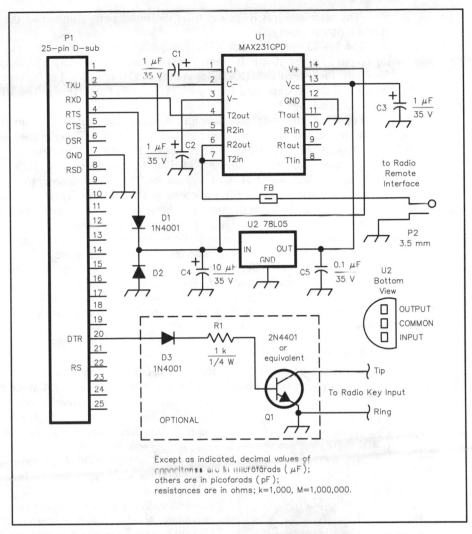

Figure 5.12—Schematic diagram of the computer/radio interface. A 25-pin connector is shown. If you need a 9-pin connector, see the wiring in Figure 5.11.

C1, C2, C3—1-μF, 35-V tantalum capacitor (Digi-Key P2059).
C4—10-μF, 35-V disc-ceramic capacitor.
D1, D2, D3—1N4001 diode (D3 is optional; see text).
FB—Ferrite bead (Digi-Key P9822ND).
P1—25-pin female, solder cup (Digi-Key 225F-ND) and 25-pin metallized hood (Digi-Key 925 GM-ND).
P2—3.5-mm male power plug (Digi-Key CP-3501-ND).
Q1—2N4401 transistor (optional; see text).
R1—1-kΩ, 1/4-W resistor (optional; see text).
U1—Maxim MAX231 (Digi-Key MAX231 CPD-ND).
U2—78L05, 5-V, 100-mA voltage regulator (Digi-Key AN78L05).

port. The interface gets its power from the serial port, eliminating the need for an external power supply.

The RS-232 transmit data (TXD) output of the PC is connected to the receiver input (pin 5) in the Maxim IC, which provides a corresponding TTL output on pin 6. Similarly, the receive data (RXD) input of the PC is connected to the output (pin 4) of an RS-232 driver, translated from the TTL output of the HF rig. The TTL input and output are tied together.

The HF rig supplies information to the computer only when requested. In other words, the PC is the link master and the radio is the slave. To eliminate possible computer noise problems, a ferrite bead is mounted on the TTL interface.

DC power for the circuit is provided by the request-to-send (RTS) output of the PC serial port. Your software must activate the RTS output in order to put +12 V dc on the output, versus −12 V dc in the opposite state. Many logging and radio control programs do this. To be on the safe side, however, fire up your software and measure the voltage on pin 4 of the serial port. Make sure you have +12 V dc on pin 4 before you attempt to connect the interface. Diodes D1 and D2 provide reverse-voltage protection, but it's best not to put them to the test if you can avoid it!

The CW keyer interface, which can be deleted if you don't need it, is controlled through the data terminal ready (DTR) output of the serial port. When the DTR output is high, the transistor switch turns on. The result is similar to closing a mechanical key contact. Do not use this keying interface with rigs that don't use a closure to ground for keying.

Construction

This converter fits within a DB-25 connector shell. The result is shown in Figure 5.13. It isn't pretty, but it works! The circuit was installed on a small piece of perforated board (available at Radio Shack) and cut to fit within the shell. Most of the parts were obtained by mail order from Digi-Key Corp. (See the Resources Chapter.)

Wiring was done point-to-point using #28 wire-wrap wire. Connections to the 25-pin connector were made with the same wire. Several layers of electrical tape were applied to the inside surface of the connector shell halves to prevent shorts to the circuit board. A 6-foot length of shielded multiconductor cable was used to interface to the radio. The plug shown is correct for ICOM radios. Check your rig to verify the connector type you need.

Figure 5.13—If you do use a 25-pin connector, you can squeeze the entire circuit into the connector shield. It's tight, but it fits!

Operation

Assuming that, by this time, you've become familiar with the software you plan to use, adding the radio interface is a snap. Install the radio interface cable between one of your PC serial ports and your radio. Modify your software setup to recognize this new configuration by selecting the correct serial (COM) port and identifying the HF rig. The software typically provides support for numerous makes and models of radios.

With many programs, after the first screen you will see the frequency and mode of the radio prominently displayed. Change bands and modes on the HF rig and the screen will follow along. Try entering a new frequency from the keyboard and you should see the radio tune to the requested frequency. Similarly, by using the logging software keyer commands, you should be able to transmit CW messages from the keyboard.

Other Serial Port Applications

Since several wires on the serial port can be individually controlled, changing the voltage on any wire is not a very big task. Alternate the wire between a *1* state and a *0* state—change it repetitively between high and low—and you have a signal generator.

Figure 5.14 shows a speaker, connected with series resistor and blocking capacitor to pin 4 on the serial connector. The return is made though pin 5, ground. Using the lowest bit on the modem control register, located at 3FCh for COM1, a short *BASIC* program generates a tone:

```
10 OUT &H3FC, 1
20 FOR A=1 TO 2:NEXT A
30 OUT &H3FC, 0
40 FOR A=1 TO 2:NEXT A
50 GOTO 10
```

The actual tone generated depends on the speed of your computer. Line 10 sets the voltage on pin 4 high and line 30 sets it low. Line 50 loops the program control back to line 10. Lines 20 and 40 slow the program down to generate a lower tone. For the highest possible tone using a vanilla *BASIC* package, omit lines 20 and 30. The same idea can be used as a rudimentary square wave generator for testing.

X10 Interface

The X10 control system is used by several manufacturers to interconnect burglar alarms, remote light and appliance switches and for other home electronic devices. Home Automation Systems (see the Resources Chapter) sells an X10 controller that uses a *Windows* screen to control devices through your computer's serial port. If you

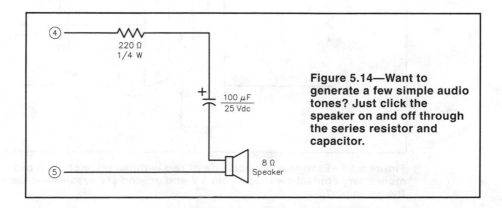

Figure 5.14—Want to generate a few simple audio tones? Just click the speaker on and off through the series resistor and capacitor.

are considering automating your station, and want some of the "heavy" control work—120 V or 240 V ac switching—done for you, consider this approach. Other X10 controllers, with less capability and lower prices, are available from many other sources including Radio Shack. With a little work, the Radio Shack controllers can be modified to be switched by the control signal from the serial port. This allows you to use the convenient X10 appliance modules to switch 120 V ac.

THE GAME PORT IS FOR MORE THAN FLIGHT SIMULATOR

The game port is an inheritance from the PCs that were popular before the current IBM or clone PCs. It did not take long for designers to discover people liked to play games, and there was nothing easier or less expensive then having a devoted connection to a computer for a game controller. These game controllers typically have two variable resistors and up to four momentary contact push buttons. A typical shoot-em-up game used the two variable resistors to measure the left/right and forward/back positions, for steering a gun or rocket ship, and four push buttons for shooting missiles and ray guns. This simple interface made it very attractive for hams to tie into their PCs with nothing more than a few switches and variable resistors.

The game port wiring, as used by a pair of joysticks, is shown in Figure 5.15. Notice the buttons are momentary contact switches, and no de-bounce circuitry is

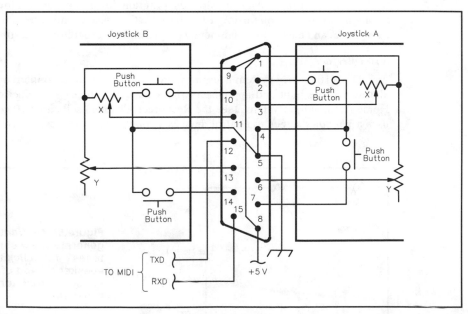

Figure 5.15—Each joystick consists of two variable resistors and two momentary contact switches. Plus 5 V and ground are available at the pins of the game port.

shown. Typically, the software should take care of contact bounce (see the discussion of contact bounce later in this chapter).

Caution: If you add a card to your PC with a game port, make sure there is one and only one game port set on. Many multi-purpose and combination cards—such as I/O cards and sound cards—come with a game port. Select only one, and deselect the others with the jumpers or DIP switches on the cards.

Connecting to the Game Port

Gary Sutcliffe, W9XT, described the game port connected to a demonstration temperature measuring probe in the October 1994 issue of *QEX*. The port is connected to a register, usually at address 201h. In its normal use the game port measures the resistance of potentiometers on a joystick's X and Y axes to determine the stick position. It also has digital inputs to detect switch closures. The game port supports two joysticks as well as four switch inputs.

The conversion of resistance to a digital format is done with one-shot circuits (sometimes called monostable multivibrators, or just monostables). When a one-shot is triggered, its output goes high for the time determined by a resistor and capacitor. The larger the values of R and C, the longer the period the output will be high. The game port has four such one-shots. The timing capacitors are fixed in value and are located on the game port board. The resistors are on the joystick, and their resistances vary with the movement of the stick.

The game port's monostables work with resistances ranging from under 1 kΩ to around 100 kΩ. The resulting time periods will range from a few tens of microseconds to over a millisecond. The monostable's output period is measured by software with timing loops or in conjunction with the PC's hardware timers.

The Game Port Register

The game port has one 8-bit register located at I/O address 201 (hex). Figure 5.16 shows the bit functions of this register when it is read.

The first four bits are the outputs of the one-shots. Each bit reads as 0 until the one-shot is triggered. It then reads as 1 until the one-shot times out. The one-shots are triggered by a write to the game port register. The data value written is irrelevant; it is the act of writing that triggers the monostables. Note that all four of the one-shots are triggered at once with a single write operation.

The upper four bits in the game port register are used to detect switch closures, usually in the form of firing buttons on the joystick unit. Of course you can use them to detect other switch status as needed for your particular application.

Using the Switch Inputs

Figure 5.15 shows how to connect external switches to the game port. You can use a common ground for the switches if needed. The switch bits read as logical ones if the switch is open and as logical zeros if the switch is closed. Programmers using Borland's *Turbo C* can test the status of the game port register by using the INPORTB() function. This function reads an 8-bit byte from a PC I/O device register. Other C dialects will have a similar function, but the name may be different.

Microsoft's *QBasic* has a special function for testing the switch status, STRIG(). STRIG returns a 0 if the switch indicated by the argument is open and a −1 if it is closed. Listing 1 shows examples for using it. (All programs for this section can be downloaded from the ARRL BBS or Internet sites.) Odd-numbered arguments are used to check if the switch is currently closed. The even-numbered arguments check if the switch has been closed since the last time STRIG was called with the same argument. Of course, if you don't want to use the STRIG functions, you can use the INP() function.

Take switch bounce into account when using mechanical switches with the game port. Many switches make and break contact several times quickly when they are opened or closed. A computer is fast enough to sense each closure, which could cause problems. For example, suppose you wanted to count the number of times the switch was pressed. You could easily get a much higher count than you should. Switch bounce also can cause a problem, if you want to initiate an activity when the switch is pressed and continue until it is released.

An easy way to handle switch bounce is to use a delay. After you sense a change in state on the switch, wait a period of time before checking the state again. Delays of 10 to 50 milliseconds are sufficient for most switches.

Using the External Resistors

Figure 5.15 shows how to connect resistors to the game port's DB-15 connector. A sensor that varies resistance in response to some stimulus can be used in place of the resistors.

Variable resistors might be mechanically hooked up as position sensors, as is done for the joystick. For example, many rotators use a resistor to indicate direction.

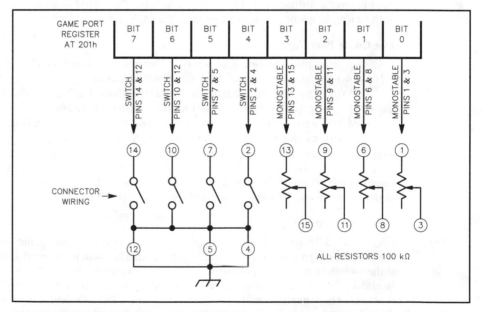

Figure 5.16—The game port register holds the values of the variable resistors and switches. Each resistor and switch is associated with a register stage or bit.

Some home-brew satellite and EME arrays use a potentiometer with its body fixed with respect to the antennas. A rigid pendulum arrangement is attached to the shaft. The pendulum keeps the shaft fixed with respect to the ground, but the potentiometer body rotates as the array is elevated. Other variable resistance devices are candidates for use, too. Thermistors are obvious choices for temperature sensing, and some humidity sensors change resistance with changes in relative humidity.

Keep a few things in mind when selecting your sensor. For best resolution the sensor should have a large change of resistance for a small change in position, temperature or whatever is being measured. The sensor should remain between 1 kΩ and 100 kΩ over the range you wish to cover.

The typical method of determining the on-times of the monostables is to trigger them and then use a software loop to count up until the output goes low. Listing 2 shows sample routines in Borland's *Turbo C* and Microsoft's *QBasic*.

QBasic has a built in function, STICK, which can be used to time the game port monostables. To use STICK, you must supply the number of the monostable you wish the value of. You must first call STICK(0) though. STICK(0) does the actual timing for all four one-shots and returns the value of the first one. STICK(1), STICK(2), and STICK(3) will return the respective values measured by the last STICK(0).

Note that the C version of the program turns off the interrupts before triggering the monostables and doing the counting. This is done because if the computer's real-time clock or other hardware interrupts while it is in the timing loop, the resulting count will be lower than it should be.

The actual count value returned will depend on a number of factors. First, of course, is the value of the resistor. Other factors include the speed of the computer. A faster computer will give a higher count (it executes the loop more times in a given period). Timing loops written in assembly language or a compiled high level language also will give higher counts than those in an interpreted one.

The *QBasic* STICK function apparently uses the PC's hardware timers to measure the one-shots. Reducing the PC's clock speed by pressing the Turbo switch does not change the values returned by STICK. You may prefer the C function, since the values returned by STICK vary by plus or minus a few counts, even when a fixed resistor is used. The C function shows smaller short-term variations in count.

Board-to-board differences also will affect the count value. Figure 5.17 shows the count value vs. resistance for the game ports on two different computers with the C program in Listing 2. A number of 1% resistors were used and the count value from the program was recorded. The 16-MHz 386SX computer actually gave a higher count for the same resistors than the 20-MHz 386DX. This is due to differences in the game port circuits of two different multifunction I/O cards.

The hardware differences and the varying response of the game port to different resistance value means you will need to calibrate each system and then convert the count value into engineering units. You may want to make a look-up table of readings and then do a linear interpolation between the two nearest entries. Another method is to analyze the calibration data with regression analysis to generate a simple equation to relate a count to the unit you wish to measure. Many spreadsheet programs and scientific calculators have such functions built in, which lets you do the analysis without dusting off your old statistics text book.

Long wires from your computer to your sensor can pick up noise that could affect

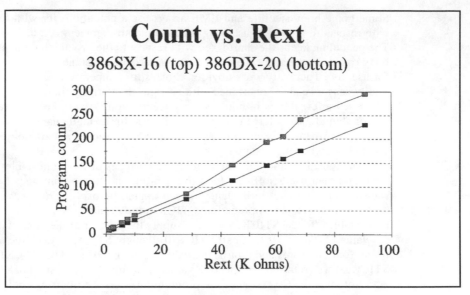

Figure 5.17—The actual count or measurement of the monostable fed by the game port is not linear, and varies with the actual computer used.

the accuracy. Keep in mind that long wires also will add resistance. So don't calibrate your antenna elevation resistor with a short cable and then run a long cable out to the tower.

Also remember to use the same language for taking your readings for calibration that you use for the final program. Using a BASIC program for calibration and an assembly language program for the final product won't give very accurate results!

Simple Temperature Measurement—Monitor your Finals

You can let your computer measure temperature near your rig's finals with a thermistor. Radio Shack sells one for about $2 (RS 271-110). The temperature sensor consists of a cable with a DB-15 on one end and a Radio Shack thermistor on the other. The thermistor is connected to pins 1 and 3 of the DB-15.

To calibrate the system, start with a styrofoam cup of crushed ice with enough water to form a slush. The temperature of this mixture is 0° C. Use a program such as those shown in Listing 2 to get the count reading.

Next, remove most of the ice and fill the cup with cold water. Once the rest of the ice melts, the temperature will gradually rise toward room temperature. Slowly stir the water. Use an accurate thermometer and record the temperature and corresponding count from the computer. (You can get a certified thermometer at most drug stores or photography shops.) When the water has reached room temperature, fill the glass with warm water and repeat the process as it cools back toward room temperature.

Figure 5.18 shows temperature vs. count for a temperature probe and a 20-MHz 386DX. You should get a similar looking curve, but it will vary depending on your type of computer, the program you use and the characteristics of your thermistor.

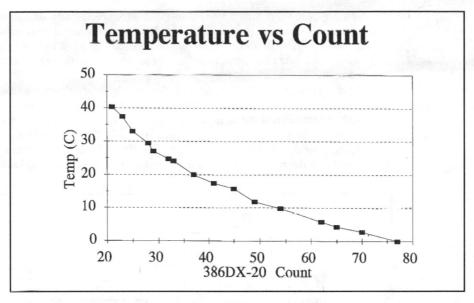

Figure 5.18—The nonlinear response of this temperature measuring system can be corrected in the software. But if you are using it to sound an alarm when your finals get too hot, you just have to calibrate the system at the critical warning temperature.

The figure shows the thermistor to be non-linear. Notice between counts of 20 and 30 the temperature changes by about 15° C, or about 1.5°/count. Between counts 65 and 75 the temperature changes only by about 5°, or about 0.5°/count. For a given count, the resulting temperature can be determined more accurately at lower temperatures.

Listing 3 shows a simple C program W9XT wrote to display the temperature. This program includes an array holding the calibration data, which it uses to do a linear interpolation to convert from counts to temperature. Because the whole system is only accurate to about 1 to 2° C, the resulting temperature value is rounded off to the nearest whole number before displaying it.

In summary, the game port offers a place to sense four independent switches as well as the position of for potentiometers. It is a convenient place to interface your PC without tying up any of the usual COM and LPT ports.

AUDIO IN AND OUT WITH A SOUND BOARD

When hams communicate on the HF and VHF bands, for the most part (excluding wideband TV and very high speed data modes) they transmit and receive audio. Sometimes the audio is direct voice signals, and other times it is data that has been converted to audio. The information on the data signal is encoded and a signal may vary the amplitude or frequency—but to stay within the FCC requirements the signals are usually within normal audio passbands.

Now suppose there was a feature in many PCs specifically designed accept one or two channels of audio, process it and analyze it—with real time results of the processing and analysis. In addition, this same card can be used to synthesize audio—frequency, amplitude and harmonics—and send out one or two channels of this synthesized audio.

There is such a card—the *sound card*. Perhaps the best-known sound card is called a *Sound Blaster*, although there are any number of manufacturers producing similar units with approximately the same characteristics. For historical and marketplace reasons, however, the term most often seen is *Sound Blaster compatible*.

Figure 5.19 is a sketch of a sound card interface. Some of the controls and jacks are mounted on the rear apron of the card, and therefore are accessible only from the

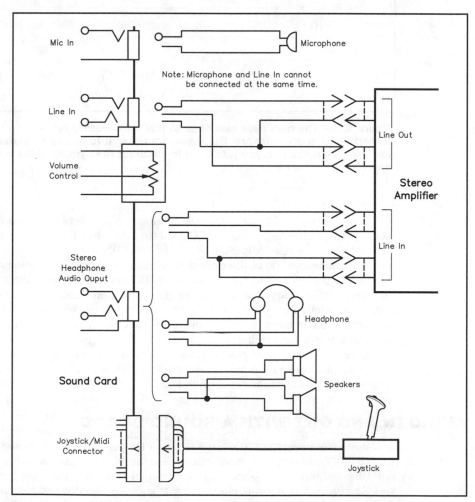

Figure 5.19—Most sound cards provide these inputs and outputs. The one shown has stereo—two channels—for input and output.

Connector		
Pin	Description	
1	MICR - Mic input, right channel	
2	MICGEN - Mic input ground	
3	MICL - Mic input, left channel	
4	SPKGND - Speaker output ground	
5	SPKR - Speaker output, right channel	
6	SPKL - Speaker output, left channel	
7	SPKRL - Speaker output return, left channel	
8	SPKRR - Speaker output return, right channel	

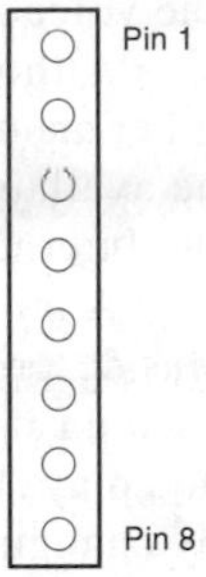

Pin 1

Pin 8

Figure 5.20—On-board connections are available on most sound cards. If yours came without instructions, this drawing might help you connect correctly to the pins.

back of a PC. Others are duplicated and available on the front panel of the PC. For example, a sound card packaged with a CD-ROM player will usually have the headphone jack on the front panel next to a manual volume control.

The game connector is the same game port described in the preceding section of this chapter. Pins not discussed there—the *MIDI* (musical instrument digital interface) pins—are used for interconnection with digital sound generation accessories.

Many sound cards clone the on-card connector supplied on Sound Blaster cards—often without any documentation. Figure 5.20 shows the interconnections common to these cards.

Call CQ Automatically—With Software You May Have

Many models of the *Sound Blaster* from Creative Labs, Inc. come with the program *READ.EXE*. This program will read ASCII text and send the results to the audio output jack of the card. Use of *READ.EXE* requires pre-loading a driver program. After this is done, the command:

READ "HOW NOW BROWN COW"

will result in the synthesized voice saying: "How now brown cow."

If you have an ASCII test file, named "CALL_CQ" located in your directory C:\HAM, the command:

READ <C:\HAM\CALL_CQ

will give you an audio version of this file.

You may want to try experimenting with the ASCII file. Instead of "CQ CQ CQ THIS IS...", try "C Q C Q C Q THIS IS"—with increased spacing. For certain letters, try phonetic pronunciation—"SEE" instead of "C", "CUE" instead of "Q."

One further command:

READ<COM1

will send the ASCII entering the computer at COM1 to the voice synthesizer, and the synthesizer will produce a voice pronouncing the information contained in the ASCII input. This last command is dependent on your machine speed. Try connecting the

ASCII output of an external RTTY or PACKET terminal unit to COM1, and see what the voice says!

Although the program *READ.EXE* is only supplied with the Sound Blaster cards, other manufacturers often supply equivalents, and shareware or freeware versions may be available on the Internet. See Chapter 6 for more information on finding files on the Internet.

A more capable method of both sending and recording voice, using a sound card, was described in the June 1996 issue of *QST*. Rick Markey, KN3C, described how he used an inexpensive ($50 for an 8-bit card at a discount store) sound card to record and play *.WAV* files. His interface for a Kenwood rig can be adapted to most other rigs by changing the audio levels and interconnections.

SSTV and Sound Cards

While earlier SSTV software used both serial and parallel ports, newer versions have migrated to the sound card. Since the video information is encoded as an audio frequency—1200 Hz for sync, and video from 1500 to 2300 Hz—the sound card is made to order for this mode. A software approach also lets you receive and transmit almost all the current SSTV modes and sub-modes, including Robot, Wraase, Martin, Scottie, AVT and others. In addition, many of these software packages can process various FAX and satellite picture modes. See Chapter 2 for more information on some of this software. A number of similar programs are available on the Internet as shareware.

Programming the Sound Card

While connecting to the sound card through a few RCA phono plugs or miniature audio plugs is relatively simple, programming for roll-your-own software is not. Sound cards are notorious, especially when used with manual installation in DOS, for compatibility problems. Hopefully, with some versions of *Windows* and other newer operating systems, installation problems have been reduced to some extent.

Many of the factors that cause installation problems—I/O address (often 220h or 240h), *IRQ* (interrupt—most often 2,5,7 or 10) and DMA (direct memory access) channels such as 0, 1 or 3—have to be accounted for. Various cards have varying capabilities, such as mono, stereo or dual channel, 8 or 16-bit capability. There are 13 or more registers and several status and address ports for a typical card.

The hardware, varying with both the age and cost of the card, often includes two *DAC*s (digital to analog converters) to provide analog audio output of the digital information resident on the card. Inputs are sampled at rates ranging from 4 to 44 kHz, with generally lower rates if two channels (stereo) are used simultaneously. For a normal Amateur Radio voice channel, with an upper frequency limit of less than 3 kHz, a sample rate of at least 6 kHz is needed—so even the older, slower sound cards are adequate for many purposes.

The cards contain one or two audio amplifiers, usually rated at 4 W or less. The outputs are low impedance, designed for direct connection to a speaker. It is a good idea to isolate the direct inputs and outputs from your rig with a matching transformer. Often, RF feedback is blamed for problems when other equipment, such as a PC, are attached to a transceiver. While RF feedback can cause problems, many times small currents due to ground loops are the real culprit.

Two sets of inputs are usually supplied on these cards. The **LINE IN** jacks go directly to the processor, and should be used when it is necessary to preserve the relative amplitude of the input audio signal. The **MIC** inputs usually have an AGC function, and therefore work best when the input signal is frequency encoded— especially when you would like to equalize the amplitude with signal fading or changes in amplitude from station to station.

Newer sound cards contain a true *DSP*—digital signal processor—chip. See the Resources chapter for more information on these chips and their extensive capabilities.

Programming this card is well within the capabilities of most experienced programmers. For the less-experienced programmer who is comfortable in *BASIC* and not detail-oriented, it is a large undertaking. The best starting point is a search on the Internet—specifically on USENET, for *FAQs*, frequently asked questions. Set your search engine (see Chapter 6) for an *advanced* or *compound* search for "Sound Blaster" and "FAQ." You should receive the latest updates. In addition, the results will probably give you other addresses to browse.

A second good source is in the software files of Microsoft Corporation. Go to their address (**http://www.microsoft.com**) and search there for "sound blaster." The use of the specific brand name—*Sound Blaster*—will not limit the information you get just to this one manufacturer. Information applicable to many varieties of sound cards is often listed under the Sound Blaster name as a general category.

CONNECT THE ANALOG WORLD TO YOUR DIGITAL COMPUTER

Many of the things hams would like to measure and control in their stations are analog—continuously variable voltages and currents—and therefore have to be converted to a digital format before a PC can be used. To supply this conversion, *A/D* or *analog-to-digital* converters are used.

One of the best ways to learn about these devices, if you have never used one, is to read the manufacturers' data sheets and application notes. Generally the converters are rated by speed (the number of conversions per second) and number of bits (how small a change in analog input signal can be detected). For example, an A/D that can make 100,000 conversions per second can theoretically be used with input signals having frequency components up to 50 kHz.

The number of bits—really the accuracy—usually ranges from 8 to 12. This means the input signal range is divided into 2^8 parts for an 8-bit converter and 2^{12} for a 12-bit converter. Thus, if you want to measure a voltage from 0 to 5 V, a 12-bit converter will measure voltage differences (changes) as small as 5/4095 or about 1.22 mV. An 8-bit converter will only allow you to measure voltage differences of 5/255 or 19.6 mV. For sources of more information on these devices, see the Resources Chapter.

You can buy a commercial A/D converter. One modestly priced (about $80) unit is offered by Marlin P. Jones (see address and model information in the Resources Chapter). This unit includes an electronic switch that allows you to monitor eight analog signals simultaneously, and report their values in sequence to your PC parallel port.

Single-Chip Dual-Channel A/D

The description and schematic of this converter was first published in the 1996 edition of *The ARRL Handbook for Radio Amateurs*. It connects to a PC parallel port, and you can measure two analog channels at once. In the *Handbook* it is shown measuring voltages proportional to the forward and reverse power as seen by an SWR bridge, but you can use it for any voltages from 0 to 5 or more. Construction and test is just a few evenings' work. The software to run the chip can be downloaded from the ARRL BBS or Internet sites. It is also included in 1996 or later editions of *The ARRL Handbook for Radio Amateurs*.

Circuit Description

The circuit consists of a single-chip A/D converter, U2, and a DB-25 male plug (Figure 5.21). Pins 2 and 3 are identical voltage inputs, with a range from 0 to slightly less than the supply voltage VCC (+5 V). R1, R2, C3 and C4 provide some input isolation and RF bypass. There are four signal leads on U2—DO is the converted data from the A/D out to the computer, DI and CS are control signals from the computer and CLK is a computer-generated clock signal sent to pin 7 of U2.

The +5-V supply is obtained from a +12-V source and regulator U1. One favorite accident, common in many ham shacks, is to connect power supply leads backward. Diode D1 prevents any damage from this action. Current drain is usually less than 20 mA, so any 5-V regulator may be used for U1. The power supply ground, the circuit ground and the computer ground are all tied together. If you already have a source of regulated 5 V, U1 is not needed.

In this form the circuit will give you two identical dc voltmeters. To extend their range, connect voltage dividers to the input points A and B. A typical 2:1 divider, using 50-kΩ resistors, is shown in Figure 5.21. Resistor accuracy is not important, since the circuit is calibrated in the accompanying software.

The breadboard circuit, built on a universal PC board (Radio Shack 276-150), is shown in Figure 5.22. The voltage regulator is on the top left and the converter chip, U2, in an 8-pin socket. Power is brought in through a MOLEX plug. Signal input and ground are on the wire stubs. Two strips of soft aluminum, bent into an L-shape, hold the male DB-25 connector (Radio Shack 276-1547) to the PC board.

Typical Use—Display Your SWR

Most analog SWR measuring devices use a meter, which has a nonlinear scale calibration. An SWR of 3:1 is usually close to center scale, and values above this are rarely printed. With a PC doing the calculation, there is no loss of accuracy due to nonlinear meter scales. Figure 5.21 shows two jumpers. When **A** and **B** are connected to **A1** and **B1**, the circuit acts as dual-channel voltmeter. Jumpered to **A2** and **B2**, connections are made to a conventional SWR bridge.

Generally, most SWR bridges have a switch to connect their internal meter to a sample of current representing either forward power or reverse power. As shown, these two sample wires are disconnected and tied back to R7 and R8. The current flowing through these 25-kΩ resistors provide voltages of less than 5 V. These voltages are proportional to the forward and reverse voltages developed in the directional coupler. The PC takes the sum and difference of these forward and reverse voltages, and calculates the SWR.

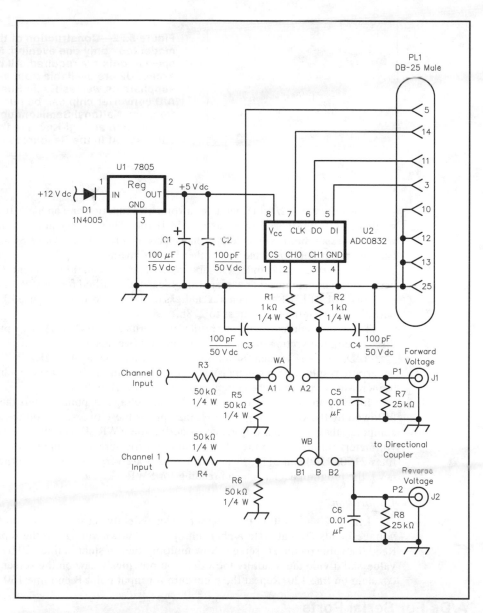

Figure 5.21—Only two chips are used to provide a dual-channel voltmeter. PL1 is connected thorough a standard 25-pin cable to your computer printer port. U2 requires an 8-pin IC socket. All resistors are ¹/₄ W. You can use the A/D as an SWR display by connecting it to a sensor such as the one use in the Tandem Match described in *The ARRL Handbook for Radio Amateurs*. A few more resistors are all that are needed to change the voltmeter scale. The 50-kΩ resistors form 2:1 voltage dividers, extending the voltmeter scale (on both channels) to almost 10 V dc.

Figure 5.22—Construction of this model took only one evening. No special tools are required. All parts except U2 are available from most suppliers as well as Radio Shack. The A/D converter chip can be purchased from any National Semiconductor dealer such as Digi-Key. See the address list in the Resources Chapter.

Software

The software, *A2D.BAS*, includes a voltmeter function and an SWR function. It is written in *GWBASIC* and saved as an ASCII file. Therefore, you can read it on any word processor, but if you modify it make sure you re-save it as an ASCII file. It can be imported into *QBasic* and most other Basic dialects.

It was written to be understandable rather than to be highly efficient. Each line of basic code has a comment or explanation. It can be modified for most PCs. The printer port used is LPT1, which is at a hex address of 378h. If you wish to use LPT2 (printer port 2), try changing the address to 278h.

To find the addresses of your printer ports, run *FINDLPT.BAS*. This program was discussed in the section on the parallel port in this chapter.

A2D.BAS was written to run on computers as slow as 4.7-MHz PC/XTs. If you get erratic results with a much faster computer, set line 1020(CD=1) to a higher value to increase the width of the computer-generated clock pulses.

Initially the software reads the value of voltage at point A into the computer, followed by the voltage at point B. It then prints these two values on the screen, and computes their sum and difference to derive the SWR. If you use the project as a voltmeter, simply ignore the SWR reading on the screen or suppress it by deleting lines 2150, 2160 and 2170. If the two voltages are very close to each other (within 1 mV), the program declares a bad reading for SWR.

Calibration

Lines 120 and 130 in the program independently set the calibration for the two voltage inputs. To calibrate a channel, apply a known voltage to the input point A. Read the value on the PC screen. Now multiply the constant in line 120 by the correct value and divide the result by the value you previously saw on the screen. Enter this constant on line 120. Repeat the procedure for input point B and line 130.

A/Ds For Serial Ports

An A/D also can be connected to any serial port. Since most PCs can have four serial ports, and only two parallel ports, devoting one serial port to an A/D rather than a parallel port may be an advantage. The chip used in the preceding section, the ADC0832, requires three input signals from a PC and supplies one output signal. A serial port has enough inputs and outputs (see Figure 5.11), but will require the converting chip described in the serial port section of this chapter to interface with most of these A/D converters.

A design using three chips is described in the *Maxim Engineering Journal*. One chip is the actual A/D converter, the second the interface (RS/EIA-232 to TTL) converter and the third chip a voltage regulator. Additional uses of PCs with A/Ds are described in the September/October 1995 issue of the *Microcomputer Journal*. It contains a description of this combination as an oscilloscope. For more information on these ideas, see the Resources Chapter.

D/A CONVERTERS—CONTROLLING ANALOG DEVICES

The complement to the A/D converters are *D/A—digital-to-analog*—converters. Once you have calculated a digital value in your PC, a D/A will give you an analog voltage proportional to the digital value. Normally the actual value is scaled. Suppose you had an 8-bit converter, and calculated a voltage of 3.5 V out of a maximum of 5 V. The 8-bit converter allows a maximum count of 255. The maximum value of 5 V corresponds to this count of 255, so a value of 3.5 would correspond to (3.5/5) times 255 or approximately 179.

The interface between the PC and the D/A would carry a value of 179, and the D/A would scale this back to a voltage of about 3.5 V. It is not necessary to be able to generate the complete output voltage range needed, since the D/A can be followed by a voltage amplifier using an op amp.

One application of a D/A is an antenna rotator control. Some rotators use a dc error voltage to sense the antenna position. When the error voltage is not 0, the rotator motor is turned on and rotates until the resulting error voltage is reduced to zero. Details of one rotator control system, based on a Radio Shack rotator, is described in an article in *73 Amateur Radio*. See the Resources Chapter for details.

General Purpose D/A Driven by the Parallel Port

This project is the complement of the parallel port A/D converter described earlier. It takes a digital number from the computer, and converts it to a voltage from 0 to 5 V dc. Only one chip, the MAX 512, is required. It operates from a 5-V supply and is connected to the computer by a standard DB-25 parallel port connector. The chip may be ordered from Digi-Key, Allied Electronics and other ham suppliers as MAX512CPD-ND. This part number specifies a 14-pin DIP. As with all integrated circuit projects, use a socket and check all voltages and wiring before you plug the chip in the socket.

If you do not have 5 V handy, use the regulator shown in Figure 5.23. IC-1 is a 7805, available at Radio Shack as part number 276-1770. A smaller capacity 5-V regulator may be used. The 7805 was selected for its ready availability at Radio Shack. Its excess capacity can be used to power other 5-V projects.

Construction

You can build the converter on a Radio Shack breadboard card (276-170). A 25-pin solder-type male plug (Radio Shack 276-1547) is mounted at one end of the board. A 2-pin Radio Shack 276-1388 connector is wired with one terminal to ground and the other to the converter output. Unregulated power is applied to the board through a polarized 2-pin connector (Radio Shack 274-222), as suggested in Chapter 22 of *The ARRL Handbook for Radio Amateurs*. Standardization on one low-power connector for your shack makes life a lot more convenient!

Software

The software needed to run the chip, *D2A.BAS,* can be downloaded from the ARRL BBS or Internet sites. It is about 60 lines long, fully commented and written in *GWBASIC*, so it may be readily modified. The parallel port address is defined on line 105 as **PORTO=&H378**. Your computer may use a different address. To find the correct address, run *FINDLPT.BAS*.

The program takes the value **AIN** from the keyboard (line 230), converts it to a number between 0 and 255, and then sends it out as a serial word to the D/A chip. If you would like to use the project with another program, use your other program to set **AIN** to the value you want to generate, and then run this program as a subroutine.

At the end of the program is the clock pulse subroutine. In the event your computer is too fast for the converter chip, you can stretch the clock pulses by changing **CD** in line 5010 to a value greater than the default value of 1.

What Can you Use It For?

This circuit gives you the capability of setting a voltage under computer control. You can calibrate the voltage to match your power supply and the actual chip used.

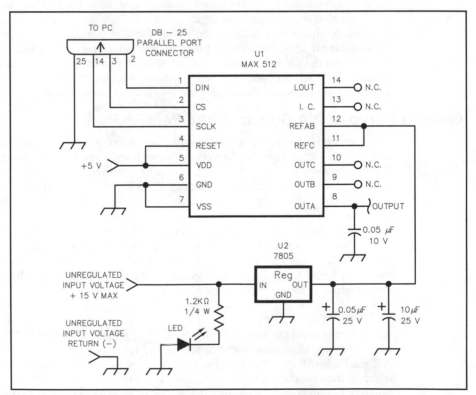

Figure 5.23—Only three wires and a ground lead are needed to connect the converter to your PC.

Tests with several chips showed an error of 25 mV or less. That's not bad—a 25-mV error over the range of 0 to 5 V dc.

Your computer can generate this voltage from any program you like. Thus, you can couple the software with a timer routine to provide a precise dc voltage for exactly the time you wish—just what the doctor ordered for battery charging.

If you would like to monitor the output of this converter, use the circuit in Figure 5.24. With a value of 5 for **AIN**, set the 10-kΩ potentiometer to light LED 1. Then, as you change **AIN**, the LED will change in response.

The D/A as a Test Signal Generator

Since the voltage output of the D/A is controlled by software, this output can be controlled to place a sin, triangle, square or other voltage function on the converter output pins. The program *SIND2A.BAS* generates a sin function. However, since the speed of execution of the software depends on the computer speed, older computers using *GWBASIC* will probably not be able to generate a very high frequency output. One test, run on a very old *relic*, was able to generate a sin wave at the fantastic rate of one complete cycle every 20 seconds. Compiling the program, with the equally vintage *IBM BASIC COMPILER* brought the speed up to one cycle every 2 seconds—a maximum frequency of 0.5 Hz!

The solution to the speed problem is to do something different, and Figure 5.25 is one good approach. A MAXIM MAX038 chip is controlled by the voltage output of the D/A converter. S1 selects sin, square or triangle waveshape outputs. Supply voltages of +5 and −5 V are required. With a 20-pF capacitor for CF (pin 5), a 5-V swing

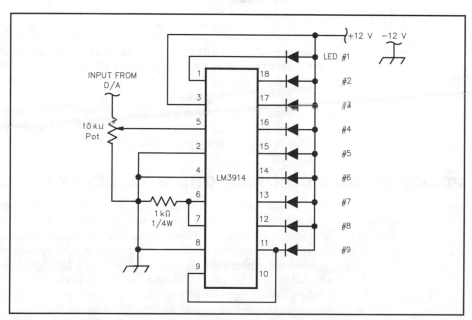

Figure 5.24—The LM3914 is an LED driver. It is connected here in the *dot* mode, so only one LED is on at a time.

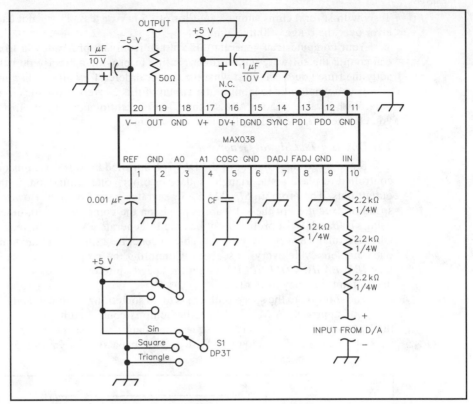

Figure 5.25—Connected to the A/D converter, the MAX038 chip provides a PC-controlled signal generator with a wide frequency coverage.

will provide a frequency range of about 2 to almost 30 MHz. The top end of the range is controlled by stray capacitance surrounding pin 5. Built breadboard fashion, CF may have to be reduced to 15 pF to approach a 30-MHz limit.

PRACTICE SAFE CONNECTIONS WITH RELAYS

When you connect any piece of equipment to a computer, there is always the possibility of causing some damage—either due to excessive loading of the computer circuits or due to ground currents. Fortunately, when there is damage it is usually limited to the port output driver—usually located on an easily replaced plug-in card.

Damage is actually quite rare, as long as you keep a few basic ideas in mind:
- Keep all ac circuits isolated with relays or optoisolators;
- Select the proper relay, and protect the circuit with a suppression diode; and
- Limit your circuit to a minimum load on any pin.

Many logic and computer microcircuits limit the per pin current to 25 mA. However 10 mA, in or out, is a safe goal. This means you can draw 10 mA when the output is at the high logic level, and allow 10 mA to flow into the pin when the output is at a low logic level. Many circuits can supply more than this value, but to determine the actual values you will have to look at the specific chip specification sheet.

These values of current do not guarantee you will have a valid logic 1 or 0 at the pin under maximum current conditions. For example, if you are driving an LED, you need only slightly less than 2 V to turn on the LED—connected from the output pin to ground with a series resistor—and therefore having a valid logic 1 is not necessary.

Relays—Good News and Bad News

Relays are one of the oldest ways to isolate circuits. When there is a need, manufacturers usually respond, and computer port driven relays are now common. The parallel port, and any other nominal *5-V TTL* connection requires a relay specifically selected for this use. Usually you will see a rating such as *pull in voltage—3.8 V* and *drop out voltage—1.2 V*. This means the relay will be energized with any valid logic *1*, and will not release until the coil sees a value less than a logic *0*.

Unfortunately, many of these "industry standard relays" cost close to $10 each, and are hard to find when you just want one or two. However, you can try other, more affordable and readily available units. Radio Shack sells a 5-V, 20-mA unit (part number 275-232) that, even without detailed specifications, seems to work well. Although 20 mA is a bit more than you would like as a load, it does not bother most printer-port connections.

A diode is needed to suppress shut-off transients (Figure 5.26A). Almost any silicon switching diode, such as a 1N914, will be adequate for a this use. In the circuit shown, the relay is driven by the current supplied by a logic 1. If you want to try the opposite configuration, and close the relay contacts with a logic 0, you may have a problem (Figure 5.26B). Returning the relay to +5 may keep it energized with a logic *1*—when you would like it shut off—since a low value of a logic *1* such as 3.5 V will mean there is still 1.5 V across the relay coil.

Relays do suffer from a limited life span, and in addition are not recommended for very fast switching. Contacts tend to bounce, and if the relay is controlling a 120 V ac circuit, this bounce may generate RFI.

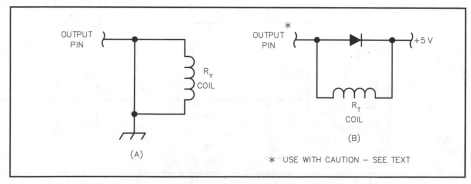

Figure 5.26—Pick the correct relay, and you can drive it directly from a PC port. See the text before using the wiring in B.

Connected to the serial (COM) port, a relay is more of a problem. Although the voltage swing is greater—at least from +5 V to −5 V—a logic 1 or 0 may be less than the supply bus. Therefore, in the off state of the relay there may be enough voltage on the pin to energize the relay.

For example, suppose the configuration of Figure 5.26A is used. The relay is supposed to go on when the RS-232 pin is at a logic 1, or somewhere between +5 to +12 V. The other end of the relay coil has to be returned to the logic 0 voltage level. Since this actual level is not really defined—except that it is −5 V to perhaps −12 V—you might be tempted to return the relay to the −12 V bus. However, if you do, and the 0 state of the pin is at −5 V, then the relay will still have 12−5 or 7 V applied and be energized!

Therefore, keep in mind you just can't tie a single relay to an RS/EIA-232 pin and expect it to work as easily as you can to a TTL or printer port pin. If you must use the RS/EIA-232 connection, you may have to use a converting chip to provide TTL levels, and then connect the relay.

EO Couplers—Relays Without the Click and Clatter

Fortunately, there is good alternative to relays, without noise, with unlimited life and ready availability. These are *electro-optical couplers*. There are several types, but each contains the equivalent of a solid-state light source, such as an LED, mounted close to a photo-sensitive device, such as a phototransistor. Energize the LED, and the transistor conducts. Since a small beam of light is the coupling mechanism, input-to-output isolation is very high. The exclusive use of solid state means no contact to wear or spark, but also often means limited power handling capacity.

Figure 5.27 illustrates two types of couplers. The MOC5010, Radio Shack part number 276-135, is a dc device. The photosensitive unit is actually a linear amplifier,

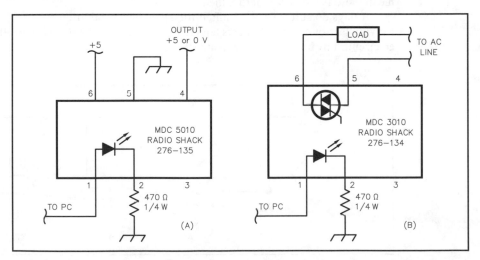

Figure 5.27—An electro-optical coupler can be used in place of a relay. A linear amplifier or switch-based unit can be used to switch dc, and a triac-base unit for ac.

but it can be used to switch 5 V on and off as shown in the figure. The input circuit is identical to the circuit you would use to connect a single LED to the printer port. For ac loads, Figure 5.27B shows a MOC3010 (Radio Shack 276-135). It contains a triac for ac switching, and can handle 250 V ac at 100 mA rms. Peak allowable current is 1.2 A.

Both devices have a maximum input current of 50 mA, but both work well with a 470Ω series resistor from a TTL driver.

Contact Bounce—The Input Side of I/O Connections

Often hams will want to sense a switch closure—perhaps even something such as the contacts of a CW paddle—and take some action in their computer when the contacts close. Unfortunately mechanical contacts *bounce*—it may take a few milliseconds before two conducting surfaces make good contact and stay in good contact. Contact opening or breaking is usually slightly shorter in time, but still has the same intermittent characteristic. During this transition time, the resistance of the circuit will vary from open to short, and every value in between, jumping back and forth in no apparent pattern. To a fast computer, this looks like a sequence of contact openings and closures.

The are several approaches to curing this problem. The traditional approach simply places a capacitor across the contacts. Since the voltage in a capacitor cannot change instantaneously, the contact closure will appear to be an exponentially decreasing resistance. This precludes using the contacts for any fast response, but it does allow the computer to see only a *single* closure. Capacitor values of 0.01-μF and higher are often used. If a capacitor is used to eliminate bounce on contact breaking, the capacitor will be discharging through the circuit it sees with the contacts open. If this circuit looks like a very high resistance, the time for this capacitor to discharge (and the contacts appear as open) may be very long!

The second approach uses a set-reset flip-flop to echo the state of the switch. For more information on the use of logic elements, such as flip-flops and cross coupled gates, see the reference in the Resources Chapter.

POWER SUPPLIES—DO YOU REALLY NEED ONE?

You will often see circuits for interfacing to a PC without any external source of power. As long as the circuit does not require very much current, and your design has some flexibility in what pins are used, this approach is very successful. Figure 5.28 has a drawing of one such scheme on a serial port. It assumes at least one of the pins for RTS, TX or DTR is high and one is low. Therefore at least one pin should be at +12 V, and the other at −12 V. Often the output points (V+ and V−) will go to a small voltage regulator, thus providing + and −5 V. With several hundred microfarad capacitors, the voltage will be maintained even if all pins drop (or go up) for a short period.

The same system can be used with the parallel port. Usually, one pin is selected to stay high—limiting the flexibility of the port—but a constant supply equal to a logic 1 is available there. However, no voltage regulator can be used since the supply is already at the lowest possible value of a logic 1, and any regulator would just drop this value further.

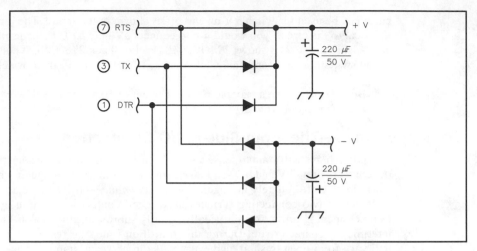

Figure 5.28—You may not need a power supply to run a single chip connected to a PC port. If the chip only needs a few mA, the port may be able to supply it.

If an external supply is used, the usual precautions to prevent ground loops are needed. Many designers recommend the return wire (the 0 V wire on a +5-V supply) should not be connected to chassis ground, but only to the ground bus of the circuit you are connecting to the computer port.

OTHER APPROACHES—IS THERE LIFE AFTER THE PC?

The present cost of $100 (or less, if you come haul it away) of an old clunker is very attractive. Get one of these PCs and you can devote it to station control or what ever idea you have. But before you do, there are some other almost PC-compatible approaches to be considered in the same price range.

Several dedicated *controller boards* are available. While their price tends to be slightly higher, they are PCs packaged on 6×6-inch or perhaps 8-inch boards. I/O is PC compatible, and they are designed to be programmed in most popular languages. Usually, there is provision for the program to be stored in a *ROM*—a read-only memory chip. Typical of these controllers is a series offered by Micromint.

In the under $100 class, but with limited program memory, is the *Basic Stamp* series of micro-miniature processors made by Parallax, with similar offerings from others. These consist of a microprocessor, a carrier board and I/O modules. They are usually programmed though your PC's parallel port, and the program then resides in the Stamp. See the Resources Chapter for more information on these devices.

Hams + PCs + Modems = Internet

WHAT IS THE INTERNET?

This is a difficult question at best. More of a concept than a physical entity, the Internet has transformed the way we gather information. Users often form their own opinion of what it is based on their personal experiences rather than by any physical description.

The media often refer to the "Information Superhighway." Is this the Internet? The concept of a highway is a good metaphor for describing the physical connections. A better one is to relate our society. Our society is composed of people and the Internet is composed of information. People travel in their cars on highways, roads, streets and lanes; Internet information travels on the superhighway. The Information Superhighway consists of fiber-optic and microwave backbones carrying hundreds of millions of bits per second. Closer to home, an *ISP* (Internet Service Provider) may send data out to the "street" at 1.544 Mbit/s using a T-carrier. On a still lower level, you may leave your driveway at 28.8 Kbit/s using a standard dial-up telephone line. In our society, people make friends and join with those who share common interests; the same is true of the Internet. Almost every conceivable group has a presence, from nuclear physicists to teen rock idols. It is not surprising that hams too have a sizable presence there.

Hams have a lot in common with Web users—particularly the desire to communicate. Hams have regular schedules to chat with each other; Web surfers meet in *IRC* (Internet Relay Chat) chat rooms with their friends for the same purpose. When they want to start a conversation, hams call CQ and web surfers say hello. The sidebar illustrates some of the parallels of Amateur Radio to the Internet.

The Internet developed from the earliest landline BBS systems, improving and adding features as the telephone system permitted. Faster modems and high-capacity trunking were the prerequisites. New computer applications soon followed, taking advantage of these higher speeds, allowing the GUI (Graphical User Interface) to become commonplace. The pace of development for the Internet has been nothing short of phenomenal. If Amateur Radio had developed at the same relative pace, we might have had CW, AM, SSB and Packet all developed in the same month. The desire to communicate is so powerful it is shaping our society in ways unimagined just a few years ago.

Caught In The Web

Most of us have heard of the "Web" from the media and many believe this is the Internet. It is not the actual Internet. The Web does play a major role and has become very popular, because it provides the GUI (pronounced *gooey*) graphical interface

Anything Surfers do, Hams can do, too [Almost]

Let's look at some of the things that hams do that also are found on the Internet. Almost every form of Amateur Radio communication has a parallel on the Internet.

Amateur Radio	*The Internet*
•Saturday morning sked with friends	•IRC chat room
•Voice communication	•I-Phone, FreeTel and other programs that digitize audio with a sound card
•A rig	•A computer
•Slow-scan television	•CUSeeMe and other video conferencing programs
•Fast-scan television	•As modem and computer speeds increase, the ability to "stream" .mpg files
•Send a file by ftping it over packet radio	•FTP a file
•Connect to a distant terminal by telnetting over packet radio	•TELNET command
•Packet radio BBSs	•BBSs
•Packet radio e-mail	•e-mail
•The airwaves are free	•The Internet is free (although you pay to connect to it)
•All Amateur Radio communications pass over two wires, the antenna feed line	•All Internet communications pass over two wires, the telephone or data circuit

that humans need to communicate efficiently with computers. *Windows* may be considered the first popular use of a GUI and the Web a close second. The first Internet users had to be satisfied with simple keyboard commands. As *Windows* applications grew in popularity, so did the need for an easy, graphical mouse-driven interface for the Internet.

Three components have to come together to make this possible. They are *URLs* (Uniform Resource Locators), *HTTP* (Hyper Text Transfer Protocol) and *HTML* (Hyper Text Markup Language). In combination, they form the basis for an efficient means to control and supply information. These tools make it not only easy, but also a lot of fun to access the Internet's vast supply of information. Commands are issued by clicking the mouse on a hyperlink. Instead of "letting your fingers do the walking," now it's possible to let your mouse do the talking.

A hyperlink is a special spot on the screen (often designated in blue). A click on it will execute a very long string of arcane instructions. For example, the web command to get government census data for Newington, Connecticut, and display it as a map showing the location of ARRL Headquarters, could be typed as:

http://tiger.census.gov/cgibin/mapsurfer?act=in&infact=2&map.x=211& map.y=180&lat=41.6865654&lon=72.7307892&wid=0.125&ht=0.125&iht=359&iwd= 422&off=CITIES&tlevel=&tvar=&mlat=41.68726&mlon=72.73069&msym= redpln&mlabel=Newington,+CT&murl=

No, the word processor didn't go berserk; that is the actual address where the map information is stored. It is obviously a lot more efficient to point-and-click the mouse on a hyperlink than it is to type a long string of unrelated symbols.

For most of us, running a *Browser* program on a *Windows* machine is all that is necessary to take advantage of these powerful tools. To be able to "hang-ten" as a net surfer no longer requires that you be a computer maven. Navigating the Internet is easy, and if you have not already joined the gang at the beach, consider the rest of this chapter as an invitation. Amateur Radio has a sizable (and ever-growing) presence on the Net.

Getting Started

The prerequisites for a ham station are a rig, a feed line and an antenna. The prerequisites for the Net are a computer, a modem, a telephone line and an ISP. There is not much difference in the concept: The rig sends information down the feed line and the modem sends information down the telephone line. The antenna radiates information all over the world, and the ISP sends information all over the world. Typically, you will need a *Windows* machine with a 14.4 Kbps or faster modem. Free software may be

obtained from your ISP. One of the first questions you might ask is, how expensive is it? That depends on what you want to do.

A connection to an ISP will typically cost $20/month or less for unlimited service over a dial-up phone line. If all you want is e-mail, the cost may be zero. Companies have sprung up offering 100% free e-mail service. The catch is that advertising is sent when you go to pick up your mail. Most users have found that the advertising is fairly innocuous. See the Resources Chapter for information about Juno Corporation. Some libraries offer free limited Internet services. Ask your local librarian what is available.

Choosing an ISP

Choosing an ISP is the first step. *America Online*, *CompuServe* and *Prodigy* had their beginnings before the Superhighway was even paved. They started out as private networks and have only recently started to provide full Internet services. Today you can choose from hundreds of local Internet Service Providers. See the Resources Chapter for a listing of national providers. The best way to find local providers in your area is to ask other hams who are on the Net. A call to your local library also may be helpful. Local telephone and cable companies are now offering Internet access. Understanding a few concepts can go a long way in choosing the most effective provider.

As mentioned earlier, if all you want is e-mail, you don't need an ISP (see Juno Corporation above). This is a limited case, so let's explore the requirements for full Internet access. For our purposes let us consider full access as the ability to access the Internet, using a unique IP (Internet Protocol) address assigned to your computer, with nothing censored or withheld by the provider. This also is called *direct* access. Access speed is important. The majority of home users find a 28.8-Kbps modem on a regular dial-up telephone line is adequate. Large organizations, or those expecting many simultaneous sessions, may want to consider a digital leased line operating up to 1.544 Mbps.

Try to obtain an ISP that provides reliable 24-hour-a-day service at 28.8 Kbps or higher. Here is where the nuances of choice come into play. Figure 6.2 lists some of the factors to consider when choosing an ISP. Of particular concern is the actual connect speed and the ability to connect without long distance phone charges. Most providers will advertise connectivity at 28.8 Kbps or higher. The actual speed, however, will depend on the quality of the local telephone circuits. Today's modems adapt to line conditions, dropping the connect speed as necessary. As a rule, the farther you are from the provider, the lower the connect speed will be. Connections made within the same town or central office will typically range from 21.6 to 28.8 Kbps. Long distance or connections made over noisy circuits may be achieved only at 14.4 Kbps or lower. See the sidebar "How Fast Am I Really Going?"

Fortunately, the cost of Internet access has dropped as the competition among ISPs has increased. As cable TV and local telephone companies get into the act, we can expect 56 or 128 Kbps access to become available at a cost comparable to today's 28.8 Kbps access.

Shell Accounts, WinSocks, PPP and SLIP

Shell Accounts, PPP and SLIP refer to the type of type of Internet connection your ISP provides. Because the Internet was initially developed under a UNIX environment, it is not surprising to find many UNIX references still apply. A *Shell* is the

◆ COST

For direct unlimited Internet access, $20/month is typical.

Check with your local telephone company and long distance carrier for limited free access.

◆ LOCAL ACCESS

Can you access your ISP with a local telephone call?

Even if your ISP provides a free call, is the connection relayed to another city? This usually slows down the actual connect speed below 28.8 Kbps.

◆ ISP CONNECTIVITY

The number of modems your ISP has is also a factor. The ISP that has the most modems for the fewest customers improves your odds of not getting a busy signal when you call.

◆ QUALITY OF TELEPHONE COMPANY LINES

The quality of the "local loop" to the central office is a big factor. A line with even a small amount of noise may slow the speed considerably. The line may sound fine for voice conversations, although it may have problems passing data at the highest possible speed. A wet windy day usually aggravates poor telephone line quality.

◆ CONDITION OF THE TELEPHONE HOUSE WIRING

Before you blame the telephone company for a noisy line, check the wiring inside your house. Accessories, such as extension phones, fax machines and answering machines, attached to the telephone line can load the line so much that modem connect speed is reduced. The ringer circuits

◆ RFI PROTECTION

Modems are susceptible to RFI, perhaps even to a greater degree than a telephone set. Sometimes you may have a fairly serious case of telephone RFI without even knowing it. You have no way of hearing what is on the line after the initial connection. Just because your telephone is clean, this is no guarantee that your modem is. A rudimentary check may be may be downloading a file while noting the transfer rate (characters/second). If the rate slows down or stops when you transmit, you definitely have a problem. Any of the advertised telephone line filters mounted near the modem will likely help.

◆ ISP EXTRAS

Does your ISP offer you space on their computer for a web page; do they censor newsgroups? Ask about any special features they may offer.

Figure 6.2—To save time, money and hassles, consider these factors when choosing an Internet Service Provider.

program that reads and interprets user keyboard commands in a UNIX environment. Korn and C-Shell are the two most popular ones. If your provider offers a *Shell Account,* you will have Internet access just as if you were sitting at a UNIX terminal.

How Fast am I Really Going?

A common problem for modem users is determining the speed of the connection. All too often, confusion occurs when a "connect" speed is displayed on the screen. The modem is always between the telephone line and the computer. This is visually obvious if you are using an external modem; however, an internal modem also is logically between the telephone line and the computer.

Two different connect speeds occur: the speed the modem uses to talk to the computer and the speed the modem uses to talk to the telephone line. *DTE*, for Data Terminal Equipment, is the connection between the computer and the modem. *DCE*, for Data Communications Equipment, is the connection from the modem to the telephone line. You might say the modem is capable of doublespeak—it can speak out of both sides of its mouth (ports) at the same time.

As a rule, the DTE speed should be as high as possible to ensure that you don't lose data. It should always be as high and preferably higher than the DCE speed. Many 486-class machines can communicate with the modem at 115 Kbps. This is a good choice if your modem and computer can support it. On the other hand, the DCE speed will be determined by the modem upon the initial telephone connection. Your modem *negotiates* with the host modem to determine the highest possible speed for the prevailing noise levels on the telephone line and the quality of your host's modem. This speed may change from day to day and it is the best overall indicator of performance. You should strive to get an efficient connection that repeatedly results in the highest possible speed. Sometimes, this is a trade-off between different hosts and the quality of the telephone circuits to these hosts. In order to make this determination you must be able to see what the actual DCE speed is. The DCE speed can be displayed upon the initial dial-up if an *init* (initialization) string with a **W2** in it has been given to your modem.

Modem software frequently comes prepackaged with a larger application, so it may be difficult to determine exactly how the modem is set up. An *init* string of characters is always sent from the computer before any communications takes place. Most modems respond to a universal set of commands called the *AT Command Set*. These commands are used for dialing and configuring your modem. The complete explanation of the AT Command set is usually printed in most modem user manuals.

The actual construction of the init string may be performed behind your back, often during the initial software installation. This may be when a Web Browser, *WinSock*, terminal program or dialing script is set up for the first time. Usually, you are asked a few questions by the setup program and your answers determine what the resulting init string will be. All too often the choice of displaying the DCE or DTE connect speed is omitted. If you want to see the DCE connect speed, you can always manually edit your modem init string to ensure that a **W2** appears in it. Most modem packages give the option of editing the init string. Just add a **W2** to the end of the existing string. Figure 6.3 illustrates how the DCE speed changes with line and host modem performance.

This terminal would be "connected" over a telephone line to your host's UNIX computer. The host computer becomes the bridge between you and the Internet. This means the software required to issue Internet commands is located on your host's computer, not yours. Your computer is merely acting as a dumb terminal. This type of connection has obvious limitations, since you would be limited to keyboard and text I/O. For additional information on UNIX, see the Resources Chapter.

Lacking a graphical interface, Shell Accounts are not as popular as they once were, and many ISPs don't bother to offer them anymore. The only advantage is the possibility of connecting with a dumb terminal or a computer that does not have a graphical (Windows) interface. For example, you could use a pocket size electronic Notebook (Sharp Wizard, for example) to pick up e-mail or even telnet and FTP files. An Internet terminal in your shirt pocket is useful if you travel a lot and want to keep in touch. See Figure 6.4 for a comparison of a Shell account and a PPP/SLIP connection.

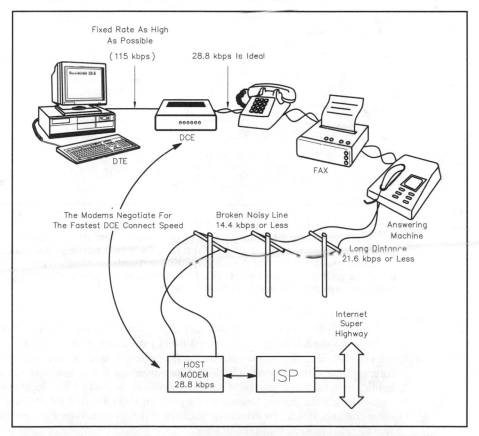

Figure 6.3—Overall modem transfer rates depend on many factors. Use the highest speed possible between your computer and the modem. 115 Kbps is recommended. Long runs of telephone line or lines in poor condition can lower the connect speeds.

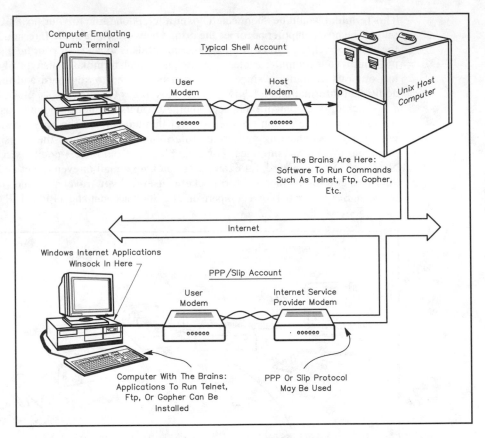

Figure 6.4—A shell account and a PPP/SLIP account work differently. When using a Shell account, your computer emulates a remote (dumb) terminal connected by modem to a UNIX computer. Only text screens are possible, because graphics cannot be displayed on a dumb terminal. With a PPP/SLIP account your computer processes both text and graphics, including high-level Internet applications such as Web Browsers.

    PPP (Point-to-Point Protocol) and *SLIP* (Serial Line Internet Protocol) refer to the protocol for handling the transmission of packetized data between the modem and the Internet. Technically they mimic the *IP*, putting your computer closer to the actual Internet than a Shell connection does. The advantage is that you may run any Internet application, such as a graphical browser, because the software is located on your machine and not the host's. One common piece of software that all PPP and SLIP users must run is a *WinSock* (Windows Socket). *WinSocks* provide the interface between *Windows* applications and the modem.

    A popular WinSock is the *Trumpet WinSock.* When installing it, you will be asked to provide values for MSS (maximum segment size), MTU (maximum transmission unit) and RWIN (receive window). These values will depend on network traffic, your hardware setup and software configurations. There is no one right answer. The optimum values change, depending on which application you are using at the time. As a rule, you can experiment to see which values give you the highest transfer rate when ftping a zipped file. A good starting point would be to use MSS=512, MTU=576 and RWIN=2048. The WinSock setup also will ask whether you will be using a SLIP or a PPP connection, which baud rate you want to use between the computer and the modem and if you want to use hardware handshaking. Choose the highest baud rate that your computer and modem will accept and hardware handshaking. This will ensure that data transfer will not be slowed down by a bottleneck in your machine. After all, what is the sense of having a 28.8 Kbps connection to the Internet if your computer will only take data at 14.4 Kbps?

Your ISP may offer a choice between a PPP and SLIP account. PPP is the newer and is claimed to be the official Internet standard. It is more widely used than SLIP and Microsoft has indicated that it will favor PPP over SLIP. PPP offers compression, has built-in error detection and can handle both IP and *IPX* (Internet Packet Exchange for Novell networks) protocols that SLIP cannot. There is a compressed version of SLIP called CSLIP, but it is not governed by any standards group. Of minor concern is that PPP is more complex than SLIP and takes up more processor power. If offered a choice, choose PPP.

Internet Commands

Many of the standard Internet commands are really UNIX commands in disguise. If we are running a *Windows* machine, we must run an application that mimics them. Often it is impossible to tell if an application is performing a UNIX command or is a standalone *Windows* application. For our purposes, it doesn't matter—their origin is not important. The common denominator is the WinSock program. It plays the crucial role as the interface between the *Windows* applications and the telecommunications software. *Windows* programs are said to have *hooks* into the WinSock. This means any application can and will use the WinSock. Figure 6.5 shows a typical set of Internet applications installed in an "Internet" *Windows* group. Telnet, FTP and PING mimic *UNIX* commands. The others are application programs that will be described later in this chapter.

Telnet

Telnet allows you to log on to a remote computer just as if you were sitting in front of it. Many computer sites are open to the public, although they require a login procedure. The usual procedure requires you to give your user name and a password. Public sites often recognize **guest** or **anonymous** as the name for a login and your e-mail address as the password. This allows the public to gain access and use some of the facilities of the site. Other sites may require that you register with them before they will allow you access. Usually an e-mail is sent to the system administrator, identifying who you are and what password you would like to use. When permission is granted, you will be able to login using the prearranged user name and password.

Telnet may be issued as a direct command from a host Shell account, or may be run from a *Windows* application program such as *EWAN*. There are many shareware telnet programs to choose from. Telnet is the technique used to access packet radio gateways from the Internet. Registration is required for these gateways to prohibit the public from initiating a packet radio transmission without a license. Your call letters

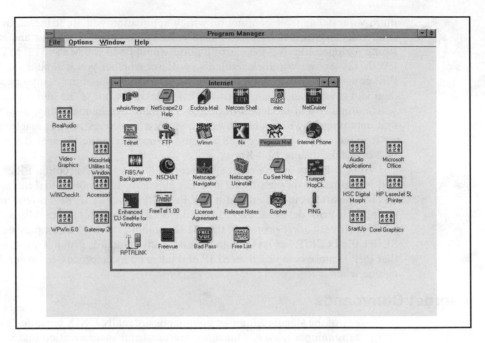

Figure 6.5—A typical set of Internet Windows applications programs. It is a good idea to place all your Internet applications into the same group.

are generally used as the login user name with a password of your choice. There is more about this in the section on Packet Gateways. When you are connected to a remote computer by telnet, you don't have free run of that machine; generally you are only allowed to run only a few selected programs.

The command is issued by typing the command **telnet** followed by the address of the host computer. For instance to connect to the Clarkson University packet radio gateway, K2CC, you would type (**telnet k2cc.ampr.org**).

To connect to *NASA's Spacelink*, type (**telnet spacelink.msfc.nasa.gov**).

Typing **telnet** without the address may, on some operating systems (such as a Shell host account), put you into another command mode. The prompt will change to *telnet* and you will be able to issue a whole new set of commands. See the sidebar "Telnet: With and Without an Address." Sometimes an optional port number is given after the address portion. This will allow you to access a specific program on the remote computer. That program may be customized to automatically bypass any login requirements, immediately presenting you with a menu.

Until recently, telnet was used mainly to access information databases. Since the Worldwide Web has grown in popularity, most people are content to search for information on it, rather than telneting to computers running *Gopher, Archie* and *WHATIS* search programs. They are mentioned because they are still very useful for those who are limited to a text only display, and they often do faster searches than a Web search program.

Telnet: With and Without an Address

Typing **telnet** at the command prompt may switch you to the telnet command mode, if you are using a host that supports this mode. This is an unusual instance where a command has two personalities. If telnet is issued without an address, it performs as a command and connects to that address. If it is issued with a following address, the operating system changes to another command mode with a new prompt. The prompt changes to *telnet*. The following will appear on your screen if you type **help** at the telnet prompt.

    telnet> help

Commands may be abbreviated. Commands are:

close	close current connection
display	display operating parameters
mode	try to enter line-by-line or character-at-a-time mode
open	connect to a site
quit	exit telnet
send	transmit special characters ('send ?' for more)
set	set operating parameters ('set ?' for more)
status	print status information
toggle	toggle operating parameters ('toggle ?' for more)
z	suspend telnet
?	print help information

    telnet>

FTP—File Transfer Protocol

FTP is a TC/PIP protocol or a program that implements the protocol, allowing a user to access and transfer files from another system over the Internet. FTP uses the familiar hierarchical directory structure that our PCs use. Use the *DIR* command to list all the files in a given directory, or *CD* to change the directory. The directory displayed when you first enter a ftp site depends on whether the site is operating under UNIX, VMS or VM. The UNIX environment is by far the most common. PC users should be cautioned, since UNIX commands are case sensitive. Typing errors often occur when inexperienced PC users venture into the UNIX world for the first time. Figure 6.6 is a list of commonly used FTP commands.

FTP may be implemented as a direct command followed by an address if your host supports this, or it may be run as a Windows application or even run as a browser feature. Not all computers on the Internet allow access to their files; there are thousands that do, however. Many support *anonymous ftp*, the ability to login using *anonymous* as your login name and your e-mail address as the password. For example, the ARRL allows anonymous login. To ftp to **ftp.arrl.org**, you would use *anonymous* as the user name and your e-mail address as the password. Figure 6.7 is a screen shot from a popular ftp Windows application, WS_FTP. The screen is divided into two sections: the left side shows the local directory where the downloaded files will be stored and the right side shows a directory listing files that may be downloaded. In this case the

🖫 CD

Change the directory. Use the CD command to select a current directory on the remote computer. It is used the same way as the DOS CD command. For example if you type **CD ARRL/CONTESTS** you will move to the to the subdirectory contests under the arrl directory.

🖫 PWD

Display the current directory. Use this after you have issued the CD command to see what directory you are currently in.

🖫 DIR

Display all the files in the currently selected directory. Other information may be displayed such as file size, date, time and type.

🖫 LS

Same as DIR, however, this is a UNIX command.

🖫 ASCII

Sets the download mode for ASCII transfers. Use this for files with .txt, .doc, hlp, asc, readme and info extensions.

🖫 BIN

Sets the download mode for binary transfers. Use this for files with .zip, .exe, .gif, .jpg, .bmp, .avi and .wav extensions.

🖫 GET

Downloads (gets) the file from the remote computer and stores it on your computer.

🖫 PUT

Uploads (puts) a file to the remote computer. Many, but not all, anonymous ftp sites allow users to upload files. Submission procedures might be found in files named readme or how_to-upload.

🖫 MGET

Same as GET, a string of multiple files may be downloaded.

🖫 MPUT

Same as PUT, a string of multiple files may be uploaded.

🖫 EXIT

Ends the ftp session

🖫 QUIT

Ends the ftp session

🖫 BYE

Ends the ftp session

🖫 HELP

Displays help information

?

Will send this (or similar) command list to your terminal.

Figure 6.6—These are the standard keyboard FTP commands. FTP *Windows* applications simply automate the use of these commands.

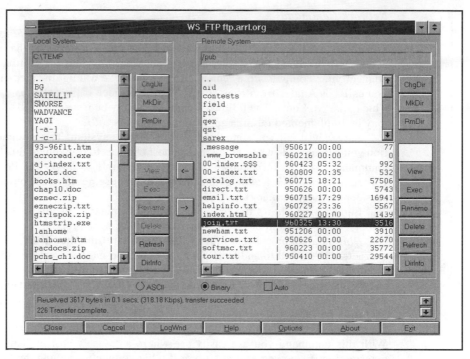

Figure 6.7—Ftp'ing a file is easy when the WS-FTP shareware application program is used. The file *join.txt* has be selected for downloading from the */pub* subdirectory. The file will automatically be placed in the selected directory (C:/TEMP here) on your computer.

file *join.txt* on the ARRL FTP Site has been selected. The file *join.txt* may be downloaded to **c:\temp** on our computer by clicking on the left pointing arrow, or we may choose to view it simply by clicking on the "view" button on the left side of the remote window. Downloading files from remote computers is as easy as point-and-clicking.

The ARRL ftp site is set up to provide immediate information. Other available files are stored on the ARRL BBS and elsewhere on Internet. Most of the files can be found at (**oak.oakland.edu**).

Before a file may be ftp'ed, you must decide if it is to be transferred as an ASCII or Binary file. All program files (those ending in .EXE) and most compressed files must be transferred using the binary mode, while text files must generally be sent as ASCII. The commands shown in Figure 6.6 would be used if you were not using an ftp application program. For instance, if you were using a Shell account without a graphical interface, you would type **GET ASCII join.txt** to download the file *join.txt*. If you are using a Browser program ftp'ing is even easier. All you have to do is click on the desired file and it automatically downloads to your system, usually after asking where you want it stored.

Network Commands

There will be times when the Net does not work as expected. *Finger*, *Ping* and *Traceroute* are simple UNIX commands that can reveal a lot about the innards of the actual network. Generally, you have no idea what physical connections are used to connect your computer to a remote site. It's just like a long distance phone call—if you call Los Angles from New York, you have no idea if the call was routed through Chicago or St. Louis. The following commands may be issued as UNIX commands or may be implemented through application programs.

Finger will tell you something about a remote system. The amount of information you get depends whether the remote host chooses to implement this function. The command takes the form *finger UserID*. For example to *finger* the President of the United States (e-mail address **president@whitehouse.gov**), you would type (**finger president@whitehouse.gov**).

Figure 6.8A shows the result of a finger command. In this case it was issued through an application program, rather then typing it in directly.

Ping is a command that returns the round-trip time that it takes for a block of characters to be sent to and from a remote host. You may be surprised to find that the time it takes to travel to a host has little bearing on its physical distance. Figure 6.8B shows that the average time for 15 round trips to the ARRL host, **arrl.org**, took 3.331 seconds.

Ping performs only an end-to-end check. *Traceroute* and *Hopcheck* are more useful commands, because they show all the routes used and the transit time to each one. With this command you can easily see where a route is broken. This is useful for determining if your server is at fault or if other connections along the Internet are out of service. Figure 6.8C shows the route from a Netcom user in Stamford, Connecticut to **arrl.org** in Newington, Connecticut.

The *Trumpet HopCheck* application program is used to check the route between two users. By noting the node location identifiers, we can determine that the data traveled more than 1200 miles to reach its final destination 75 miles away. The data starts out in Stamford, CT (stm-ct, line 1), travels to Newark, NJ (nwk-nj, line 3), then to Washington, DC (was-dc, line 4), then to Chicago, IL (chw-il, line 5), then to Boston, MA (lines 8,9,10) and then finally to the ARRL in Connecticut (mgate.arrl.org, line 12). An out-of-the-way route like this is typical of the Internet; distance between sites has little bearing on the route or time taken. This is about as close as we can get to perceiving the physical nature of the Internet. The Internet is elusive and the route may be completely different the next time a check is made.

Names and Addresses

There three common types of names or addresses. They are addresses for personal e-mail, host sites as specified by the *DNS* (Domain Name System) and *URL*s, (Uniform Resource Locators). The ideal address is easily remembered by humans and efficiently manipulated by machines.

By convention, e-mail addresses are not case sensitive. There are many instances when a URL (Web address) address will contain case-sensitive parts, however. It is a good idea to get into the habit of always being aware of the case when typing any kind of Internet address.

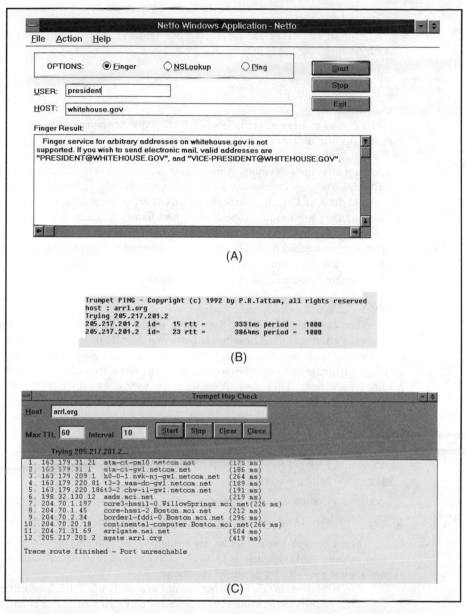

(A)

(B)

(C)

Figure 6.8—Information about the President's e-mail address is available by "fingering" him. In A, *NetInfo*, a Windows applications program, does the work. In B, the time for a round-trip connection is calculated by the *Trumpet Ping* program. The *Trumpet Hop Check* in C program displays the route used to connect two sites within Connecticut. The data travels through many states before it is returned to Connecticut. In step 5, we see the data has reached as far west as Chicago.

E-mail Addresses

E-mail addresses are much like our familiar postal address system. A postal address might be the following:

Joe Ham
73 Any Street
Hamtown, WY
USA

Joe's e-mail address might be **joeham@73anystreet.hamtown.wy.usa**

This is in the form of **user@host**. All e-mail addresses use the @ symbol to separate them into two parts. The user name appears before the @ symbol and the host name or location after the @ symbol. A user name is chosen when you first sign up with a host provider. You may choose any name that is not already in use by another user on your host. At the ARRL, staff member call signs or department names are used as user names because they are unique, shorter than real names and easily remembered. The host portion of an e-mail address may be thought of as either a location or name. It doesn't matter, because they both refer to the same computer. The host name or location for the ARRL is **arrl.org**. If you wanted to send an e-mail to the Volunteer Examiner Coordinator Department at the League, you would simply address it to **vec@arrl.org**

DNS

The *DNS* (Domain Name System) provides an easy-to-remember format for host names. Periods are used to separate parts in a domain name into subdomains. Domain names are read from left to right, with the largest category appearing at the right end of the string. In the United States six domains have been identified that should cover any type of user. They depend on what the user does rather than physical location. These domains are:

.com	Commercial organizations
.edu	Educational and research institutions
.gov	Governmental agencies
.mil	Military agencies
.net	Communication networks
.org	Private groups such as nonprofit organizations or foundations

Some typical domain names are **arrl.org**—this indicates the ARRL is an organization, **mit.edu** —Massachusetts Institute of Technology (an educational institution) and **whitehouse.gov**—a part of our government.

Physical domains do exist, but are not as widely used. Each country is assigned a two letter country code, similar to an amateur call sign prefix. For example, the United Sates is assigned **.us** and Canada **.ca**. The DNS is ready for worldwide expansion of the Internet. Over 300 country codes have been assigned; only about 100 countries have Internet service, however.

Individuals do not get domain names. They are assigned by InterNIC, the Internet Network Information Center, to groups who demonstrate that they have a need and the ability to access the Internet. Your ISP will be assigned a domain name; you as a customer will only be issued a user name provided by the ISP.

URL

A URL is not too different than a Swiss Army Knife; one tool that does just about everything. URLs, Uniform Resource Locators, are in a way an address, a protocol and a file name all combined into a unique name. The most common protocols implemented by URLs include http (hypertext transfer protocol), ftp, telnet, Gopher and WAIS (wide-area information service). When a URL is issued, a specific piece of information from a unique site is requested using a specific protocol. URLs were developed by the Worldwide Web project as an efficient means of locating and obtaining any kind of information that could be sent over the Internet. They consist of a string of characters without spaces.

URLs take the general form of: *protocol://hostname/directory-path/filename*. The most common use of URLs define hot links used in Web browsers. Browsers use the http protocol for transferring information to your computer. The information may be graphics, text, audio, video, a file or just about anything else a computer can process. For example, the URL, **http://www.arrl.org/hamradio.html** tells you the protocol is *http*, the site is on the Worldwide Web (*WWW*), the site (host) address is *arrl.org*, and a file named *hamradio.html* will be sent to you. If you are using a browser program, your computer will process the html file, filling the screen with text, graphics and hot links (other URLs) in a matter of seconds. See the following section on Web Browsers and hot links for more detail. Not all Worldwide Web sites use the letters WWW at the start of their address; while it is common, it is not a requirement for an http resource.

If the URL is given as: **ftp://ftp.arrl.org/pub/join.txt** we have requested that the *ftp* protocol be used to send us a file from the host named *ftp.arrl.org*. The file resides in the *pub* directory and is named *join.txt*.

THINGS TO DO ON THE INTERNET

In this section we will look some of the most popular features of the Internet: e-mail, news groups, Web browsers, conference servers and mailing lists. For our purposes we will assume you are running Windows. All the applications mentioned can be downloaded from the Internet and are offered as shareware. This does, however, present a Catch-22 situation. How do you get these programs if you don't already have Internet connectivity? Good question. Most ISPs will provide, as a part of their package, a Web browser program that will get you started. Once you are on line with their browser, you may download another browser if you wish, or download all the Internet applications you can imagine. There are so many Internet applications, you could probably download a new one every day. Asking for a helping hand on the local repeater will almost certainly result in an offer of help, and perhaps even some starter software.

E-mail

Those familiar with packet radio know that packet mail can take days to reach its destination. On the Internet it often takes a matter of a minute or two, although occasional delays can extend this time to several hours. Many who work in offices with a LAN have an Internet e-mail connection without even knowing it. Ask your network administrator if in doubt. The global e-mail system might be thought of as many LANs, all interconnected by the Internet. The Internet does not process e-mail any differently than any other data; it only provides the path for data to travel over.

If you use any of the on-line information services, your e-mail is not being sent directly to the Internet, but rather it is preprocessed by their software. If you are using a direct connection from an ISP, a mail program will be required. Many, such as Pegasus and Eudora, are available as shareware. These programs allow you to save to disk all received e-mails, send multiple copies to different users, reply with just the click of the mouse, print the mail, and even receive word-processing files as an attachment. Pictures saved as a graphic file are quickly "attached" and sent. With some e-mail programs, viewing them is as easy as clicking on the "view attachment" icon. There is something special—a sense of anticipation—when an e-mail is received with a picture attached to it.

Figure 6.9 shows a screen shot from the Microsoft Mail program. It should look very familiar to Windows users. The top level File, Edit, View are standard Windows commands. The middle window shows two messages waiting in the Inbox, ready to be read. The message from Mabey about the ICOM IC-7 is opened in the forward window. All e-mails have a Subject Line; in this case the subject is ICOM IC-775DSP and the text of the e-mail follows.

Mail programs make it as easy as possible to send mail. You don't have to remember any actual e-mail addresses. Figure 6.9 shows a typical address book. The address of any mail previously sent or received will be stored. A click of the mouse is all that is necessary to recall the address. In this example, Joel Kleinman, N1BKE, has been selected. We do not actually see his Internet e-mail address—the program knows it and automatically inserts it. We can identify our friends by their nicknames, real names, call signs, actual Internet e-mail address or whatever you choose.

There is one problem with some mailers. While is easy to send mail, it may not be that easy to successfully send or receive a file—a picture or a document—as an attachment. Most files generated by word processors consist of 8-bit information, as are most picture files and executable (.EXE or .COM) files. Some mail programs will only allow attachment and transmission of 7-bit information. In that case, you will need a program such as *UUENCODE* or a *MIME*-compatible program to send a file. To receive such files you will need *UUDECODE* or a *MIME decoder*. Generally, both capabilities are needed. There are a number of shareware programs available to do the job, but first ask your internet provider if you need 7/8-bit external encode/decode capability.

Newsgroups — Usenet

Newsgroups are the equivalent of a worldwide BBS system. *Usenet* is the name of the largest one, with millions of daily readers. To access a newsgroup, you will need an application program called a newsreader. In addition, your ISP must provide access. Some provide limited access, blocking those groups they feel are inappropriate. Some newsgroups are moderated—to ensure articles are suitable for a particular group. The unmoderated groups do leave the door open for objectionable material. This is generally not a problem because this type of material is normally posted to a

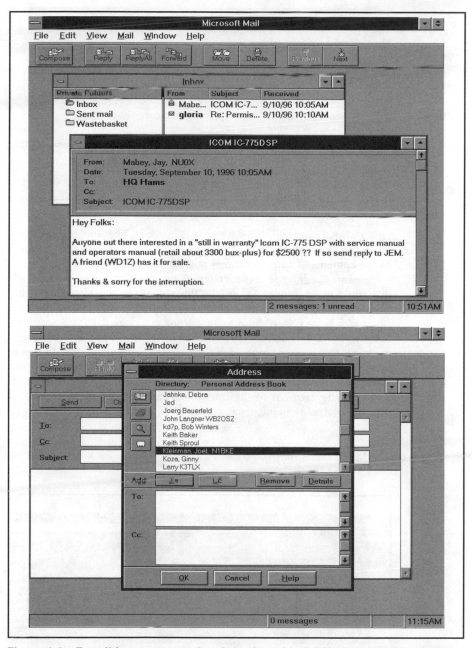

Figure 6.9—E-mail is easy to send and receive with the Microsoft Mail program. Incoming mail is listed in the Inbox; clicking on a particular item opens it. Clicking on the *Reply* icon is all that is needed to send a reply. This and similar programs include an e-mail address directory, eliminating the need to type actual e-mail addresses.

Table 6.1
Newsgroup Organization

These are the seven top-level categories. All other topics will included under one of these.

comp	Computer hardware and software
rec	Recreational topics—sports, movies, hobbies travel
sci	Science topics
soc	Social Science and cultural discussions—ethnic, religious, occupational
talk	Controversial topics—politics, abortion, guns
news	Discussions about Usenet
misc	Catch-all category—everything else goes here

group whose name will indicate what is inside it. There would be little sense in looking for chicken recipes in the "Vegetarian Cooking" group, and you might be offended by the contents of some messages posted to **alt.sex.whatever**!

Before the Internet expanded to its present size, seven main areas were selected that would accommodate any article. Table 6.1 shows the these areas. Alternative groups exist whose key words give a good idea of the type of articles posted. A newsreader can search by key word for a particular topic. Figure 6.10 is a screen shot taken from the *WinVN* newsreader program. A search was made on (**radio.amateur**). Three groups matched, and it is obvious what their content might include. For example, the first one, (**rec.radio.amateur.antenna**), will have articles about Amateur Radio antennas. This screen shows only 14 of the 16,018 possible groups. Groups come and go on a daily basis, but the trend is toward more and more groups. Almost any subject you can imagine is already being discussed in some group.

Threads

Inside each group there may be hundreds of articles with many of them "threaded"

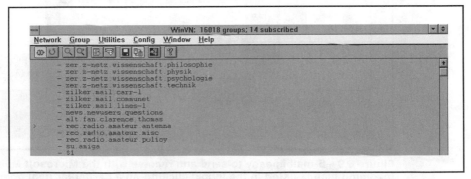

Figure 6.10—*WinVN,* **a popular newsgroup reader, shows a few of the 16,018 possible groups. Three Amateur Radio groups are listed. You simply click on a particular group to read what is inside it.**

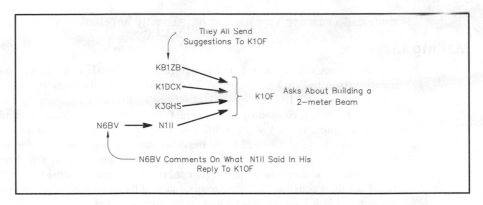

Figure 6.11—In this drawing of a news thread, K1OF asks an initial question. All answers are threaded or linked to each other. Newsreader programs group all the messages together ('threads them'), so you can follow a line of discussion.

together. A thread is formed when someone posts an article or message and others respond to it. For example, K1OF might ask if anyone knows how to build a good 2-meter beam. The answers he receives will be *threaded* or linked to his initial query. In this case N1II responded by saying "you should check out N6BV's antenna design software." N6BV then posted the reply, "I will e-mail you the design program N1II suggested." A newsreader program will show you all the articles having a common thread. By selecting K1OF's original posting, you will be able to see the threads linking N6BV to N1II to K1OF. Threads make it possible to read all the correspondence on a single topic at one time. The threads can be several layers deep lasting for many weeks, if the initial topic was of interest. Postings are usually deleted automatically after a period of time. Often, threads of lasting interest are archived as a *FAQ* (frequently asked questions) or other files.

Netiquette

Every system needs some rules, and the informal rules governing behavior on the Internet is known as *netiquette*. Before you post a question (remember it will be sent throughout the world), find out if your question has been asked before and if you are asking it in the right place. Always read the FAQ document for your intended group before posting material. Often, a little research will reveal an answer before you ask the question. Because users often post questions that have been asked previously, the acronym *rtfm* has become common place. It means, in very strong terms, that you should read the manual (or FAQ). See the Resources chapter for other common abbreviations.

If you ask a controversial question or make a controversial statement, you may be *flamed*. A flame is a *very* negative reply. Words typed in capital letters are akin to shouting. Use the same (or better) manners that you would use on the air and you will get along just fine on the Net. *Usenet* is the best possible place to gain in-depth information. It is likely there is someone out there who knows more than you do about the topic. All you have to do to avoid being flamed is to ask a new question and post it to the right group. But don't let the threat of being flamed discourage you. If you can't find an answer, ask! You may be pleasantly surprised.

Mailing Lists

A mailing list (sometimes called a reflector) is similar to the newsgroups—topics are discussed and answers are given. The only difference is the delivery system. When you join a mailing list you will ask questions and receive answers by e-mail. A *list-server* provides a common e-mail address that is used for all correspondence. This makes it simple to post a query; all you have to do is send it to the list-server. The server re-mails your message to all the other subscribers. The listserver is usually an unattended computer. Be cautioned: joining too many mailing lists will result in a lot of e-mail. If you don't have the time to read them, you might consider dropping off the list. Like their cousins, the newsgroups, mailing lists are sometimes moderated. Most are not. Table 6.2 shows several ham-related mailing lists.

To obtain information, subscribe to (or unsubscribe from) a list, send an e-mail to the listserver. The text in the body of the e-mail will be interpreted by the listserver computer, resulting in your addition or removal from a list. A single listserver may serve many different mailing lists, so the name of the particular list you want to join must be included. For example, if you are interested in *The ARRL Letter* (see Table 6.2), you may subscribe to it by sending an e-mail to: **listserv@netcom.com**. Include the body of the letter, subscribe letter-list   to subscribe to it or **unsubscribe letter-list** to remove yourself from the list. To obtain information about the listserver itself, the body should say, *help*. There is no need to include a "subject" line for these inquiries, unless your mailer requires one. The listserver will ignore it.

After subscribing, the listserver will usually respond with a confirmation and

---

Table 6.2
Listservers

List Name	E-mail address of listserver	Notes
letter-list	listserv@netcom.com	Distribution of the ARRL Letter
arrl-exam-list	listserv@netcom.com	License exam schedule
arrl-nediv-list	listserv@netcom.com	Bulletins from the NE Division director
arrl-ve-list	listserv@netcom.com	Info for ARRL Volunteer Examiners
ema-arrl	listserv@netcom.com	Info on the Eastern Mass. ARRL section
fox-list	listserv@netcom.com	Info on radio direction finding, fox hunting
fieldorg-1	listserv@netcom.com	Discussions about the ARRL field organizations
ham-tech	listserv@netcom.com	Technical discussions about Amateur Radio
ham-wx	listserv@netcom.com	Weather info
ky1n-list	listserv@netcom.com	Info about VE exams in New England
barc-list	listserv@netcom.com	Info about the Boston Amateur Radio Club
barc-races	listserv@netcom.com	Info about RACES and Emergency Management
newsline-list	listserv@netcom.com	Distribution of the Amateur Radio Newsline

---

specific instructions, including how to unsubscribe. If you lost the unsubscribe instructions, the help message (above) will give you the missing information.

USENET BY E-MAIL

You can receive some Usenet newsgroups via e-mail if you don't have a newsreader or your ISP does not provide access to the newsgroups. For instance, if you want to receive all the postings to the rec.radio.amateur.misc newsgroup by e-mail, send an e-mail to (**listserv@ucsd.edu**). In the body of your message type: *add info-hams*. If you want to reply by sending a posting to the newsgroup, send an e-mail to (**rec-radio-amateur-misc@cs.utexas.edu**).

Chat/Video Conference Servers

Servers in general do just that—they serve you by providing information. The listservers mentioned above send you information in the form of e-mail messages. Servers are central places where you connect and then are reconnected to others. They are similar to a conference call or party line. Some servers provide real time video, voice conferencing and text exchange. Hundreds of people use these popular systems, so they all include some means of identifying users with common interests. Groups or topics are formed—it is not surprising to find that hams have their own groups.

CUSeeMe, *Connectix Video Phone*, *VidCall*, *Intel Proshare* and *VDOPhone* are video conferencing programs. Audio conferencing programs include *IPHONE*, *FreeTel*, *GlobalChat*, *Homer*, *Ircle*, *Maven* and *NetscapeChat*. Descriptions of *IPHONE* and *CUSeeME* follow. Information on the others may be found by performing a web search on their name. The Resources Chapter contains more information on cameras.

There are many servers that do not have an Amateur Radio presence, such as game playing servers. Your opponent may be a remote computer or even a real person. If you would like to play Bridge, Chess, Checkers, Poker, Backgammon or just about any other game you can think of, you will find a server to accommodate you.

IRC

The Internet Relay Chat is the most popular conference. It supports real-time text exchanges, with thousands of users. IRC groups users into channels or chat rooms. This creates a diverse atmosphere where you will encounter many different personalities. IRC users log onto channels, just as hams do when they join a net on a specific frequency. You may join an existing channel or simply start your own. This is not much different than calling CQ or breaking into an existing QSO. Identifications are made by the use of nicknames. If the name you choose is already in use, you will be told to choose another one. Naturally, hams often use their call signs. There can be thousands of channels to choose from. Figure 6.12 shows a screen shot from an mIRC, an IRC application program. The program has a built-in search feature that will search all the possible channel names by a keyword. In this example "radio" was used, and the channels with the word "radio" are listed. When this search was made, there were 4 out of 3075 channels with the word "radio" in them.

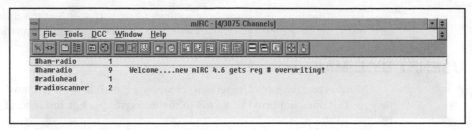

Figure 6.12—Potential QSOs are easy to find with the *mIRC* program. A scan of 3075 IRC channels for the word "radio" reveals four channels (top screen bar). A click of the mouse is all that is necessary to join of these QSOs.

IRC Networks

IRC is comprised of three major networks with several small ones. The major ones are EFNet, UnderNet and DalNet. The large networks have a different personality from the smaller ones. The EFNet is the largest and suffers the most abuse, mainly from teenaged hackers and from lag (delays). If you run an IRC application program, you may not even know what network you are using because most of the connection process has been automated. A Web site that lists the various networks and servers is (**http://www.geocities.com/SiliconValley/park/6000/servers.html**).

In an effort to reduce network congestion, some servers will accept users only from a local area. After all, why use a server halfway around the world to talk to your friends across town. If a server refuses you, just try another one—there are many to choose from. Most servers use port 6667 (DalNet uses 7000). Your server list will indicate the port to use.

Figure 6.13 shows a typical network configuration. Individuals (clients in IRC terminology) log into specific servers and the servers are interconnected by high speed digital links. Surprising as it may seem, the three major networks do not interconnect with each other. Knowledge of the network you have logged into is necessary. You can be logged into the EFNet on channel **#hamradio** and not be able to talk with your friend who is logged into the **#hamradio** channel on the DalNet. For example, KA1OF can talk to K3EIN, DL8EBM and WA2TQI because they are all logged into the same network and are using the same channel. Although W9KTH and K3OSK are both logged on the **#hamradio** channel, they can't talk to each other or to the gang on the EFNet. WT1I and N1EKD can talk to each other, but they can't talk to K3OSK because he is not on the **#cooking** channel.

The best way to obtain a current list of IRC network servers is to perform a Web search on "IRC Servers" or point your browser to the Web site listed above. EFNet is the largest of the three networks with over 20,000 users. Since it is large it seems to attract the lion's share of misfits. Operation can become chaotic at times, and the smaller nets may offer a more amiable atmosphere. Occasionally the network servers lose touch with each other and a "netsplit" occurs. When this happens, you may lose some or all the parties you were in contact with.

The most popular ham radio channel is found on the EFNet. Try channel **#hamradio**. Here you will find activity at almost any hour of the day or night. It is very common to have at least one or two DX stations present. **#hamradio** is a great place to stop by for

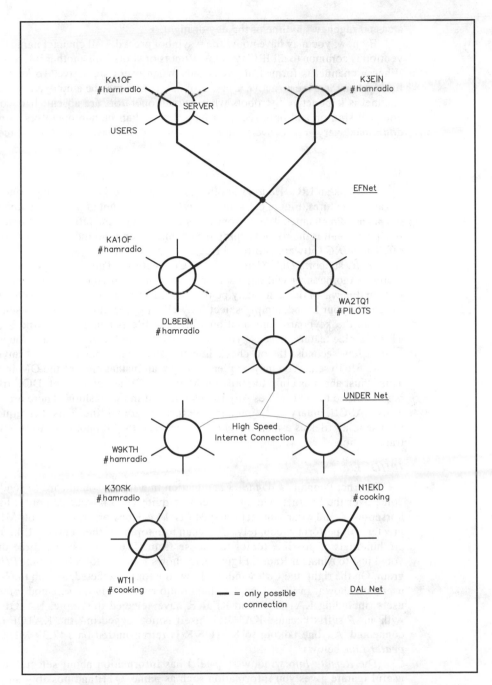

Figure 6.13—Three major IRC networks are shown operating. Communication is possible only within a network, not between networks.

a casual ragchew anytime of the day or night.

By now, you may have noted the # symbol precedes all channel names. This convention is common to all IRC systems. Robots or "bots" are another interesting factor. When a channel is formed, it exists only when users are active. To keep a channel listed when there are no active users, a robot program may be employed. The **#hamradio** channel is kept active by robots when human operators are absent. It is conceivable you will sign on and only see the robots rather than human operators. Since robots don't make very good conversationalists, you will just have to wait for a "real" ham to appear.

mIRC

mIRC is an IRC *Windows* application program. It is user friendly and has some advanced features. Figure 6.14 shows a *mIRC* screen shot of a typical conversation on the **#hamradio** channel. The current users are listed on the left side. **@HamBot** is not a live person—it is the robot keeping the channel open if all the other users should sign off. The *mIRC* software is offered free for home users.

mIRC supports *DCC* (Direct Client Connection). This allows you to connect directly to another user without a server in the path. Your connection is faster and more private this way. Files can easily be transferred. If you have a file that you would like to send to your friend, simply select it by clicking the mouse, and it is sent. You can continue the keyboard conversation while the file is being sent in the background. This is a nice feature, because you can send a picture file and see who you are talking to in a few seconds. If you check into the **#hamradio** channel, ask if anyone has a picture file to send. You may be pleased to get an instant view of the OM in his shack. This is just about as close to 100% QRM-free SSTV as you can get. DCC file transfer is not limited to picture files Any file can be sent in this fashion. There are no restrictions—ASCII, binary, .gif, .jpg and .exe formats are all fine. This technique is easier than sending files as e-mail attachments, because they do not have to be encoded for transmission.

IPHONE

Internet Phone is a *Windows* application that uses a sound card to send digitized voice over the Internet. The quality can be quite good if your computer has enough horsepower, and your connection speed is 14.4 Kbps or greater. A 66-MHz 486 or greater will perform adequately. Users can join topics of their choice. Like IRC, there are hundreds of possible topics to choose from. There are usually three or four devoted just to Amateur Radio. Figure 6.15 shows four windows from the *IPHONE* program. On the right, the *Call* window shows the topics selected, and on the left current users are shown. In this example, "ham radio rptrlink" is the selected topic. Several users, including KA1OF-R and KF5KF, have selected this topic. KA1OF is shown with an *-R* suffix because KA1OF himself is not logged in—the KA1OF repeater is connected. Anyone talking to KA1OF-R is retransmitted on 147.39 MHz (see *Repeater Link* below).

The *Remote Info* window (top left) has information about selected users. This useful feature gives you information such as name, QTH and possibly an e-mail address, before the QSO (chat) starts. The *Internet Phone* window is the control panel. When someone calls, one of the 10 button icons will indicate the caller's nickname.

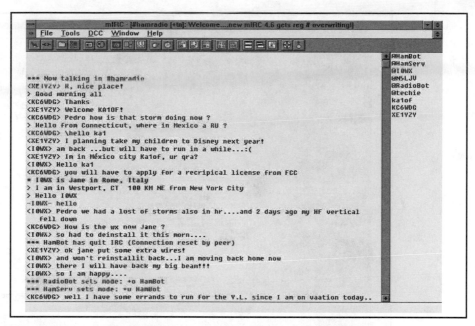

Figure 6.14—This is what a QSO looks like on the #hamradio IRC chat channel. Current users are listed on the right side of the slider bar. Stations from Italy, Mexico and California are enjoying this conversation.

Just click on a button to answer the call. These buttons also function as a memory dialer and can be used to initiate calls. The off-hook telephone icon is used to hang up the call. The *Remote Statistics* window (lower left) tallies the number of lost packets. Good audio quality is maintained with up to 10% lost packets.

Work Repeaters over IPHONE

Mark Brown, N9YNQ, has developed *Repeater Link,* the first application that directly connects on-the-air hams by voice. *Repeater Link* works in conjunction with *IPHONE* and a repeater. Audio from a sound card must be linked to the repeater. This is easily accomplished by interfacing to a rig with a VOX feature. The rig will key the repeater when sufficient audio is received over the *IPHONE* connection. No physical connection to the repeater is necessary if this technique is used. A better method, but not as practical for most hams, is to couple the audio directly from the PC's sound card into the repeater's audio circuits.

The program acts as a control operator by keeping nonhams from using the link. It automatically checks to see if the calling party's call sign in the FCC database. If it finds it, the audio path to the sound card will open. As you might expect, quite a bit of excitement is generated when a ham from "down-under" checks into the local 2-meter repeater.

The possibilities are quite exciting for this new mode. Before long it may be possible to link with a distant repeater by simply issuing on-air Touch-Tone com-

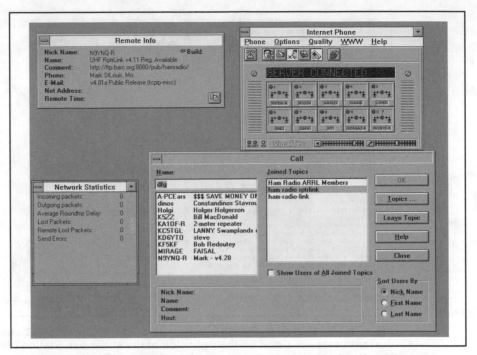

Figure 6.15—Speaking with amateurs over the Internet is fun if you have a sound card and use the *IPHONE* program. Highlighted in the *Call* window is the *ham radio rptlink* topic. Users who have joined this topic are shown to the left.

mands. Before long, HT-to-HT worldwide communications may be possible using this approach.

CUSeeMe

CUSeeME is video conferencing software that allows person-to-person and group conferences. *CUSeeME* was started in July 1992 as a research project led by Cornell University in partnership with other organizations. Cornell provides freeware versions of *CUSeeME*, which can be downloaded from the Internet. Contact (**ftp://cu-seeme.cornell.edu/pub/CUSeeMe/**).

A commercial version is available from White Pine Inc. You may purchase or obtain a 30 day demo of the commercial version from their site. The White Pine product is called *Enhanced CUSeeME*, and their site is (**http://www.cu-seeme.com**).

If you feel video conferencing is out of the question because you don't have a camera, think twice! The program will allow "lurkers," those without a camera, to able to view any of the participants. Amateurs are picking up on video conferencing. You may hear someone in a QSO on 2 meters or 20 meters mention something about seeing each other. Even if you are just listening to the QSO, it may be possible for you to join the video conference if you know what reflector (see next section) they are using. A connection may be established on a person-to-person basis by connecting directly to a user's IP address or to a reflector site that will have many simultaneous participants. You may even use the *CUSeeME* software without the Internet by connecting two dial-up modems.

Reflectors

Often participants log into a common site. This site, called a *reflector*, receives video and then resends it (it is reflected) to others on the reflector. The reflectors are not interconnected like the *IPHONE* servers. Instead of having thousands of potential contacts, you may be limited to a dozen or so. There are dozens of reflectors scattered around the world, however, with new ones popping up every day. Each reflector has a unique IP address and is often sponsored by a university or a commercial organization. Even NASA has several reflectors. They broadcast NASA TV and are intended for receive-only applications; you cannot send video to them. *CUSeeMe* has no way to organize users by topics, so the only control over who you see is through reflector choice.

The original development performed at Cornell University used Macs as the platform. As the program grew in popularity, a *Windows* version was developed. The system requirements are a 28.8-Kbps modem using a SLIP or PPP connection, 10 Mb of hard disk space, a 486 DX/66 or better processor and a 256-color 640×480 video card. Versions are available for most versions of *Windows*. Mac users will need a minimum of a 68030 running at 25 MHz, MacOS 7 or higher, and 5 Mb of RAM. Obviously, a camera is required to send. One popular camera is the Connectix QuickCam. See the

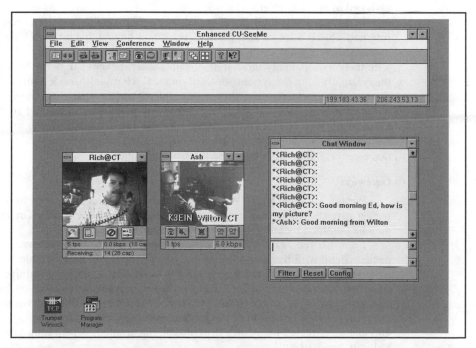

Figure 6.16—Rich and Ash enjoy a video QSO. Not only do they see each other, they can type back-and-forth using the Chat Window.

Resource Chapter for details. An alternative video source is a video capture board used with a camcorder.

The picture quality is good, but the picture size is on the order of 320×120 pixels. Numerous small picture windows may appear on the screen at one time. Figure 6.16 shows Rich connected to Ash, K3EIN. Text is sent in the Chat Window. Keeping the number of video windows to a minimum will allow faster transfers. It is fascinating to watch a picture materialize because the frame is updated only by changes in the scene. If a picture is not changing, you will not be sent anymore data. This is a clever technique to conserve bandwidth. Audio also is supported, although the quality is inferior to standalone audio programs such as *IPHONE* and *FreeTel*. Simultaneous audio and video at 28.8 Kbps does not give good results, since the audio quality is poor. There is, however, an effective keyboard chat window. Here all participants can read what the others are typing. This works well because the overhead for the text transmission is small compared to video. Audio plus video is just too much for the program to handle at 28.8 Kbps.

Packet Radio Gateways

Packet gateways offer worldwide real-time connectivity between the Internet and the AmprNet (Amateur Radio Packet Radio Network). Both use the TCP/IP protocol and many of the same commands. For example, you can telnet, ftp, IRC and send e-mail to and from both systems. The AmprNet is a part of the Internet and has been assigned its own domain (block of IP numbers). Any IP address starting with 44 is assigned to the AmprNet.

In this section we will focus on ways of connecting to packet radio sites from the Internet. This is a lot of fun, particularly if you have a distant ham friend who is on packet. Many packet users don't realize that they can connect on a real-time basis with their friends many thousands of miles away, because they mistakenly associate the relatively long delays encountered on local RF node-to-node routes. RF connects a few miles apart are often slower than Internet paths spanning many thousands of miles. From the Internet there are dozens of gateways connected to hundreds of **ampr.org** nodes. Just about any place on earth is accessible, if you know the route. Antarctica even had its own packet radio gateway. The trick to successful long distance packet connects is knowing the correct route.

Gateways

Warren Toomey, VK1XWT, has compiled a comprehensive list of all the known packet gateways. It is commonly referred as the "Resource List." The latest version may be obtained by anonymous ftp from (**minnie.cs.adfa.oz.au**).

Look for the *resource* file in the *hamradio/gateways* directory. If you have a packet friend who lives near one of the listed cities, you may be able to contact him from your computer via the Internet. Upon login, most gateways require a password. This is to prevent nonamateurs from accessing a transmitter. All you have to do to "get permission" is to ask for it. Send the sysop (his e-mail address is usually given before a password is required) an e-mail stating who you are (real name, call sign, etc) and a suggested password. If permission is granted, before long you will be able to log in and with full access.

Internet gateways are like their packet cousins; in fact, they are likely residing

```
*Welcome to the Launceston Packet Radio Gateway *

Station name    : ice-gw.vk7ztt.ampr.org  [44.136.221.170]
Run by          : Tony VK7ZTT and Scott VK7YSH
Equipment       : 80386 SX (25MHz), 40 MB Disk, 2MB Ram.
Radio Interface : Interface name is "radio" with output on 144.800MHz,
1200Bd.
Location        : The Gateway is located at the premises of ISP,
                  IC Technologies, in the city centre of Launceston.
                  This is a free service provided to the Amateur community.
Local Area Info : Launceston is located in the North of the Australian Island
                  State of Tasmania and is the State's second largest city.
                  An FBB style BBS serves the Launceston area on 147.575 MHz.
Services        : We provide Telnet, FTP, SMTP, AX25, and Netrom access.
                  The gateway also provides basic JNOS BBS services.
                  The sysop welcomes comments, type 'sp sysop' to send a
                  message.

73, Tony.

Current msg# 0.
BBS,TAMPA,CSIRO,?,A,B,C,D,E,F,H,I,IH,IP,J,K,L,M,N,NR,P,PI,R,S,T,U,V,W,X,Z>
```

Figure 6.17—Long-distance Internet gateway connects are possible. The contact here was made with a Tasmanian gateway, vk7ztt.ampr.org. This information screen is obtained by using the "I" (info) command.

on the same computer. Just for fun, K1OF connected to the farthest place on earth he could reach using an Internet packet gateway. Figure 6.17 shows an actual "off-the-air" transcript of the information provided by a packet gateway in Tasmania. By connecting through their "radio" port it would be possible to connect with an Australian ham using only an HT and a packet modem. You will often be the first DX connect for many of these stations. This is thrilling for both sides and often results in a QSL request. Although QSL cards may exchanged, they do not count toward most awards when stations are worked through a gateway.

Conferences

One of the best ways to generate a live keyboard-to-keyboard QSO with a distant station is to join a conference or *converse* server. Many packet gateways provide their own conference server for local or regional connects, while others support the Worldwide Converse Server for international QSOs. The Worldwide Converse Server is similar to running an IRC dedicated to Amateur Radio. See the Sidebar "A Typical Converse Server QSO" detailing the connection process and QSO. Many gateways support a conference server. If they do, *CONF* or *CONV* will be given as a command line option. You my reach the gateways listed in the *resource.txt* file by telneting to them.

A Typical Converse Server QSO

The following is an excerpt of an actual QSO initiated over a Worldwide Converse Server.

Many of the packet gateway stations listed in the resource.txt file provide access to converse servers. **Bold** print indicates what the reader would type. Responses to Converse Server commands are given in *italics*.

In this example, KA1OF telnets to **hg5bdu.kfki.hu (148.6.80.11)**. This is KFKI, a Hungarian gateway. Once connected, he issues the **conf** command and is connected to the worldwide conference. He then types **/who** to see who is logged on the channels. As you can see, there are logins from all over the world. KA1OF is initially listed as being logged into channel 0. This channel is supposed to be used only for initiating a QSO. He notes that channel 162 is not in use (a random choice) and asks that if anyone wants a short QSO, they should meet him there. He then types **/ch 162** to switch to channel 162 and waits for someone to join him. Hubert, VE3HDL, joins him and the QSO starts. When the QSO is finished, KA1OF types **/bye** to disconnect from the conference server returning to the Hungarian gateway command line.

KA9Q NOS - KO4KS-TNOS/Unix v2.02/ELF (hg5bdu.kfki.hu)

Please login with your call sign, and use your name for the password.

login: **ka1of**

Password: *****

[TNOS-2.02-BFHIMT$]

Read users area to be informed!

Welcome ka1of, to the hg5bdu.kfki.hu TCP/IP BBS (KO4KS-TNOS/Unix v2.02/ELF)

Last on the BBS: Wed Sep 18 20:06:34 1996

You are the only user currently on the BBS

For help on using this system type 'HELP command'.

Area: 'ka1of' Current msg# 0 of 0.
?,A,B,C,CALL,CONF,D,E,F,G,H,I,J,K,L,M,N,O,P,Q,R,S,T,U,V,W,X >

conf

*** *TNOS Conference @ KFKI-Bp. Type /HELP for help.*

*** *There are 99 users online*

*** *There are 14 groups available*

*** *ka1of signed on at 20:06.*

*** *Now on Channel 0 (27 users).*

*** *Net 'Take your QSO Off channel 0, Do NOT sit on channel 0 !!!!'*

Welcome, ka1of!

/who

Channel	Users
	Take your QSO Off channel 0. Do NOT sit on channel 0!!!
	ka1of py2va g0ejg dg3bfl wa9fef ve3hld ac6g ve2pl vegcks
	ok2uzl dd8ds kb0vib lx1bi-roger hb9iat dc0ij g6rbp py2je

```
                    g0fdi hb9omj dd8ds ke6hvb dg7kap dc9tw dl4mhb dj9ze dl3sei
                    ik8scr
   1940     sp3mis
   2211     sq2cfn
   8085     g0wfs q7rwp
   12345    sleeping-channel    pse ring the bell
            db6wn pa3esk dg4kam
   32767    TCP/IP
             wa3dsp g6crv
```

anyone for a short QSO, please switch channel 162
/ch 162
*** Now on Channel 162 (1 user)*

*** *ve3hld signed on at 20:15.*
hello ve3hld, rich here
QTH is Westport, CT abt 50 miles NE NYC
<ve3hld>: Hello Rich , Hubert Here
<ve3hld>: Oakville Ontario Canada
how far Is that from Toronto?
<ve3hld>: It is 25 miles west of Toronto on Lake Ontario. Home of the Ford
Winstar.
FB, on ur QTH, we had a very rainy day here
<ve3hld>: We have had a lot of rain, but not like yours and to-day it has
<ve3hld>: cleared and the temp is 22c or 72 f. A really nice day.>>
Wow that was a nice day.. temp here only got up to 58 , burr
**Hubert, are you using a radio or using the Internet net directly to get into
this server?**
<ve3hld>: I am using a radio -25watts through a repeater in Oakville then a
<ve3hld>: satellite connection in Toronto.>>>
I'm coming through the Internet directly, no radios
<ve3hld>: You are also paying for your Internet, I'm getting mine free.hi hi.
Are you active on HF?
<ve3hld>: No I am not. Have not got into that yet. I only have a temp home made antenna.
I spent a week in Toronto last October, it was very nice.. had warm WX by luck
<ve3hld>October is about the nicest month in our area as far as I am concerned.>>
Hubert, what is the farthest place you ever worked on packet?
<ve3hld>: I have not been on it long and you are the farthest so far. This
<ve3hld>: is my first day on this Wormhole because our satellite has been
disconnected.>>
**Well I better get going, tks vy much for the QSO, I hope to meet u again
73's**
<ve3hld>: Yes Rich nice meeting you will say goodbye for now. Good Packeting.
 <ve3hld>: 73
good luck
/bye
*Exiting *** TNOS Conference @ KFKI-Bp.*

Area: 'ka1of' Current msg# 0 of 0.
?,A,B,C,CALL,CONF,D,E,F,G,H,I,J,K,L,M,N,O,P,Q,R,S,T,U,V,W,X >

The WEB

What's the WEB? We have the *Worldwide Web*, *internet*, *The Internet*, the *Web*–and the *WEB*. What's what and what's the difference? Internet, no matter how you spell it, with or without capital letters, is a communications system. Earlier in this chapter we discussed where it came from and the various services now available on it. The Web, no matter what you call it, is one of the services available on the Internet.

Technically, the Web is a system for sending around information prefixed with the word *hyper*—*hypermedia, hypertext*. . . . If you don't want a precise definition, you can look at it as point-and-click information. Look at the screen, put your mouse cursor on the (normally) blue or purple words, and click. Up comes new text, audio or perhaps a clip of live motion video. When you write a letter on your computer, you use *a word processor*. People who write Web pages use the *html* language—hypertext mark-up language. Just as your word processor puts codes into your letter to control the type and size of print, html puts codes in a page to control how it will look when you call up a Web page on your Web browser. Normally, the formatting codes are not visible when you look at a letter on your screen; likewise, the html codes are not visible when you look at a Web page.

So what is the Web? It is a set of computers, working to a standard or *proto-col*, that provides information on one end and displays information on the other end—with the information inside a wrapper called html. In official computerese, the computer having the information is called a *server*, and the computer asking for the information is called a *client*. Your Web browser is *client software*. And of course, tying together all these computers is the Internet. See the Resources Chapter for more information and suggested books.

URLs

A URL is a uniform resource locator. Uniform, because it follows a set pattern, and resource, because most anything you can call up by way of the internet is called a resource. A URL, discussed earlier in this chapter, is an address and descriptor. In this section we are going to deal with URLs beginning with the pattern **http://**

This pattern stands for a Web page, accessible with a Web browser. Very often, the next part of the address is www.companyname.com, so you will see (**http:// www.companyname.com**) as the URL or address for many major companies. In fact, it is common enough so that if you want to go to the Web page of a company, and you don't know its address, you can try this pattern. It usually works! Most Web browsers (see the next section) will accept company name, in place of a full URL, and fill in the rest by itself. An address in this form is most often the homepage of the organization. Following the .com (or .org, .gov, .edu, .net or .mil) is the specific address of various files and services—usually separated with a forward slash. Generally, either capital or lower-case letters may be used; some UNIX-based sites are case-sensitive, however.

Browsers

The software that allows you to look at Web pages, browsers are constantly evolving. Many are available, either in a trial version or with a slightly reduced capability, free, when downloaded from the manufacturer. *Mosaic* was the first to be widely used at home, and was made even more popular when CompuServe distributed a few versions to be used on its Web service. However, it is being made obsolete by changes to the html language.

In the mid 1990s, *Netscape* became the browser of choice for many people. It also was distributed free in trial versions and totally free to employees of non profit and educational organizations, and some others. For the latest (perhaps free) version, go to (**http://www.netscape.com**) and follow the instructions.

Netscape is in a hot commercial competition with the Microsoft *Internet Explorer*. A free version of *Internet Explorer* can be downloaded from (**http://www.microsoft.com**).

In addition to browsing, these software packages usually include various other internet services, such as e-mail, voice capability for chat, audio download and video clip download. If these extra services are not a part of the browser, there are usually instructions telling how to download *helper, assistant* or *plug-in* applications. As a result, many people have to choose between using the e-mail software provided by their Internet provider and the e-mail (or other applications) software bundled into their browser. Others may not be able to use anything other than that provided with their internet service.

Search Engines

Every day, another way. If that is not the motto of the people who provide ways to search the Web, perhaps it should be. This entire book, multiplied in size by 100, could be devoted to this topic—but unfortunately a significant part of it would be obsolete before it ever saw light of day.

If you want to find something on the Web, you probably will use a search engine. Some people object to this term, calling it *computerese jargon.* The use of the word *engine* in the computer field became popular some years ago, when referring the core software in database systems that did the work—analogous to the engine in an automobile. But no matter what you want to call them, more and more of them are coming on-line.

A typical search engine can be set to search the Web or newsgroups (USENET), and search on a specific word, specific term (in quotation marks) or concepts. They can usually be set to search on one word or term, or even use logical operations such as *AND, OR, NOT* and others. Each comes with instructions, and each operates differently. If your search doesn't get the results you want, try again with a different set of words on the same search engine, or try a different engine.

Some engines search only the first line of the Web page for key words. Thus, if the author of a page was not careful, you can miss a valuable page completely if your key word is not in the title. Other search engines search entire texts, and still others have other search criteria.

There are engines that list sites only by key words supplied by the person registering the site with the engine. Thus, if the site's sponsor does not list the keyword *carp* when registering a new site on Goldfish, your search on *small carp* will not pick up his site. Some search engines take 6 hours to pick up a new site (after manual registration); others take up to 6 months. Thus, one search may find material posted two weeks ago, and others miss it completely. With all these faults and problems, you still might find the worst problem is that there is just too much material. Almost anything goes!

Searches are generally of two types, *broad* and *narrow*. Using square brackets to represent the *search for* box on the screen, a broad search might be for something such as [Kenwood]. A narrow search might be [Kenwood Amateur Equipment]. A still more narrow search, with logical operators, would be [Kenwood AND Amateur Radio AND service bulletins]. An alternative approach could be [Kenwood AND service bulletins NOT Audio], thus hopefully not including any responses from their audio line.

Will it work? Sometimes, depending on the search engine used. Some search engines allow logical operators but require you to give a key word. The pages will be listed, starting with those pages that contain this key word, followed by everything else. If your search is too broad, your first response will be something like *First 10 of 35,000 responses*! Unless you have the stamina to view 35,000 Web page titles, this is a clue to narrow your search.

If you have never done a search before, a good starting place is a search on search engines. The usual standard is search.com (**http://www.search.com**). You may be able so save a large amount of time by picking the correct search engine and reading the instructions.

A few popular search engines are Yahoo!, AltaVista, WebCrawler, Excite, Infoseek and Lycos. Many have specialties—you just have to try them and see.

Special Searches

Often, a search on a general search engine is not the best way to go. You might first try to imagine who might have the material you want, or a link to the material you want. For example, for updates on Microsoft software, go directly to the Microsoft site rather than a general search site. Do you want Amateur Radio information? Go to (**http://www.arrl.org**) (where else?). How about shareware? Go to (**http:// www.shareware.com**).

Home Pages and Links--What Are They All About?

When you do go to a Web page, the first thing you will usually see is the *Home Page*. Everything at this Web site is linked to this home page. A *link* is a graphic object or a few words of different colored text. When you put your mouse pointer on or near this text, the arrow changes to a "pointing hand" icon. Click the left mouse button and your browser takes you to a new page with a subject and title related to the colored text you just pointed to. Want to go back to the page you just looked at? Hit the **BACK** button on the menu bar of your browser or follow the instructions on the Web page you are viewing.

Behind each link is a statement, written in html. It says, in effect, "If the user clicks here, go to this URL—http://www.XXXX.yyy. The letters XXXX.yyy may stand for the location of a page at some other site, a page at this same site, or even a location on the same page you are viewing. As an example, suppose you go the ARRL home page at (**http://www.arrl.org**).

On the actual Web page (Figure 6.18) links are shown in color, but they are printed here underlined. Click on text representing a link, such as *On the Air* (fifth underlined item from the bottom in the figure), and your browser will take you to the new page, in this case Figure 6.19. Click on *Shuttle Amateur Radio Experiment (SAREX)* and Figure 6.20 results.

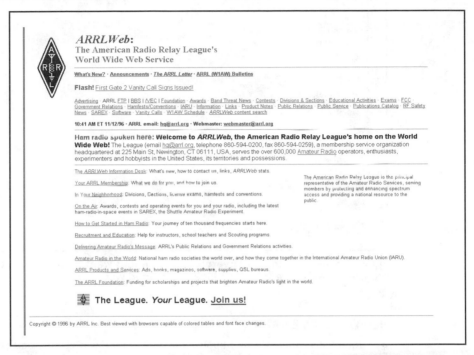

Figure 6.18—ARRL's Home Page. Clicking on an underlined item will cause a new page of information to appear about that item. Clicking on the "On the Air" (5th from bottom) item will cause the page pictured in Figure 6.19 to appear.

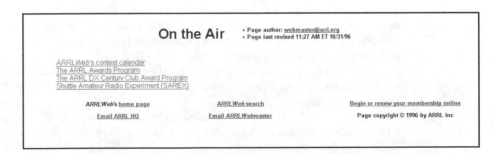

Figure 6.19—The "On the Air" web page showing more ARRL links. Clicking on "Shuttle Amateur Radio Experiment" takes you to a new screen pictured in Figure 6.20.

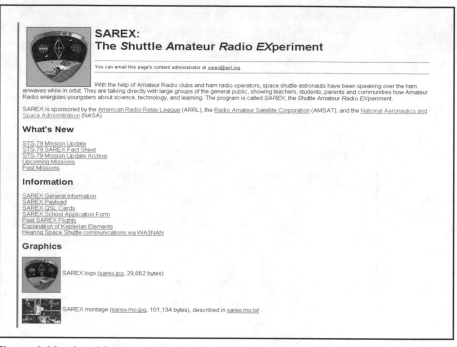

Figure 6.20—Anything and everything you might want to know about the SAREX program is available from this nicely designed web page.

But Why Call It a "Web?"

Imagine a spider's web. Suppose the outer strand was elastic, and you could pull it tight, so the web became a closed volume. Next imagine many, but not all the places that web strands cross had other strands connected across the center to other junctions. Starting to sound a little confusing? Well, welcome to the Web! There is no top, no bottom, no start and no end—everything is closed back on itself.

Sometimes you can jump from site to site and finally choose a link to go back to where you started. Other times the links take you in totally unexpected directions. Often, the author of a Web page will add a set of links having nothing to do with the topic of the page—they are there just because he or she likes them and wants you to have a little fun too!

Take a look at Figure 6.21. It is a simplified drawing of a set of Web sites and the interconnections. It starts with the ARRL home page. Each of the addresses shown is preceded by **(http://)**.

At this site there is a page of links. One takes you to the home page of the QCWA, an association of radio amateurs who have been licensed for over 25 years. Located at **(http://www.efn.org/~qcwa)**, one of their links will take you back to the ARRL. Another one leads to "Amateur Radio in Kansas City," which also links to AMSAT (and back to the ARRL). AMSAT leads to TAPR. TAPR has several pages,

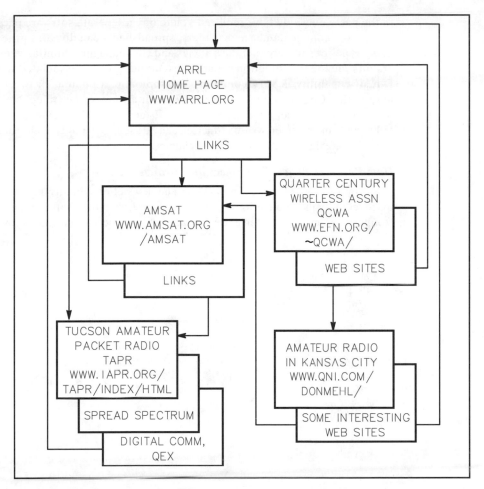

Figure 6.21—There is no beginning or end to the links traveled on the Worldwide Web.

one of which is devoted to spread spectrum. The ARRL publication *QEX* is referenced on this page, with a link back to the ARRL. Any question now why it is called a "web"?

Fortunately, depending on the amount of memory and hard disk cache space you have, it is manageable (or navigable). Two important navigational tools are usually located on the menu bar of your browser. The **BACK** button will take you back to each of the pages you had just visited. If you used the **BACK** button and want to go forward, just use the **FORWARD** button.

Chat and Other Functions

Modern software packages usually include other functions—functions that in the past you would have required you to buy a separate software package. Word processors contain database managers, spreadsheets can do word processing, and many types of software include utilities and file managers. Similarly, many browsers include internet function capabilities not necessarily associated with the Web. E-mail capability is very common. *Netscape 3.X*, a popular browser, is distributed with a Chat program called *CoolTalk*. It allows voice (telephone) conversations over the internet while the browser is loaded. If an audio card is not installed at either end, an on-screen writing function can be used. General chat channels and voice (*IPhone*) are discussed earlier in this chapter.

Ham Resource Pages, Fun Places and Strange Sites

Almost every magazine, newspaper and newsletter contains the latest set of sites discovered by the publication's staff. They range from the useful to the entertaining, from curiosities to the bizarre. Be forewarned—sites can come and go overnight!

Resources Guide

In this chapter **the boldface text, such as this,** are keys to the chapter text that suggested you look in this Resources chapter. Web addresses and messages you would normally see on a computer display **are shown like this**. A Web address in the middle of a sentence is printed without parentheses, but any Web address followed by a punctuation mark is printed within parentheses to avoid confusion. The parentheses are not part of the address. Italics are used for *book names* and *software packages*. Costs quoted do change with time, as do postal addresses, e-mail addresses and Web addresses.

CHAPTER 1

If you don't already have a bookshelf full of personal computer books, your local book store or mail order supplier would be happy to remedy this situation. One readily available book on **PC basics** is *The Little PC Book*, by Lawrence Magid (© 1993, Peachtree Press, 2414 Sixth St., Berkeley CA 94710, Telephone 800-283-9444. ISBN 0-938151-10). A second, somewhat more comprehensive book is *Peter Norton's Inside the PC* (© 1995, Sams Publishing, 201 W. 103 St., Indianapolis, IN 46290; ISBN 0-672-30624-7). For a **reference book on hardware**, ranging from the 8086 chip to Pentiums and 8-bit bus structure to 64-bit paths, *The Indispensable PC Hardware Book*, by Hans-Peter Messmer (©1995, Addison-Wesley, ISBN 0-201-8769-3) is a good choice.

A document titled *pc-hardware-faq*, by Willie Lim and Ralph Valentino, is readily available on the Internet. You can find it in the files of the **computer.sys.ibm.pc.hardware** newsgroup, or just do a search for other sites holding it. Updated periodically, it contains references to other sources of information.

The **basics of digital circuits and concepts** are covered in Chapter 7, Digital Signal Theory and Components, of *The ARRL Handbook for Radio Amateurs*. The same book has a chapter devoted to Safety (Chapter 9), which is worth reading before you work on any piece of equipment.

An interesting, personal **story of the early days of commercial computers**, from a ham's (W3HTF) point of view, is *From Dots to Bits: A Personal History of the Electronic Computer* by Herman Lukoff (©1979, Robotics Press, Portland, OR; ISBN: 89661-002-0).

Most engineering texts on **Fourier Analysis** contain the equations for analyzing the harmonics of pulse waveforms, such as multiples of the 16-MHz clock described in the text. A convenient summary is in *Reference Data for Radio Engineers*, published by Howard W. Sams and Company. Recent editions contain summary charts of the harmonic energy.

Electronic Circuit Analysis by Johnson, Johnson and Hilburn (©1992, Prentice Hall, Englewood Cliffs, NJ, ISBN 0-13-249335-7) contains a chapter with this material. If the computer clock is symmetrical—the up-period and the down-period are equal—then the resulting spectrum consists of only odd harmonics of the frequency of the full period waveform.

For an understanding of **Part 15 Rules** you could read the actual government document. However, there is a handy summary and explanation in *The 1996 Reference Guide,* published by *Compliance Engineering Magazine* (Vol XII, No. 2). Contact them at 1 Tech Drive, Suite 17, Andover, MA 01810 for availability and price of this issue. It also is available at some public and university libraries. Modems must be qualified under FCC Part 68, in addition to Part 15. Recent changes in the FCC rules have eased the type acceptance of PCs. Included in the new rules is, among other things, permission for qualified manufacturers to test their own equipment for RFI.

A good starting point for **understanding RFI/EMI** is the EMI chapter (Chapter 28) of *The ARRL Handbook for Radio Amateurs*. The ARRL also publishes a book devoted to this topic, *Radio Frequency Interference—How to Find It and Fix It*. Another good source of help and information is the *FCC Interference to Home Electronic Entertainment Equipment Handbook*. Although it is now out of print, it may be available at libraries that offer government documents. You can look for current government publications at (**http://www.gpo.gov**) on the Internet. The Lab Notes column in the September 1995 issue of *QST* contains additional EMI information.

The **Linux** operating system is a version of **UNIX**. It offers some advantages—and disadvantages—over the more commonly used DOS/*Windows*/OS/2 systems. The April 1995 issue of *QEX* describes this operating system. *QEX* is published by the ARRL.

You might be asking yourself what these "guys"—*UNIX* and *Linux*—are doing in a book about computers and ham radio? Most of us have heard the term *UNIX*, but rarely associate it with Amateur Radio. The general impression is that *UNIX* is some form of military-industrial strength operating system that has no place in our shacks.

Not so. By now we have all become accustomed to hearing about the Internet and packet radio, so it should come as no surprise to learn *UNIX* has its roots in both areas. If you have ever sent an e-mail or ftp'ed a file from the Internet or telneted to a friend on packet radio, it is very likely you have already used *UNIX/Linux* without knowing it. *UNIX* is the operating system of choice for Internet servers using the TCP/IP protocol. All the now familiar (assuming you're a Web surfer) terms like FTP, Telnet, login, ping and pop are really *UNIX* commands. You might consider *UNIX* to be the "operating system" of the Internet.

Linux is a free version of the *UNIX* operating system created by a Finnish graduate student, Linus Torvalds. Some pronounce it as "Lih-nucks" and others as "Lean-ix," but for free who can complain? It is distributed free with all the source code included. For Amateur Radio purposes, we will only consider *Linux*. It is a true 32-bit operating system and will run on 386s and above.

If you want to run *Linux*, it can be selected upon boot-up from DOS. After it is selected, DOS is effectively removed, and your system behaves just as if the PC had been booted from *Linux*. This is a nice feature, since it allows us to maintain the more frequently used DOS operating system. Linux can be downloaded free from the Internet, but it is *big*—over 20 Mb. The preferred method is to buy a $15-$30 CD ROM.

Just Computers, PO Box 75414, Petaluma, CA 94975-1414 offers a selection of CDs with or without paper documentation. *Slackware 3.1* and *Red Hat* CD ROMs are available for $19 and for $49 with a 1600-page documentation package. The *Debian* CD costs $22 and $49 with the documentation package. Orders may be placed by e-mail (**sales@justcomp.com**) by phone 707-586-5600, by fax at 707-586-5606. On line Web ordering also is available at (**http://www.justcomp.com**).

InfoMagic, 11950 N. Hwy. 89, Flagstaff, AZ 86004, is another supplier with on-line ordering capability. They offer the *Linux Developer's Resource 6 CD Set* for $27.50. It comes complete with all the Linux archives and includes a complete on-line *Installation & Getting Started Guide*. They may be reached by telephone at 800-800-6613 or 520-526-9565 and by fax at 520-526-9573. On-line ordering is available at (**http://www.infomagic.com**).

Red Hat Software, 3203 Yorktown Avenue, Suite 123, Durham, NC 27713, sells the *Official Red Hat Linux* for $49.95. This package includes two CD ROMs and a book. They may be reached at 800-546-7274 or 919-572-6500 or by fax at 919-572-6726. For e-mail orders contact (**sales@redhat.com**) or (**http://www.redhat.com**) on the Web.

UNIX plays a large part of the technology behind the Internet and the Web. Check the section of this chapter devoted to resources and additional information for Chapter 6.

There are many alternative methods of **keeping and selecting an operating system** on your computer. *System Commander* is a commercial software package, with an advertised capability of allowing you to put as many operating systems as you wish on your computer. Thus, according to the manufacturer (V Communications, Inc., 4320 Stevens Creek Blvd., San Jose, CA 95129, 800-648-8266), you can put DOS, Windows 3.X, Windows 95, OS/2 and any other system you like on your hard disk. Each time you boot, a menu of available operating systems is presented for your selection.

In the References Chapter of *The ARRL Handbook for Radio Amateurs* there is a table of the lower 128 **ASCII characters**, plus several other handy tables.

George Murphy, **VE3ERP**, periodically issues a disk of **freeware programs** consisting of ham electronics calculation routines. Many of the source formulas are taken from *The ARRL Handbook for Radio Amateurs,* and the routines are written in *BASIC.* These programs often are posted on the Internet and various telephone bulletin board systems, such as the ARRL *HIRAM* BBS. For information on the latest update, contact VE3ERP at 77 McKenzie St., Orillia, ON L3V 6A6, Canada, and ask for information on *HAMCALC.*

There are many books on **upgrading your computer**. If you are planning to buy a used computer for several hundred or perhaps a thousand dollars, the cost of a $35 or $40 book can be a good investment. *Upgrading and Repairing PCs*, by Scott Mueller (©1996 Que Publishing, 201 W. 103 St., Indianapolis, IN 46290; Telephone 1-800-428-5331, ISBN 0-7897-0825-6) is typical of the books available.

The BIOS on some older computers may not recognize the size of the nice, new hard drive you just purchased. This is particularly true of drive sizes over 1 Gb. Many hard drive suppliers recognize this (and other) problems. To make it as easy as possible to upgrade your drive, they supply an installation routine and software to allow you to use their **large hard drives on older machines**. Typical of these drives and software is the material supplied by Maxtor Corporation, 211 River Oaks Pkwy, San Jose, CA 95134. Their 1 Gb drive comes with software called *Max*Blast*. This software allows the user to set up the new Maxtor disk to its maximum capacity.

To see what you might do with a **CGA display** by **rewiring the connector**, see "The Absent CGA Color Text," by Paul Danzer, N1II, in the January 1989 issue of *Modern Electronics* on page 36.

Software comes in all shapes and sizes. Some **software installs** easily—and some not so easily. Today, most software is distributed with at least one level of compression. The sidebar on *Zipping and Unzipping* covers this first level of compression. Much *WINDOWS*-compatible software comes with a second level of compression. It must be installed to work, and part of the automatic installation process includes the expansion from this second level of compression.

After unzipping, look for a file called *READ.ME* or *README.1ST.* These files usually provide the installation instructions. If there are no such instructions, select **RUN** in the File menu, and then **BROWSE** to find a file called *SETUP.EXE* or *INSTALL.EXE.* Run one of these files, and the *WINDOWS*-hosted software will be installed. If in doubt, and given a choice, accept the default directory for installation.

Some *DOS* software comes with *READ.ME* or *README.1ST* files, and some does not. Some include automatic installation programs also called *SETUP.EXE* or *INSTALL.EXE*, and some do not. If the software does include one of these .EXE programs, simply run it from a DOS prompt. To be safe, if your computer does have *WINDOWS*, to install a *DOS* program first exit *WINDOWS,* and then install from the direct *DOS* level. Some *DOS* programs have problems installing (and running) from a *DOS* prompt in Windows.

You will find more information on **memory upgrading and expansion** in *The Complete PC Upgrade and Maintenance Guide,* by Mark Minasi (©1996, Sybex, 2021 Challenger Dr., Alameda, CA 94501, ISBN 0-7821-1956-5).

To Unzip, Pull Here!

To save space on disks and communications (on-line) time on Internet and telephone lines, most software is distributed in a compressed form. The most popular compression today is called **ZIP**, with *PKZIP* and *PKUNZIP* used—in one of their many forms—for compression and decompression (expansion). These programs are available in both *Windows* and DOS versions, and some versions are shareware.

Most people find it best to unzip files either in a new, empty directory or on a floppy drive disk, assuming there is enough room on a single floppy. Thus, the unzipped files are in just one place, and you can check them easily with a virus checker. Normally, to unzip a file with a DOS version, the command is **PKUNZIP NEWFILE.ZIP**. The file extension .ZIP tells you that you have a zipped file. In a computer running *Windows*, you can use the file manger FILE/ASSOCIATE command to make your unzipping program automatically unzip a file ending with .ZIP if you double-click on the file name under the file manager.

Some software is distributed in a self-uncompressing format. The file is then supplied as **NEWFILE.EXE**. Run **NEWFILE.EXE** by typing **NEWFILE**, followed by pressing the ENTER or RETURN key, and the file uncompressses itself!

⌑ CHAPTER 2

The **W1AW schedule,** including the times of transmission of **FEC bulletins,** is printed each month in *QST*. **Coastal station schedules** do occasionally change. Some stations maintain a Web page with updated schedules. Other station schedules can be found by searching Internet and newsgroups under *SWL* and *utility short wave stations*. If you are not familiar with searching, see Chapter 6 of this book. Many coastal stations will reply to a brief letter or phone call with a schedule, but remember, you cannot divulge the contents of private messages received over the air to anyone else.

The **common SSTV frequencies** listed in Figure 2.13 were taken from the "Considerate Operator's Frequency Guide," usually printed each January in *QST*. You will also find it as Table 3.1 in Chapter 3, Basic Operating, in each edition of *The ARRL Operating Manual*. There are no "frequency police" who will arrest you for not following this guide, but as a courtesy to your fellow hams, you will want to follow the frequency suggestions in the Guide.

A good source of information on **packet radio** is *Practical Packet Radio*, published by (naturally) the ARRL. **Packet formats** are quite complex, and a good source of up-to-date information is TAPR—the Tucson Amateur Packet Radio organization. They are located at 8987-309 E. Tanque Verde Rd, #337, Tucson, AZ 85749-9399. Contact them by either phone (817-383-0000), fax (817-566-2544) or e-mail **tapr@tapr.org**

TAPR is a nonprofit research and development corporation with more than 1000 members worldwide. It was founded in an attempt to develop a low-cost TNC kit. This effort resulted in the now famous TNC-1. TAPR's second development, the basis for most TNC's currently in use, is the TNC-2. Although TAPR no longer provides complete TNC kits, they do have a number of digital products available.

Contact **Kantronics** at 1202 East 23rd St, Lawrence, KS 66046-5005 (telephone 913-842-7745) for more information on **G-TOR** hardware. For **CLOVER**, contact **HAL Communications** at 1201 W. Kenyon Rd, PO Box 365, Urbana, IL 61801 (telephone 217-367-7373).

APRS software is available in DOS, *Windows* and Mac versions. DOS versions are available for FTP download from (**tapr.org/tapr/SIG/aprssig/files/upload**).

A basic registration costs $29. Additional options are: GPS $9, DF $9, WX $9 and the latest copy on disk cost $9. Contact Bob Bruninga, 115 Old Farm Ct, Glen Burnie, MD 21060. If you have a Java-capable browser, you may visit Bob's Web site at (**http://web.usna.navy.mil/~bruninga/aprs.html**) or contact him by e-mail at **wb4apr@amsat.org**

WinAPRS and *MacAPRS,* written by Mark and Keith Sproul, may be registered with Mark Sproul, 698 Magnolia Rd, North Brunswick, NJ 08902. You will find these shareware programs at (**http://aprs.rutgers.edu/aprs/**). The downloadable versions are fully functional, although you will not be able to save your settings until you register. WinAPRS costs $60 and MacAPRS $50. The authors' e-mail addresses are: Mark Sproul, KB2ICI, **sproul@ap.org** and Keith Sproul, WU2Z, **ksproul@noc.rutgers.edu**

Getting On Track with APRS, published by ARRL (order no. 5854), covers Mac, *Windows* and DOS APRS software and applications.

Garmin International, 1200 East 151st St, Olathe, KS 66062, makes a low cost line of handheld GPS units that are popular with amateurs. Contact a local marine electronics dealer in your area or ask Garmin (**http://www.garmin.com/** or Telephone 913-397-8200 or fax at 913-397-8282) for a list of dealers in your area. A Web search on *Garmin* will likely return a list of participating dealers. Many of these dealers state prices and will take orders over the Web.

Tigertronics makes a multimode interface that fits in the DB-25 connector shell. The are at 400 Daily Ln, PO Box 5210, Grants Pass, OR 97527. Telephone is 1-800-8BAYPAC. They also have a Web page at (**http://www.tigertronics.com**).

⊞ CHAPTER 3

This chapter contains the names of a number of commercial and shareware programs. If you are interested in obtaining a copy, the following listing of addresses (real and hyperspace) are the places to go for this material.

Logging Programs

FD1200 Field Day Logging Program by Harry Bump, KM3D, may be obtained by mail, PO Box 392, Richland, PA 17087, telephone 717-866-6879. E-mail: (**harry.bump@hamdata.leba.net**). A $10 donation is requested.

DXbase version 4.6 is available from Scientific Solutions Inc., 736 Cedar Creek Way, Woodstock, GA 30188, Telephone 770-924-2210, or by e-mail (**jlennox@mindspring.com**) or via (**http://www.mindspring.com/jlennox/**). The retail price is $89.95.

DXLOG and *ClusterLog* version 1.96 are available from Whisper Woods Enterprises, PO Box 277, Upper Black Eddy, PA 18972; 610-982-9632, e-mail (**whspwood@interserver.com**). The retail price is $49.95.

HyperLog version 3.06c is available from HyperSoft, 3065 Hitt Rd, Cumming, GA 30131; 770-844-8874, orders only 800-274-0890, HyperSoft BBS 770-844-9023, e-mail (**76370.2431@compuserve.com**). The retail price $44.95 if the software is downloaded or $49.95 by US mail.

LOGic 4 version 4.02 for Windows is sold by Personal Database Applications, 2616 Meadow Ridge Dr., Duluth, GA 30136; 770-242-0887. The retail price is $99.

Log Master and *Log Ranger* are provided by Sensible Solutions, PO Box 474, Middletown, NJ 07748; 908-495-5066, 908-495-5066, BBS 908-787-2982. The retail price is $89.95 and includes your choice of one of the following: A one-year (new or renewal) ARRL membership, a SAM call sign database or a radio/computer interface.

LOGPlus! is available from DMW Systems, 9909 121st Ave NE, Lake Stevens, WA 98258; 360-653-8304, BBS & fax 360-653-9652; e-mail: (**n7xr@everett.com**). Their Web site is (**http://www.everett.com/users/logplus**). The retail price is $48, with the manual on disk.

LogView is sold by MFJ Enterprises, PO Box 494, Mississippi State, MS 39762; 601-323-5869. Retail price including *LogView, PacketView* and *RigView* is $109.95.

Log Windows version 2 is sold by Advanced Electronic Applications, PO Box C2160, Lynnwood, WA 98036; 206-774-5554. AEA also has a conference area in CompuServe's HamNet Forum. The retail price is $99.

WJ2O Master QSO logging program is available from WJ2O Software, PO Box 16, McConnellsville, NY 13401; 315-245-1010 or 800-944-WJ2O for 24-hour answering service. The retail price is $59.95.

Propagation Programs

CAPMan Version 3.0 is available from Lucas Radio/Kangaroo Tabor Software, 552 Wewoka Dr, Boulder, CO 80303. Tel 303-494-4647, fax 303-494-0937. E-mail: (**70511.2570@compuserve.com**). Price class: *CAPMan* $89.95, *CAPMap* $29.95.

PropMan is available from Collins Avionics and Communications Division, Dept. 120-130, 350 Collins Rd NE, Cedar Rapids, IA 52498-0120, Tel 800-321-2223 or 319-395-5100. Price class: $49.95 plus tax, shipping and handling.

SKYCOM 2.0 is available from Fuentez Systems Concepts, Inc., 2460 Remount Road, Suite 102, N Charleston, SC 29406, Telephone 803-745-9496. Order from EEB, Telephone 800-368-3270 or 703-938-3350. E-mail: (**skycom@fuentez.com**). Web: (**http://www.fuentez.com/skycom/whatis.html**). The price is $59.95.

HFx Version 1.06 is available from Pacific-Sierra Research Corporation, 2901 28th St., Santa Monica, CA 90405. Tel 800-820-4PSR, fax 310-314-2323. E-mail: (**hfx%mgate@psrv.com**). URL: (**http://www.psrv.com/hfx/**). Price class: $129.00.

VOACAP is available by anonymous FTP from (**ftp.voa.gov**) in the subdirectory (**/pub/software/voacap/voawin.exe**). The *VOAWIN.EXE* file is a self-extracting executable file, approximately 5.7 Mb in size.

Satellite Tracking Programs

InstantTrack is available from AMSAT, 301-589-6062, $50 AMSAT members, $70 non-members, $200 commercial, (**http://www.amsat.org**).

NOVA is available from Northern Light Software Associates, 2881 C.R. 21, Canton, NY 13617, telephone 315-379-0161, e-mail (**w9ip@webcom.com**). DOS or *Windows* versions are $59.95; also from Bob Myers Communications, PO Box 17108, Fountain Hills, AZ 85269-7108, telephone 602-837-6492, fax 602-837-6872, e-mail (**bmyers@primenet.com**).

Call Sign Databases and QSL Managers

SAM Callsign is available from RT Systems Inc., 8207 Stephanie Drive, Huntsville, AL 35802, telephone: 800-723-6922 or 205-882-9292

QRZ CD ROM is available from Walnut Creek CDROM, 4041 Pike Lane, Suite E, Concord, CA 94520-9960, telephone 510-674-0783, e-mail (**info@cdrom.com**).

Radio Amateur Callbooks may be reached at 800-278-8477 or 908-905-2961. Fax is 908-363-0338 and e-mail is (**103424.2142@compuserve.com**). Their mailing address is 1695 Oak St, Lakewood, NJ 08701. These books also are available from the ARRL.

The HamCall CD ROM may be obtained from Buckmaster Publishing, 6196 Jefferson Highway, Mineral, VA 23117. Telephone 800-282-5628 or 540-894-5777.

The PROLOG QSL Manager is available for $23 from Datamatrix, 5560 Jackson Loop NE, Rio Rancho, NM 87124. For telephone orders call 800-373-6564, for the BBS call 505-892-5669.

ARRL Software

All League products may be ordered directly from the ARRL, on the Web or from distributors. See the advertisements in *QST* for the names and locations of local distributors. See the rear of this book for ordering information and a complete list of ARRL software products.

If you have any questions, contact the ARRL, 225 Main St, Newington, CT 06111, telephone: 860-594-0200, e-mail (**pubsales@arrl.org**).

Frequency Lists

The *Ham_DB & Open Repeater Database* and *FCC Master Frequency Database* are both available from PerCon Corp., 4906 Maple Springs / Ellery Road, Bemus Point, NY 14712, telephone 716-386-6015, e-mail (**sales@perconcorp.com**).

The Klingenfuss Super Frequency List is available from Klingenfuss Publications, Hagenloher Str. 14, D-72070 Tuebingen, Germany. Telephone: 49-7071-62830, fax 49-7071-600849. Price: DEM 50 (US $36.25) plus DEM 5 (US $3.62) shipping and handling. The price in dollars varies with current exchange rates.

CHAPTER 4

MathCad is published by MathSoft, Inc., 101 Main St., Cambridge MA 02142-1521; telephone 617-577-1017; fax 617-577-8829. Demonstration versions of *MathCad 6.0 PLUS* are available on diskette directly from MathCad. Contact Charles Camiel at 800-MATHCAD (800-628-4223) or use anonymous FTP (**ftp.mathsoft.com/pub/software/wrkmodel**); the file name is *WRKMODEL.EXE*. You can also get the file from MathSoft's Web site (**http://www.mathsoft.com**). *WRKMODEL.EXE* is a self-extracting file; only the Print and Save functions are disabled in the demonstration software.

Check Appendix C of this book for information about **ARRL Radio Designer** and **MicroSmith**. Shareware versions of *SPICE* software are available on the Web at (**http://www.shareware.com/**). Search for *SPICE* under your preferred operating system.

For more information on **narrow-band audio filters**, see A. B. Williams and F. J. Taylor, *Electronic Filter Design Handbook* (New York: McGraw-Hill, 1988), 2nd edition.

In the *Technical Correspondence* column of *QST,* January 1997, David Nordquist, KE9ED, discussed his experiences with the *Maple V* **mathematics software.** Robert Evans, KB6YJW, Director of Electronic Publishing for Brooks/Cole, and Marketing Director Carolyn Crockett worked out a plan for *QST* readers to obtain the student edition of *Maple V* or *Scientific WorkPlace* (which integrates a *Maple V* kernel with a scientific word processor) for $37—50% off the reduced $74 price of a recent edition (2.0 or 2.1 for *WorkPlace* and Release 3 for *Maple V*). Both *Maple V* and *Scientific WorkPlace* come with a printed manual. An abundance of add-on functions and tutorials may be found on math Web sites. Demos of the software can be downloaded from Brooks/Cole's Web page at: (**http://www.brookscole.com/brookscole.html**).

Other sites to visit include: tutorial material at (**http://curiac.acomp.usf.edu/maple/symbolic.html**); a library of additional functions, etc, (**ftp://ftp.maplesoft.com/pub/maple**). Those interested in the Maple User Group should contact Maple-(**list@daisy-uwaterloo.ca**). A huge technical Web site with math and other materials is at (**http://www.birkhauser.com**).

Both programs run on '386 or higher IBM-compatible computers under *Windows 95* or *Windows 3.1*. *Maple V* can be set up to run under DOS alone, and also is available for a Macintosh running System 6.07 or higher. *QST* readers can order the software by calling Brooks/Cole at 800-354-9706; major credit cards are accepted.

TK Solver **and** *Mini-TK* are distributed by UTS Software, 1220 Rock St, Rockford, IL 61101. For a free copy of *Mini-TK*, see their Web site at **http://www.uts.com** or call them at 800-435-7887. Current retail price for the full *TK Solver* is $200.

The original circuit for the **Ugly Weekender** receiver was described by Roger Hayward, KA7EXM, in "The 'Ugly Weekender' II, Adding a Junk-Box Receiver," *QST*, Aug 1992, pp 27-30.

Also see Ulrich L. Rohde, KA2WEU, "Designing Low-Phase-Noise Oscillators," QEX, Oct 1994, pp 3-12 for more information on **oscillators**. A book by the same author is *Digital PLL Frequency Synthesizers—Theory and Design* (Englewood Cliffs, NJ: Prentice-Hall, Inc., 1983), section 4-1, "Oscillator Design."

EZNEC is distributed by Roy Lewallen, W7EL, PO Box 6658, Beaverton, OR 97007. *Suggested retail price:* $89 postpaid (add $3 outside US/Canada).

Contact Brian Beezley, K6STI, 3532 Linda Vista, San Marcos, CA 92069, telephone 619-599-4962 for any of his products. *Suggested retail prices*: **AO 6.5, NEC/ Wires 2.0, YO 6.5, NEC/Yagis 2.5, TA 1.0**. Any one program: $60; three bundled together: $120; five bundled together: $200. Prices are postpaid; add $5 for international shipping.

You can contact MicroSim (20 Fairbanks, Irvine CA 92718) at 800-245-3022 (sales) or 714-455-0554 (fax). Ask for their evaluation version of *DesignLab,* which is supplied on a CD-ROM. Their Web site is (**http://www.microsim.com**).

IntuSoft is at P.O. Box 710, San Pedro, CA 90733-0710. You can call them at 310-883-0710 and ask for a copy of their *ICAP* demo CD. The CD contains the demo programs plus a large number of information files and price lists. You can download the demo version from their Web site at (**http://www.intusoft.com/**).

MICRO-CAP is made by Spectrum Software, 1020 S. Wolfe Road, Sunnyvale, CA 94086, Telephone 408-738-4387. Check their Web site at (**http://www.spectrumsoft.com/**) for more information. The trial version is posted there.

🖫 CHAPTER 5

VisualRadio 2 is available on CompuServe in the HamNet Forum, Library 6, *Software and Pictures*. You can find it on the Internet in several places, including the HamNet page at (**http://www.webcom.com/~sjl/HamNet_Companion/**).

Many programs, such as *VisualRadio,* are combinations of control programs, loggers, databases and communications programs. You can usually download a version in compressed or *.ZIP* form. It is a good practice to virus check every download before unzipping, after unzipping (and before installation) and after installation but before running it.

After unzipping (and virus checking), you should read the *READ.ME* file—to find the cost, if it is shareware, and to find what computer resources you need to run the program. Many people make it a habit to delete any program without a *READ.ME* that contains this information.

The ARRL Handbook for Radio Amateurs, **71st edition, 1994**, described **a repeater based on a PC**. The section was written by ARRL Assistant Technical Editor Bob Schetgen, KU7G. It is a good model for the process to be followed when you plan to take a PC and devote it to a major single use, such as a repeater controller. If you have any questions on the controller, contact KU7G at the ARRL by e-mail at **KU7G@arrl.org**, or contact the *Handbook* Editor at the ARRL.

There are many **computer-related books to use as source material** for computer interfacing projects. If you intend to use *BASIC,* one book is *The GW-Basic Reference* by Inman and Albrecht,©1990 by Osborne/McGraw-Hill, ISBN 0-07-881644-0. Since *GW-BASIC* is an older language, there are not many newer books devoted to it. Another book with several **interfacing examples** is *Controlling the World With Your PC*, by Paul Bergsman (©1994, ISBN 1-878707-15-9). It is available from Hightext Publications, P.O. Box 1489, Solana Beach, CA 92075. While the title of the book certainly overstates the scope of the contents, it does have a few interesting examples, including motor control.

The parallel port was described as general purpose input/output device by W9XT in the November 1993 issue of *QEX*. The text describes the interrupts associated with bit 4 of the control register, and the application of this control signal. A schematic of a general purpose port expander is shown with application information.

A **list of parts suppliers**—name, address, telephone number—is printed annually in Chapter 30, the References Chapter, of *The ARRL Handbook for Radio Amateurs*. In addition, the disk included with this book (1996 and later editions) contains the program *TISFIND*, which allows you to search for a supplier by name, product or several other categories. To get updated information, you should get the most recent edition. Other parts suppliers advertise in *QST*, the ARRL's monthly magazine sent to members. For more information on *QST*, see Appendix C.

Digi-Key Corporation, 800-344-4539,(**http://www.digikey.com/**) will send you a copy of their catalog on request. As most other suppliers, have a surcharge for small orders. At last check, they asked for an extra $5 for orders under $25, but they do ship almost immediately if you place a telephone order. Both Digi-Key and Allied (800-433-5700 or **http://www.allied.avnet.com/**) carry Maxim, TI and most other major part lines.

Radio Shack, which started its life as a ham store in the Boston area, now carries a limited parts line in all its stores. However, the advantage of suggesting the use of Radio Shack parts is easy availability—there seems to be an outlet with the familiar red and black sign in almost every shopping center. They will order parts they don't stock. **Marlin P. Jones** (800-432-9937 for orders and catalogs) offers many computer parts and accessories, besides a line of small electronic kits. Their catalog is the sort hams have sat and scanned on many a rainy Saturday afternoon. **All Electronics** (800-826-5432) falls in the same category.

For specific computer parts and tools, **Jameco** (800-831-4242) is a good place to look. You will often see items to make your life easier—items you never thought existed—plug converters, test sockets, extenders and special boards.

Etched, drilled, double-sided **DigiVFO PC boards** with plated-through holes and a solder mask on both sides are available for $20, and kits of parts including the PC board and all ICs (less power supply and enclosure) are available for $79.95 from Dover Research, 321 W. 4th St., Jordan, MN 55352-1313. Their telephone number is 612-492-3913. All kits include a $3^1/2$-inch, PC-DOS-format floppy disk containing the latest *DigiVFO* and *SIG_GEN* programs in source-code and executable form, as well as files containing the schematic and a shareware compiler called *A86*. These files are also available from the ARRL BBS and Internet sites.

The January 1996 issue of *QEX* carried another **parallel port VFO design**. *QEX* is the monthly experimenters' journal published by the ARRL. For subscription information, look at the back pages of this book.

EDN is an "industrial circulation magazine," distributed to working engineers and others in the electronics industry. Many company libraries, engineering school libraries and other special libraries keep back issues. *EDN* is published by Cahners Publishing Company, 8773 South Ridgeline Blvd, Highlands Ranch, CO 80126-2329 (**http://www.ednmag.com**). A regular column, "Design Ideas," often carries small circuits such as **the use of a PC port as the input of a frequency counter**. The counter description was in the October 26, 1995 issue on p 110.

The Indispensable PC Hardware Book, by Hans-Peter Messmer (©1995, Addison-Wesley, ISBN 0-201-8769-3) mentioned earlier in this chapter contains a summary of the **use of** *DTR, DSR, DCD* and the entire alphabet soup of signal names associated with modems and **serial data flow control**. Another good source of modem control information is in the *pc-hardware-faq*, by Willie Lim and Ralph Valentino (also mentioned previously). It can be found by searching newsgroups in the Internet, and is usually in the files of the **computer.sys.ibm.pc.hardware** newsgroup.

You can get up-to-date information on **sound cards containing a** *DSP* by performing a search on the terms "sound card" and "DSP" on the Internet. Since this is a very "hot" topic, information is frequently added and new files posted very often. Johan Forrer, KC7WW, wrote a very informative article titled *Programming a DSP Sound Card for Amateur Radio* for the August 1994 issue of *QEX*. The sound card described is a *Cardinal Digital Sound Pro-16*, which is based on an Analog Devices *Personal Sound Chip Set (PSA)*, consisting of the ESC614 iSA(PC) bus ASIC, AD1848 stereo CODEC and ADSP-215 DSP chips.

Another useful place to look is at the shareware Web page—(**http:// www.shareware.com**). Search for programs with the keywords *DSP, sound cards* and *FFT*. Download the files, and look at the README or .DOC files for information.

Analog Devices, Inc. at One Technology Way, P.O. Box 9106, Norwood MA 02062-9106, Telephone 617-329-4700 or (**http://www.analog.com/**) publishes an *Application Reference Manual*. The best way to receive a copy is to contact their local office. Check an industrial directory in your local library for office addresses and telephone numbers. **Maxim Integrated Products, Inc**. published a *New Release Data Book* (Vol IV), dated 1995. Contact them at 800-998-8800 to ask for a copy. The *Maxim Engineering Journal* also is available from Maxim. In the issue labeled Volume 22, on page 10 there is a description of the use of the PC serial port to drive an A/D converter. Maxim also will supply software (*EJ #22 C Program Software*, Rev 1, March 19,1996) for the converter.

A commercially built 8-channel **A/D converter** (model 5293-RB is about $80 plus shipping) is available from Marlin P. Jones at 800-652-6733 (fax 800 432 9937) or (**http://www.mpja.com/**).

For more information on the use of PCs with A/D converters as oscilloscopes, see the September/October 1995 issue of *Microcomputer Journal.* On page 30, Jan Axelson discusses using **PCs as test instruments, including oscilloscopes** and logic analyzers. *Microcomputer Journal* is published by CQ Communications, 76 North Broadway, Hicksville, NY 11801. Their telephone number is 516-681-2922, fax 516-681-2926.

A circuit for **antenna rotor control** was described in *73 Amateur Radio*, November 1987, page 44. "Let The Computer Steer Your Beam," by Paul Danzer, N1II). The rotor circuit is a typical "zero out the position error" used by several 5-wire control rotors.

Logic elements, such as flip-flops and gates, are covered in Chapter 7, Digital Signal Theory and Components, of *The ARRL Handbook for Radio Amateurs* (see the appendix for ordering information).

The *Basic Stamp* **series of micro-miniature processors is made by Parallex**, and can be bought from Micromint, Inc., 4 Park St, Vernon, CT 06066. Call them at 860-871-6170 (fax 860-872-2204). Parallex, Inc. is at 3805 Atherton Rd #102, Rocklin CA 95765. A clone of this line of microcomputers made by Scott Edwards Electronics, is available by contacting Marlin P. Jones (800-652-6733). These clones are called (in the catalog) *counterfeit stamp* kits.

CHAPTER 6

These **three companies offer free e-mail services:**

Juno Online Services, New York, NY, telephone 800-654-5866 or on the Web at (**http://www.juno.com**). System requirements call for 4 Mb RAM, 10 Mb hard disk, *Windows 3.1* or later (including *95*), and a 9600 baud or faster modem.

Freemark Communications Inc., Cambridge, MA, telephone (800) 693-6245 or (617) 492-6600. Their Web address is (**http://www.freemark.com**). System require-ments are 4 Mb RAM, 3 to 5 Mb hard drive, *Windows 3.1* or later (including *95*) and a 2400 baud or faster modem (9600 recommended).

HoTMaiL, Telephone 408-222-7000, e-mail (**info@hotmail.com**) or on the Web at (**http://www.hotmail.com**). Requires a Web Browser—Netscape 2.0 or 3.0 is rec-ommended.

The following is a **list of national ISPs**. No guarantee is made to the accuracy, because this is a very competitive and volatile market. Many new local providers are coming on-line everyday. Check with the hams in your area to see who they are.

Uunet Technologies, Inc.
Product: AlterDial
Web Site: **http://www.uu.net/**
Points of Presence: 100 U.S. cities
Customer Service: 800-900-0241

America Online Inc.
Product: America Online
Web Site: **http://www.aol.com/**
Points of Presence: 166 U.S. cities, AOL users also can connect via SprintNet
Customer Service: 800-827-3338

AT&T WorldNet
Product: AT&T Business Network
Web Site: **http://www.att.com/worldnet/**
Points of Presence: Major Cities
Customer Service: 800-394-8840

CompuServe Inc.
Product: CompuServe Information Service
Web Site: **http://www.compuserve.com/**
Points of Presence: 420 U.S. cities

Concentric Network Corporation
Product: Concentric Network
Web Site: **http://www.concentric.net/**
Points of Presence: 197 U.S. and 7 Canadian cities

Global Network Navigator (An America Online Subsidiary)
Product: GNN
Web Site: **http://gnn.com/gnn/**
Points of Presence: more than 700 U.S. cities (most major ones;
     SprintNet & GNNNet)
Customer Service: 800-819-6112

IBM Global Network
Product: IBM Internet Connection Service
Web Site: **http://www.ibm.com/globalnetwork/**
Points of Presence: 111 U.S. cities, over 400 access numbers world wide
Customer Service: 800-426-3333

MCI Telecommunications
Product: InternetMCI
Web Site: **http://www.internetmci.com/**
Points of Presence: 60 U.S. cities
Customer Service: 800-444-8722

Netcom On-Line Communications Services Inc.
Product: NetCom Internet Services
Web Site: **http://www.netcom.com/**
Points of Presence: 175 U.S. cities
Customer Service: 800-353-5600

Performance Systems International Inc.
Product: InterRamp
Web Site: **http://www.psi.net/**
Points of Presence: 150 U.S. cities
Customer Service: 800-774-0852

Performance Systems International Inc.
Product: Pipeline USA
Web Site: **http://www.psi.net/internet/**
Points of Presence: 140 U.S. cities
Customer Service: 800-395-1056

Prodigy Services Co.
Product: Prodigy Network
Web Site: **http://www.prodigy.com/**
Points of Presence: 325 U.S. cities; world's largest dial-up access provider to the
  Web
800-PRODIGY

Microsoft Corp.
Product: The Microsoft Network
Web Site: **http://www.msn.com/**
Points of Presence: Over 100 U.S. cities

UNIX and its variations are a small but important presence in Amateur Radio. For information on obtaining software, see the text on Chapter 1 resources earlier in this chapter. The following information will give you an idea of what is happening in this area:

Linux, a variation of *UNIX*, is not as popular as DOS or *Windows 95*, but it excels in running TCP/IP applications. To that end, Steve Bible, N7HPR, and Greg Pool, WH6DT, have conspired to push the envelope of amateur resourcefulness by building a Web for Amateur Radio. See their article "Amateur Radio on the World Wide Web" in the July 1995 issue of *QST*. Excerpts appear below. The full impact of this marriage of the Web and Amateur Radio is unclear at this time. However, one thing is obvious: the Internet and Amateur Radio have so much in common that a divorce is very unlikely.

The Web on Amateur Radio

According to Steve and Greg the following five basic steps are necessary to create your own Web over packet radio:
1) Introduction of the *Linux* 32-bit operating system.
2) Configuring *Linux* for amateur packet radio.
3) Installing and configuring the World Wide Web server program, *httpd*.
4) Installing and configuring the World Wide Web client program, *NCSA Mosaic*.
5) Installing and configuring Microsoft *Windows 3.1 Web Client*.

In the end, you'll have a complete TCP/IP packet server station with the AX.25 protocol integrated into the operating system. This system also will be able to communicate with existing packet client stations that use AX.25.

Amateur Radio Programs for Linux

Terry Dawson, VK2KTJ, maintains the Linux HAM HOWTO guide. Point your Web browser to (**http://gateway.unipv.it/linux-ht/HAM-HOWTO.html**). Specific programs include satellite software such as Microsat Ground Station Software, by John Melton, G0ORX/N6LYT, and Jonathan Naylor, G4KLX, and SatTrack, a satellite tracking program by Manfred Bester, DL5KR. For packet radio, Brandon Allbery, KF8NH, has ported version 1.09 of *JNOS* to *Linux*. This allows users familiar with *JNOS* to switch over to *Linux*. As you can see, programming for *Linux* is an international effort.

In an effort to make the configuring of packet radio for *Linux* easier, keep an eye on the work of Bruce Perens, AB6YM, and his Debian Linux Distribution 5. His *Linux For Hams* CD-ROM will include, in addition to packet radio, call sign searching and satellite tracking programs.

Table 7-1

Linux Documentation Project and HOWTO Manuals

Linux Installation and Getting Started, Version 2.2.2
Network Administrator's Guide, Version 1.0
Kernel Hackers' Guide, Version 1.0
Linux System Administrator's Guide, Version 0.3
Linux HOWTO Index
Linux Busmouse HOWTO
Linux CDROM HOWTO
Linux Ethernet HOWTO
Linux Hardware HOWTO
Linux Installation HOWTO
Linux Kernel HOWTO
Linux Mail HOWTO
Linux NET-2 HOWTO
Linux PCI HOWTO
Linux Printing HOWTO
Linux PPP HOWTO
Linux SCSI HOWTO
Linux Serial HOWTO
Linux Sound HOWTO
Linux XFree86 HOWTO

Just as hams use Q Signals, Internet "QSOs" or messages often contain **abbreviations, acronyms and symbols**. There is no official guide—this list was compiled from various Internet messages, on-line services and chat groups. There are many more in occasional use, but these are the most common.

BBL—Be Back Later
BFN—Bye For Now
BRB—Be Right Back
BTW—By The Way
FUBAR—Fouled* Up Beyond All Recognition
FWIW—For What It's Worth
FYI—For Your Information
IMHO—In My Humble Opinion
IMO—In My Opinion
IOW—In Other Words
LOL—Laughing Out Loud

LOL—Laughing Out Loud
NBD—No Big Deal
OIC—Oh, I See
OTL—Out To Lunch
OTOH—On The Other Hand
PITA—Pain In The Arteries*
RSN—Real Soon Now
RTFM—Read The Fine* Manual
SNAFU—Situation Normal, All Fouled* Up
TIA—Thanks In Advance
WTH—What The Heck*

:-)—Happy (smiling)
:-(—Unhappy (frowning)
g —grin
s —smile

* – Use Your Imagination!

Cameras are available from several sources. *Connectix Corp.,* telephone (800) 950-5880, manufactures two golf-ball size cameras that are widely used for video conferencing. The following information was obtained from Connectix's Web site at (**http://www.connectix.com**).

They sell only through retailers such as CompUSA, Egghead Software, Computer City, Price Costco, Fry's and ComputerWare, and mail order companies including MacConnection, MacWarehouse, Tiger Direct and MacMall. A description of the Windows products is given; however, a similar product is available for Macs.

Color QuickCam for Windows is the color version of the most popular digital video camera, the original QuickCam. It sells for about $199 (after an introductory rebate). Color QuickCam captures brilliant pictures in 24-bit color at a 640×480 resolution, and records *Windows* AVI-based movies. Similar to the original QuickCam, it plugs into a standard parallel port of PCs, and can be used for adding video to World Wide Web pages and video e-mail creation. Color QuickCam achieves faster frame rates than the original camera through a new patented compression technology developed by Connectix—VIDEC. Besides retaining the same plug-and-play simplicity, Color QuickCam version 2.0 enhanced software includes Auto-Capture, Timed exposure and Auto brightness and hue.

QuickCam for Windows is a plug-and-play video camera for Windows-based personal computers and sells for around $99. QuickCam is extremely easy to use, requires no external power, and users don't have to change hardware configurations. It translates images into a digital video signal compatible anywhere in the world, and is an enhancement of Connectix QuickCam for Macintosh, a leading digital input device for the Mac platform.

For up-to-date **information and tutorials on Internet and the Web**, a good starting point is (**http://www.w3.org**). There are many books out on the subject, but they tend to become obsolete in a year or so. You would do better with a search on the Internet, under the key words *hypertext* and *tutorial*. If your Internet provider is CompuServe, try their Help Forum. Many of the on-line tutorials are kept up-to-date, with revisions every few months. *QST* has printed a number of articles about the Internet and the Web, directed toward hams. The most recent of these are:

Exploring the Internet—Part 1 (Ford): September 1994, p 43
Exploring the Internet—Part 2 (Ford): October 1994, p 43
Exploring the Internet—Part 3 (Ehrlich): November 1994, p 52
Exploring the Internet—Part 4 (Ehrlich): December 1994, p 47
Amateur Radio on the World Wide Web, Part 1—Welcome to the Web! (Pool): June 1995, p 24
Amateur Radio on the World Wide Web, Part 2—The Building Blocks of a Packet Radio Web (Pool): July 1995, p 37
Surf the Ham Webs (Ford): February 1996, p 62
There's No Place Like Home (Michael Gauland, AA7JF), August 1996, p 59

Home pages are fairly easy to put on the Web, but there are a number of interesting complications when it comes to including graphics. Generally, the larger the graphic, the longer it takes to load. Graphic files in the .GIF format are generally slower than those in .JPG format, and depending on the compression used, .JPG files can vary. However, small size .GIF files are still the most common used.

Many people turn off all graphics when browsing, to save down load time. Note the **visually handicapped** are precluded from taking advantage of your home page if you transmit information as graphics, and those who turn off their graphics also will miss this information. Generally, you might want to check out the "alternate" command. Change the usual command to insert an image (**<IMG SRC="URL">**) to (**<IMG SRC="URL" ALT="******">**). The ***** represents text that will be displayed if the image is turned off in a user's browser.

Appendix
A

PC Filenames

Thanks to *FCUG*—the Fairfield County Users Group, Fairfield County, Connecticut Reprinted with their permission.

EXTENSION CONVENTION

Your DOS manual spells out the rules for the naming of files, but just to review: Remember that a file name may have up to eight characters (in DOS and pre-*Windows 95*) in the main body, and then, as an option, you may follow the main body with a decimal point and up to three additional characters. The acceptable characters are letters A through Z and numerals 0 through 9. Lower case, if used, will automatically be converted to upper case. The following punctuation marks may also be used:

$$\_ \char`\^ \sim ! \$ \% \& \text{---} \{ \} ( ) @ \char`\` \char`\'$$

There are four extensions which have special meaning to DOS and they are used for the following purposes, exclusively:

.COM: This identifies a program file. Typing just the main body of the file title at the DOS prompt followed by <ENTER> will start the program running.

.EXE: Also a program file, same as .COM for most intents and purposes.

.BAT: A batch program. Such a program contains one or more DOS commands which will execute in sequence when the main body of the file name is typed followed by <ENTER>. AUTOEXEC.BAT is a special batch program that is executed automatically whenever the system is booted.

.SYS: A system file, also called a "device driver," it contains system and/or hardware information for DOS. CONFIG.SYS is a special file that causes the designated device drivers to be installed whenever the system is booted.

Many other common extensions are in general use and, mostly by tradition, have come to identify certain specific types of files. The list is by no means complete and should be used only as a guide, since no complete industry standard exists.

Common File Extensions

.Ext	Type	Description
.!!!	Temporary	Various
.$$$	Temporary	Various
.ALL	Misc.	WP-Printer file
.ANI	Misc.	Animation
.ARC	Archive	Archive File
.ARJ	Archive	Archive File
.ASC	Document	ASCII-various
.ASM	Language	Assembler Source
.AVI	Movie	Microsoft Movie
.BAC	Backup	Various
.BAK	Backup	Various
.BAS	Language	BASIC Source
.BGI	Graphic	Borland Graphic Driver
.BIN	Language	Binary
.BK!	Backup	WordPerfect
.BKP	Backup	Various
.BMK	Misc.	Windows
.BMP	Graphic	Win-graphic bit map
.C	Language	C Source Code-ASCII
.CDR	Drawing	CorelDraw
.CFG	Misc.	Configure-Various
.CFH	Drawing	Print Shop pictures
.CFL	Drawing	Print Shop pictures
.CGA	Resolution	Graphics Adapter
.CGM	Graphic	Graphics Metafile
.CHK	DOS	CHKDSK file
.CHP	Misc.	Chapter-Ventura
.CHR	Misc.	Character-Various
.CHT	Misc.	Harvard Graphics
.CLP	Misc.	Clipboard - Various
.CMD	Misc.	Norton-4DOS Macro
.CNF	Misc.	Configure-Various
.COB	Language	COBOL Source-ASCII

.CPS	Misc.	Central Point-vaccine
.CUT	Misc.	Dr. Halo-graphics
.DAT	Data	Various
.DB	Data	DataBase File-Paradox
.DBF	Data	DataBase File-dBase
.DCT	Data	Data Tble-Win/OS-?
.DEV	Driver	Device Driver
.DIF	Data	Data Interchange Var.
.DIR	Misc.	Directory
.DIZ	Archive	BBS-File-ID
.DLL	Data	Dynamic Link Library
.DOC	Document	Various
.DRS	Resource	Display/Printer Resource WP
.DRV	Driver	Device/Screen Driver
.DRW	Drawing	Designer
.DTA	Data	Various
.DTF	Data	Data File-Q&A
.DTP	Misc.	Desk Top Publishing
.DVP	Exe	Prog Inform. DeskView
.DVR	Driver	Device Driver/Filter
.DWG	Drawing	AutoCAD
.EGA	Resolution	Enhanced Graphic
.EPS	Misc.	Encapsulated Postcript
.FFI	Font	Power Pack
.FIL	Misc.	Filler File
.FLC	Movie	Autodesk Animator
.FLI	Movie	Autodesk Animator
.FLT	Misc.	Filter/Device Driver
.FNT	Font	Font-Various
.FON	Font	Font-Windows
.FOR	Language	FORTRAN Source-ASCII
.FRM	Misc.	Form-Various
.FRS	Misc.	Resource file WP
.GEM	Misc.	Digital Research-GEM
.GIF	Graphic	Graphic Interchange
.GRP	Misc.	Win - program group
.H	Language	C Header Code-ASCII
.HDR	Misc.	File Express-Header
.HER	Resolution	Hercules Monochrome
.HLP	Misc.	Help - Various
.HRC	Resolution	Hercules Monochrome
.HST	Misc.	Host-Communications
.Hxx	Misc.	Help Overlay Numbers
.ICO	Graphic	Windows-Icon
.IDX	Index	Index-Various
.IMA	Misc.	Image-Mirage
.IMG	Misc.	Image-Various
.INC	Language	Include File-ASCII
.INF	Windows	Info-Windows
.INI	Misc.	Windows-config, init.
.INX	Index	Index-Various
.IX	Index	Index-Various

.JPG	Graphics	Compressed graphics
.KEY	Misc.	Key-various
.LIB	Language	Library File - BINARY
.LOG	Misc.	Log-ASCII
.LST	Misc.	List-ASCII
.LZH	Archive	Archive Yoshi LHARC
.MAC	Misc.	Macro
.ME	Misc.	Read Me-Various
.MID	Music	Musical Instr Digital
.MNU	Misc.	Menu
.MOD	Music	Amiga Music-Soundtracker
.MON	Resolution	Monochrome Adapter
.MSG	Misc.	Message
.MSP	Drawing	MS Paint drawing
.OBJ	Language	Object Code-BINARY
.OLD	Misc.	Old Files-Various
.OPT	Misc.	QEMM Optimize
.OV#	Overlays	Overlay number
.OVL	Overlays	Overlay
.OVR	Overlays	Overlay
.PAK	Archive	Archive
.PAL	Misc.	Harvard Graphics-palettes
.PAS	Language	Pascal Source-ASCII
.PCC	Misc.	PaintBrush-CUT
.PCX	Drawing	PaintBrush drawing
.PDF	Misc.	Adobe Acroread & others
.PIC	Drawing	Pictures Designer Screen
.PIF	Executable	Win. Prog. Info. Files
.PIX	Drawing	Pictures Inset Screen
.PMX	Misc.	PageMaker
.PRG	Language	dBase Source-ASCII
.PRN	Misc.	Print File ASCII-Various
.PRO	Misc.	Profile-File Express & Others
.PRS	Resource	Display/Printer Resource
.PS	Misc.	Postscript
.PT3	Misc.	PageMaker 3
.PUB	Misc.	Ventura Publisher
.QIF	Misc.	Quicken
.QLB	Language	Qk Basic Library-BINARY
.QMT	Misc.	Quicken
.ROL	Music	Music-ADLIB
.SBI	Music	Sound Blaster Instrument
.SCR	Drawing	Screen
.SCR	Misc.	Script
.SCZ	Misc.	WingZ-Script
.SCx	Drawing	Colorix-RIX-Screen Type
.SDA	Misc.	S/W Dist Network ASCII
.SDN	Archive	S/W Dist Netwk-SDNV
.SET	Misc.	Set-up-Lotus & Others
.SFO	Misc.	Quattro Pro
.SHW	Misc.	Harvard Graphics Show
.SND	Misc.	Sound Quattro Pro

.SS	Drawing	Splash drawing
.ST	Misc.	Stamp-Splash
.STY	Misc.	Style
.SWP	Temporary	Swap Files-Windows
.TEM	Temporary	Temporary File
.TEX	Document	Text
.TGA	Graphic	Targa-Truevision
.TIF	Graphic	Tagged Image File
.TMP	Temporary	Temporary File
.TRN	Misc.	Quattro Pro
.TTF	Font	True Type Fonts-Win 3.1
.TUT	Misc.	Tutor
.TXT	Document	Text
.USL	Font	HP Landscape
.USP	Font	HP Portrait
.VGA	Resolution	Video Graphics Array
.VOC	Sound	Soundblaster
.VRM	Misc.	Quattro Pro-Vroom
.VRS	Misc.	WPerfect DR10 - resource
.VWR	Misc.	Viewer/Filter PCTools
.WAV	Sound	Sound-Windows 3.1
.WFN	Font	Coral Draw
.WK1	SpreadSht	Lotus 1 & 2 Worksheet
.WK3	SpreadSht	Lotus 3 Worksheet
.WKS	SpreadSht	Lotus 1 & 2 Worksheet
.WKZ	SpreadSht	WingZ - Worksheet
.WPG	Drawing	WordPerfect Graphic
.WPM	Misc.	WordPerfect Macro
.WQ1	Spread Sht	Quattro Pro Worksheet
.WRI	Text	Text-Win Write
.WSP	Misc.	QPro Worksheet placement
.XFR	Font	PaintBrush
.XLC	Misc.	Excel Chart

Appendix
B

Glossary

Archie—A service used to search for files on FTP servers. An alternate service is Veronica. Remember, there are a lot—a real lot—of files on line. The search can take a long time and result in a very long list. These services are lumped under the general term *Gophers*.

ARPA—The Advanced Research Projects Agency, part of the U.S. Department of Defense, and the agency that created the ARPANet. This was the start of Internet.

ASCII—The American Standard Code for Information Interchange, a standard way of representing letters, numbers, punctuation and some symbols and printer control commends with numeric values. As an example, a lower-case **a** is an ASCII value of 97, and an upper-case **A** is a value of 65. Most computers—PC, MAC, UNIX-based and others—recognize ASCII values. See the sidebar.

bauds and bits—A list of topics hams argue about would start with SWR. Bauds and bits would be a close second. According to the Institute of Electrical and Electronic Engineers, one baud is one bit per second in a train of digital signals. Therefore, if you can successfully transmit at a 9600 baud rate, you can send 9600 bits per second. Add a transmission protocol (such as V.34 or V.32), data compression (such as V.42 or MNP5) and error correction (such as V.42), and this simple relationship quickly changes. For an up-to-date tutorial, search the Internet for **"FAQ" AND "modems"** or your local computer bookstore.

binary numbers—The idea of using binary or digital information was the natural choice for the earliest digital computers, which were made from *switches*—originally relays, then vacuum tubes and finally solid state. Analog information has continuously variable voltages on a wire. Binary information has two values, as controlled by the switch. Therefore, there could be no mistake about the value of a signal—it was either yes or no, high or low, 1 or 0.

BIOS—Basic input output system. The 1's and 0's, usually burnt into ROM or loaded in EEPROM, that control the primary input and output functions of a PC.

bit—A bit is a single binary (two valued) thing: logic 1 or logic 0, 5 volts or zero volts, high or low,....

browser—A program used to view World Wide Web pages. See Chapter 6.

byte—A byte is now 8 bits. Notice the word *now*. A byte used to be machine dependent, but presently, in common discussions, it is assumed to be eight binary places or bits.

DIP—Dual in-line package. A microcircuit with two rows (two lines) of pins. The pins allow the circuit to be plugged into a board or socket.

DSP—Today, these letters stand for a set of chips that are designed to perform a set of math functions. By programming the digital signal processor, you can make a filter or some other analog function with a degree of accuracy and precision that can only come from digital synthesis.

Freeware—Free software. See Chapter 1.

FTP—File transfer protocol, or the system that controls the transfer of files over the internet. To *FTP a file* means to transfer it over the internet.

Home page—Usually the starting point when you "find" a company's or person's page on the Internet. The first (title) page is called their *homepage*.

HTML—A standard (more or less) language used to write Internet pages. The letters stand for hypertext markup language.

IDE—The integrated drive electronics is the standard hard disk controller found in most PCs. See SCSI.

IRC—Internet Relay Chat, a method of conducting live conversations on the Net. See Chapter 6.

IRQ—PCs use a system of *interrupt requests*, or IRQs, to control the internal flow of signals. You may see a reference to IRQ3, or some other number (most commonly from IRQ0 to IRQ15). Each IRQ is supposed to control one function, but often they are shared. This becomes important when you try to install a new piece of hardware—perhaps a CD-ROM drive. You might find the IRQ suggested during the *INSTALL* program (for the drive) is already being used—if you use this IRQ for a second function you may end up with an IRQ *conflict*. Hopefully, the software accompanying your new device will suggest what to do next!

ISA—Industry standard architecture is the term used for one of the PC bus configurations. See Chapter 1 for details on the family of bus types.

numbers—Can be encoded as decimal, octal, hexadecimal (hex) or binary. The name corresponds to the number of values any one digit may take. In a decimal system, each digit can have one of 10 values—0, 1, 2, ...9. Hex encoding provides 16 values for each digit, 0 though 9, A, B, C, D, E and F. The value of F is 15. Octal has 8 values and binary only 2. A sidebar in Chapter 5 shows the relationship of binary digits to decimal.

ports—Whenever information moves in and out of a PC, it does so through a port. This is name given to the electrical connection. Each port has an address, and by looking at the address (for information coming in) or writing to the address (for information going out), the *I/O*—input/output functions—are performed.

SCSI—New computers often are equipped with the small computer system interface. It was designed to make connecting to add-on cards and devices simpler.

serial and parallel—Figure 1.1 illustrates a 4-bit digital number, with the value 1101. If the digits are transmitted down a single wire (A), one digit at a time, the digits, representing data, are said to be going in serial—just as several hikers might walk down a narrow path one after another. Take the four digits, put them on 4 wires (B), and they will be available in parallel—just as four people walking shoulder to shoulder down a broad highway. The same information is available in both serial and parallel, but generally it travels faster in parallel.

Shareware—Software that is initially free for a trial period. Sometimes the trial version has reduced capabilities, and may stop working after the trial period has elapsed. The trial period is usually 30 days, and the registration fee is normally lower than the cost of commercial software.

TCP/IP—the letters stand for Transmission control protocol/Internet protocol. Almost no one remembers what they say, but hams and many others know what they do. They are the basis of packet radio and all transmissions of information on the Internet.

Telnet—A method of logging in directly to a computer through the Internet. See Chapter 6.

URL, Universal Resource Locator. A standard way of representing services (or places) on the Internet. A URL consists of a name (such as FTP or http), followed by a colon, two slashes, and then the address of the place to which you are connecting.

USENET Newsgroup—A place on the Internet where people discuss any topic they wish. There are over 10,000 newsgroups, including many on ham radio topics. Caution: Some newsgroups contain material that you may find offensive, and some newsgroups specialize in offensive material.

UUENCODE/UUDECODE—Many internet services only allow 7-bit data to be transferred, and most computer files are 8-bit. Various coding systems, such as the one called UUencode/decode, are used to turn an 8-bit file into a 7-bit file before transmission, and back to 8-bit information upon receipt. *MIME* (Multipurpose Internet Mail Extensions) and several other coding systems are also used.

words—A word is generally machine dependent. In the past and currently common word sizes range from 4 bits to 64 bits. For real I/O, such as ASCII, a word is set at 8 bits, representing an expanded alphabet. The sidebar describes the ASCII code set.

World Wide Web (WWW)—A part of the Internet that uses hypertext, graphics, sound and video. See Chapter 6.

ASCII Codes

ASCII consists of decimal values from **0** to **255** or from **0** to **FF** in hex. Actually, as it so often happens, there are two ASCII standards—the first or original consisted of values from **0** to **127**, and the second, or *extended ASCII* codes, added the values from **128** to **255**. Each value represents one number, letter, symbol or operation. At first glance the table of 255 entries is overwhelming, but the table can be divided into manageable chunks.

Decimal values from **0** to **32** represent primarily printer operations and control signals. Some of these, such as the *bell* (**7**), are carryovers from the time when ASCII terminals replaced teletype machines. Others, such as **10**, line feed, are direct printer operations.

Starting with decimal **33** and continuing to **127** are numbers, upper and lower-case letters, common punctuation and symbols. From **128** to **255** is the extended character set, including some drawing symbols, non-English letters and math symbols.

A program to display the extended ASCII character set is included on the disk accompanying this book. The program is supplied both as a *BASIC* file (*ALPHA.BAS*) and as an executable file (*ALPHA.EXE*). The .BAS file has been saved with the text or *,A* option, so you can read it with any word processor. If you modify it with a word processor, make sure to save it as a plain ASCII file.

Related ARRL Books

REFERENCES

The ARRL Handbook

The annual *ARRL Handbook* is packed with projects and updated information, including software. Whether you're an Amateur Radio beginner, an experienced operator, electronic technician, engineering student or engineer, you'll find each chapter of *The ARRL Handbook* a stand-alone "mini-book" that covers your favorite topics and provide invaluable reference material, software, fascinating facts and some great new do-it-yourself projects. If it's ham radio, it's in the *Handbook*. With 1200 pages and 1000 charts and illustrations, *The ARRL Handbook* is an exceptional value. Softcover, with software. Also available on CD-ROM.

The ARRL Operating Manual

The Operating Manual is your most valuable resource for whatever operating-oriented questions you may have. How do I use a repeater autopatch? Where is the CW subband on 20 meters? How do I use a QSL bureau? What is grayline propagation and how do I make it work for me? How do I get started on the ham satellites? You'll find an impressive and colorful section that features dozens of US and overseas operating awards, and a handy reference section includes an ARRL DXCC Countries List, beam-heading information, a series of maps, US counties, sunrise/sunset tables, and much, much more.

DIGITAL COMMUNICATIONS

Your Packet Companion

ARRL staff member Steve Ford, WB8IMY, wrote this book for the packet new-comer. Covers many topics, from assembling a station to sending mail, from packet satellites to the latest networking systems. Its straightforward writing style and clear drawings will get you on the cutting edge of digital ham radio in no time. 1st ed., #3959 $10

Packet: Speed, More Speed and Applications

For packet enthusiasts interested in medium to high-speed packet systems or ap-plications that go beyond everyday messaging, BBSs and PacketCluster. The book covers these areas: 9600 bits/s, 56 kbits/s and Faster, Projects, Special Topics, and References. Projects includes a PACSAT modem, scaleable baud rate FSK modem and a telemetry adapter for the TNC-2. Special topics include automatic packet re-porting systems (APRS), a computer utility to show local packet connections and traf-fic, packet meteor scatter experiments, and future link-layer protocol considerations. If you're just getting into packet, you'll want to explore the ARRL's *Your Packet Com-panion*. If you're already into packet, this book is a must for your radio book shelf. 1st ed., 160 pages #4955 $15

Practical Packet Radio

The title says it all: Written by Stan Horzepa, WA1LOU, this book could make your life easier, whether you're setting up your first packet station or exploring TCP/IP or another more-advanced technique. The successor to WA1LOU's classic *Your Gateway to Packet Radio*, this book covers everything the packet-active ham needs to know: setting up a station, getting on the DX packet cluster, exploring bulletin boards and satellites, and much more. A series of Appendices includes sources of packet-related hardware and software, a Glossary of Terms and the AX.25 protocol. 1st ed., 224 pages, #5307 $15.95

Your HF Digital Companion

Steve Ford, WB8IMY, takes you on a tour through the worlds of RTTY, AMTOR, HF packet, PACTOR, G-TOR and CLOVER. You'll discover how to set up your sta-tion and communicate in each of these fascinating modes. A valuable reference sec-tion tells you where to find equipment, software and more. 1st ed., 208 pages. #4815 $10

NOSintro: TCP/IP over Packet Radio

You'll find a wealth of practical information, hints and tips for setting up and using the KA9Q Network Operating System (NOS) in a packet radio environment. The emphasis is on hands-on practicalities. You'll see exactly: how to install NOS on a PC, how to set up the control files, how to check out basic operations off-air, and how to use NOS commands for transferring files, logging in to remote systems, send-ing mail, etc. 356 pages #4319 $23

DATA BOOKS AND SOFTWARE

The 1995 ARRL Periodicals CD-ROM

On this one CD-ROM is a compilation of all 1995 issues of *QST, QEX* and *NCJ* . Here are some of the special features you'll find: the full text of every *QST, QEX* and *NCJ* article, including technical and general interest articles, columns, product reviews and New Ham Companion features; every drawing, table, illustration and photograph (many in color); more than 1000 advertisement images, indexed alphabetically by vendor and product; a powerful search engine that lets you find desired information quickly by entering article titles, call signs, names or just about any other word; Windows printing and Clipboard support, so you can print out articles or share them with other Windows applications; tools to create bookmarks at often-used articles and more. You'll need these minimum system requirements: 386, 486 or Pentium™ IBM or 100% compatible (486 or better recommended); 4 Mbytes of RAM (8 Mbytes recommended); hard disk with at least 10 Mbytes of free space; Microsoft Windows™ 3.1 or higher; 640 x 480, 256-color graphics; CD-ROM drive (double speed or faster recommended); mouse or equivalent pointing device. #5579 $19.95 plus $4 shipping/handling for ARRL members, $29.95 plus $4 shipping/handling for nonmembers

The ARRL Electronics Data Book

This valuable aid to the radio amateur, RF design engineer, technician and experimenter contains all those commonly used tables, charts, and those hard-to-remember formulas and semiconductor pin-out diagrams are found in one handy source. You'll also find hundreds of popular circuits and building blocks, including oscillators, mixers, amplifiers, other devices and their operating parameters. By Doug DeMaw, W1FB, 2nd ed., 232 pages, #2197 $15

COMPUTER-BASED DESIGN TOOLS

ARRL Radio Designer 1.5

This is the premier ARRL design tool that lets you create computerized models of audio, radio and electronic circuits so you can see how they work, and make them work better without actually building them. Here's just some of what you can do with *ARRL Radio Designer*:
- Model passive and small-signal linear circuits from audio to RF
- Predict and analyze performance of linear, small-signal active and passive dc, audio and RF circuitry (including amplifiers, filters, matching networks and power splitters and combiners)
- Optimize circuit performance to meet goals you specify
- Display the signal level at any point in a simulated circuit
- Simulate component value variations due to temperature and tolerances with Monte Carlo statistical analysis

•Simulate circuit response to a steady-state time-domain signal using impulse, step, pulsed carrier or user-defined stimuli, and much more.

ARRL Radio Designer reports S, Y, Z, group delay and voltage probe parameters for n-port networks; chain (ABCD), hybrid (H), inverse hybrid (G), gain, voltage gain, stability parameters for two-port networks, and more. Reports can be rectangular or polar graphs, or tables, displayed on screen or printed on any Windows compatible printer in the colors, fonts and line weights you specify. Circuit entry is via a text-based circuit editor. *ARRL Radio Designer* comes on two 3.5-inch floppy disks (example circuits and reports included), and includes an instruction manual containing how-to-use-it, tutorial and reference information. Requires Microsoft Windows 3.1 or higher, 8 megabytes of RAM, and a hard disk with at least 5 megabytes of free space; a math coprocessor is strongly recommended. For more information, contact ARRL. #4882 $150

The ARRL Antenna Book

With its accompanying disk, this book is the definitive source for information on state-of-the-art antenna and transmission line theory and construction. It presents the best and most highly regarded coverage of antenna fundamentals, propagation, transmission lines, Yagis and quads, as well as all popular wire antenna designs. You'll find a chapter on HF Yagi Arrays based on the latest computer modeling software. The Radio Wave Propagation chapter includes comprehensive statistical data on the range of elevation angles needed for communication from all areas of the US to important DX locations. Included with this edition is a 1.44 MB 3.5-inch diskette for the IBM PC/XT/AT and compatible computers with software for Yagi analysis, propagation prediction, transmission-line evaluation, and more.

Physical Design of Yagi Antennas

Written by Dr. David B. Leeson, W6QHS, this book is packed with information on how to design or reinforce Yagi antennas so they can survive in the most adverse weather conditions like—120-mile-per-hour winds! Covers the structural design of elements, booms and masts, plus the electrical design of Yagi antennas. 1st ed., ©1992, 340 pages, #3819 $20. The accompanying disk is available in three varieties: 5.25-inch spreadsheet diskette for IBM or compatible #3827 $10; 3.5-inch spreadsheet diskette for IBM or compatible #3835 $10; 3.5-inch spreadsheet diskette for Macintosh #3843 $10 (spreadsheet program not included with above software)

ARRL MicroSmith

This standard by Wes Hayward, W7ZOI. *ARRL MicroSmith* is a Smith Chart simulation program for the IBM PC and compatibles. You don't need detailed knowledge of the Smith Chart. Use MicroSmith to design matching networks with fixed or variable L-C components, stub-matching sections with transmission lines, and more. It's all done graphically on your computer screen. It's also useful for a variety of network analysis problems. Includes a user's guide with numerous illustrations. 3.50-inch diskette. #4084 $39

Introduction to Radio Frequency Design

Wes Hayward, W7ZOI, presents a treatment of the fundamental methods of radio frequency design using mathematics as needed to develop intuition for RF circuits and systems. He emphasizes application of simple circuit models whenever possible and prepares you to actually design HF, VHF and UHF equipment. This "timeless" reprint includes 3.50-inch software for IBM PCs and compatibles that goes with the text. ARRL 1st ed., 400 pages, #4920 $30

Solid State Design for the Radio Amateur

Packed with information on Amateur Radio circuit design and applications, it includes descriptions of receivers, transmitters, power supplies and test equipment. Much of the data cannot be found elsewhere. Essential for every technical library. 256 pages, #0402 $15

QST—ARRL'S Monthly Membership Journal

Simply put, *QST* is the best source of news and practical information from the world of Amateur Radio. All hams, regardless of license class or experience, will find it indispensable. ARRL members get all this, and more, in each issue each month:

Product Reviews: Comprehensive, readable and reliable reports on the latest transceivers and accessories.

Hints & Kinks: Clever and useful tips sent in by *QST* readers who have found a better way to accomplish a task or solve a problem.

Feature articles cover all the fascinating aspects of ham radio.

Written for beginners but enjoyed by nearly everyone, the *New Ham Companion* section covers antennas, operating, safety, and questions and answers from readers on any ham subject.

Technical articles cover cutting-edge theory and practical designs that will expand your Amateur Radio horizons.

DXing and Contesting, two of the most popular on-the-air activities, are featured prominently in each issue.

Ham Ads and display ads are the best way to find a piece of Amateur Radio gear, new or used, top shelf or bare bones.

Useful and timely *News from the FCC* and the international scene is featured in articles, and in columns such as DC Currents, Happenings and Amateur Radio World.

Other columns feature satellites, packet radio, public service, technical discussions—and much more!

Appendix
D

The ARRL Technical Information Service

Rev. 08-19-96

The following is a list of information packages and bibliographies that are available to provide assistance for technical problems and introductory information on topics of interest. To request paper copies of an information package, send a separate written request to the ARRL Technical Department Secretary. Enclose a check or money order for the amount of $2 for ARRL Members or $4 for non-members for each package requested (covers the cost of photocopying and mailing).

To request paper copies of article bibliographies, send a written request to the Technical Department Secretary and enclose a large (9×12) envelope, self-addressed and postage paid. There is no fee for bibliographies, but there is a charge for article copies as explained on each article list.

Most of these packages are also available electronically at no charge from the following sources:

The ARRL Field Services telephone BBS. The BBS can be reached by dialing 860-594-0306, utilizing standard 8-n-1 parameters, connect rates from 300 baud up to 28,800 baud.

Electronic Mail. You can send email to the League's Internet Email Information Server from CompuServe, America Online and similar services. Send a message to **info@arrl.org** (this is an Internet address; contact your service provider for details on sending email to Internet).

In the text of your message, write the single word HELP to get a set of instructions for using this service.

File Transfer Protocol (FTP—Internet only). The League has a remote FTP archive site that contains all of the files from the email server. For the current address of this site, FTP to **www.arrl.org** and retrieve the file *helpinfo.txt* or access the FTP links on our World Wide Web page at:

http://www.arrl.org/

Title   Description

ATV—Information about Fast-Scan Amateur Television
DSP—General information on Digital Signal Processing
Electrical Safety—Reprint from ARRL Antenna Book (pgs. 1-8 to 1-16)
Emergency Power—Reference to QST, April 1993 Lab Notes
EMI/RFI Pckg.—General information about EMI/RFI (see Note 1)
EMI-Audio—Interference to audio equipment (see Note 1)
EMI-Automotive—Automotive Interference solutions
EMI-Bibliography—List of QST articles about interference
EMI-CATVI—Interference to Cable Television Systems (Reprints from Communications Technology)
EMI-CB—Interference from Non-Amateur Transmitters
EMI-Computer—Information on Computer RFI
EMI-Consumer—Consumer Pamphlet on RFI
EMI-Electrical—How to track and solve electrical interference (see Note 1)
EMI-Ignition—Brief suggestions for solving ignition noise RFI
EMI-Pacemaker—Susceptibility of Cardiac Pacemakers to interference
EMI-RF Bulbs—Information about RF-driven lamps
EMI-Smoke Detector—Interference to Smoke Detectors (Reprints from QST, November 1980 and February 1981)
EMI-Telephone/FCC—FCC Information Bulletin on Telephone Interference
EMI-Telephones—Reprint from QST, October 1992 Lab Notes (see Note 1)
EMI-Television—Reprint from QST, March 1994 Lab Notes (see Note 1)
EMI-Touch Lamp—Various QST Hints & Kinks reprints (see Note 1)
EMI-VCR—Brief suggestions (see Note 1)
Frequency Counter—Reprint of 93 Hbk (pgs. 25-13 to 25-19)-Frequency Counter article
G5RV—Bibliography of G5RV articles, and reprint from Antenna Compendium I
Grid Squares—How to Locate them (Reprint from January 1989 QST, pg. 29)
Indoor Antennas—Select an Indoor Antenna (Reprint from QST, December 1992 Lab Notes)
Kits—ARRL Kit Mfg. List (August 1993 Lab Notes)
LCF Calculator—Copy of an old out-of-print LCF Calculator
Lightning Protection——Reprint of two-part Lab Notes column (October and December 1994)
Manuals—How to Locate Manuals and Documentation—(June 1992 Lab Notes)
Mobile-Marine—Maritime Mobile Installation suggestions
Moonbounce/EME—Information about moonbounce (Reprint from QST, July 1985, pgs. 18-21)
Packet—Beginner Packet, TCPIP, address coordinators
Parts List—Ch. 35 of Hbk. & QST, August 1992 Lab Notes (See Note 2)
Printed Circuit Boards—Sources for PCB prototypes and supplies (October 1993 Lab Notes)
Propagation Basics—Propagation Introduction and Terms explained
RDF—Radio Direction Finding
Receiver Tests—Technical Descriptions
RF Safety—Radio Frequency Energy Safety
RIG—What Rig Should I Buy?? (Reprints from QST)
RTTY/AMTOR—Getting Started with HF Digital Communications
Satellites—Information about amateur satellite operation
Software—Reference to QST, April 1992 Lab Notes

SSTV—Reprint from QST, January 1993, pg. 20
Stores—US stores that sell amateur radio equipment
Synchronous Detection—Reprint from QEX, September 1992, pg. 9
SWL Tips—General information about short-wave listening
TCP/IP—Getting Started with Amateur TCP/IP
TV Channels-CATV —General Information
Vacuum Tube Data—General Information
WEFAX—Reprint from QST, February 1993, pgs. 31-36

Notes

1. Ask for the EMI/RFI Package plus any of the others. Most of the others assume that you have read the EMI/RFI Package.
2. We will send this along, but current copies of the *ARRL Handbook* contain the most up to date information.

About the Authors

Paul Danzer, N1II, was first licensed as KN2DGR, and immediately became a member of the local teenage Novice group on 40-meter CW. After receiving a BEE and an MSEE, he spent his days as an aerospace engineer, with 11 US patents in the radar and electronics fields. At night he continued hamming, including writing over 60 ham radio and computer magazine articles and one book. He now spends his days as an Assistant Technical Editor on the ARRL staff, responsible for the *Handbook, Operating Manual* and several other books. At night he is still operating 40-meter CW.

Richard Roznoy, K1OF, received his Novice license at age 12. Active for over 35 years, he still enjoys a good rag chew and an occasional DX chase. As an avid home-brewer, he has built equipment ranging from QRP stations to kW amplifiers. With a BSEE, he has held the position of Vice-President of Engineering for a computer peripheral manufacturer and a telecommunications company. For the past 12 years, as founder of the RL Design Group, he specialized in the design, construction and installation of RF communications systems. He is active on the Internet and enjoys ham related applications. He is an Assistant Technical Editor on the ARRL staff.

About The American Radio Relay League

The seed for Amateur Radio was planted in the 1890s, when Guglielmo Marconi began his experiments in wireless telegraphy. Soon he was joined by dozens, then hundreds, of others who were enthusiastic about sending and receiving messages through the air—some with a commercial interest, but others solely out of a love for this new communications medium. The United States government began licensing Amateur Radio operators in 1912.

By 1914, there were thousands of Amateur Radio operators—hams—in the United States. Hiram Percy Maxim, a leading Hartford, Connecticut, inventor and industrialist saw the need for an organization to band together this fledgling group of radio experimenters. In May 1914 he founded the American Radio Relay League (ARRL) to meet that need.

Today ARRL, with more than 170,000 members, is the largest organization of radio amateurs in the United States. The League is a not-for-profit organization that:
* promotes interest in Amateur Radio communications and experimentation
* represents US radio amateurs in legislative matters, and
* maintains fraternalism and a high standard of conduct among Amateur Radio operators.

At League Headquarters in the Hartford suburb of Newington, the staff helps serve the needs of members. ARRL is also International Secretariat for the International Amateur Radio Union, which is made up of similar societies in more than 100 countries around the world.

ARRL publishes the monthly journal *QST*, as well as newsletters and many publications covering all aspects of Amateur Radio. Its headquarters station, W1AW, transmits bulletins of interest to radio amateurs and Morse code practice sessions. The League also coordinates an extensive field organization, which includes volunteers who provide technical information for radio amateurs and public-service activities. ARRL also represents US amateurs with the Federal Communications Commission and other government agencies in the US and abroad.

Membership in ARRL means much more than receiving *QST* each month. In addition to the services already described, ARRL offers membership services on a personal level, such as the ARRL Volunteer Examiner Coordinator Program and a QSL bureau.

Full ARRL membership (available only to licensed radio amateurs) gives you a voice in how the affairs of the organization are governed. League policy is set by a Board of Directors (one from each of 15 Divisions). Each year, half of the ARRL Board of Directors stands for election by the full members they represent. The day-to-day operation of ARRL HQ is managed by an Executive Vice President and a Chief Financial Officer.

No matter what aspect of Amateur Radio attracts you, ARRL membership is relevant and important. There would be no Amateur Radio as we know it today were it not for the ARRL. We would be happy to welcome you as a member! (An Amateur Radio license is not required for Associate Membership.) For more information about ARRL and answers to any questions you may have about Amateur Radio, write or call:

ARRL Educational Activities Dept
225 Main Street
Newington CT 06111-1494
(860) 594-0200
Prospective new amateurs call:
800-32-NEW HAM (800-326-3942)
World Wide Web: http://www.arrl.org

Index

FEEDBACK

Please use this form to give us your comments on this book and what you'd like to see in future editions, or e-mail us at **pubsfdbk@arrl.org** (publications feedback).

Where did you purchase this book?
☐ From ARRL directly   ☐ From an ARRL dealer

Is there a dealer who carries ARRL publications within:
☐ 5 miles   ☐ 15 miles   ☐ 30 miles   of your location?   ☐ Not sure.

License class:
☐ Novice   ☐ Technician   ☐ Technician Plus   ☐ General   ☐ Advanced   ☐ Extra

---

Name _____   ARRL member? ☐ Yes ☐ No

_____   Call Sign _____

Daytime Phone   (   ) _____   Age _____

Address _____

City, State/Province, ZIP/Postal Code _____

If licensed, how long? _____

Other hobbies _____

_____

Occupation _____

For ARRL use only		PCHS
Edition	1 2 3 4 5 6 7 8 9 10 11 12	
Printing	1 2 3 4 5 6 7 8 9 10 11 12	

From _____

_____

_____

EDITOR, PERSONAL COMPUTERS IN THE HAM SHACK
AMERICAN RADIO RELAY LEAGUE
225 MAIN STREET
NEWINGTON CT 06111-1494

······································ please fold and tape ··